*To the young, who must bear the brunt of the burden
imposed upon them by their elders' slow awakening
to the climate crisis.*

Sandra,
Touching base after a
decades-long absence.
Larry

I PLEDGE ALLEGIANCE
TO THE
EARTH

A Prayer For the Planet

LAWRENCE K. ZEISLER

LUMINARE PRESS

WWW.LUMINAREPRESS.COM

Printed in the United States of America

Cover Design: Claire Flint Last
Cover Photo: Jody Parker

Luminare Press
442 Charnelton
Eugene, OR 97401
www.luminarepress.com

LCCN: 2019910809
ISBN: 978-1-64388-142-3

A Personal Hello

I Pledge Allegiance to the Earth is an inquiry into the nature of life. Tracing the book's lineage, a point was reached when the series of short treatises and poems foreshadowing it could no longer contain the urges they once satisfied. Knowing that a larger format was required, I took a deep breath and proceeded to write. If you sense an air of apprehension in the previous statement, you are correct. I was well aware that a book-length undertaking would demand ample expenditures of time and energy.

I feel a sound philosophy is the most fat-free prose genre. There is little margin for error when the essence of one's soul is laid bare. This book took so long to mature because of the fierce struggle to weed out any contradiction in its pages. Actually, its genesis predates transcription; I recall moments during adolescence when I'd cry questions to the tear-stained nights that my limited years of life could not answer. Youth is at once liberating and confining.

This "unsettling something" remained relatively stable until I reached the hotly reactive years following adolescence when it was made manifest in the form of distress, even anger. Now anger likes a scapegoat, and it was found in nothing less than the American ethos. In a nutshell, I was angry because I couldn't come to terms with our apparent indifference to the destruction we were inflicting upon the earth.

During those restive times, my often-boggled mind revealed its thoughts in the form of preponderant soliloquies of filibuster proportions, loaded with prophecies of gloom and doom. Needless to say, the usual audience was me. Billy Joel's ballad "Angry Young Man" fit me like a glove.

Fortunately, the turmoil underwent a metamorphosis. My compassion, once reserved for the natural world, tempered the anger sufficiently to enhance my comprehension. I realized that since humans and nature are linked, to devote one's cares to one while excluding the other makes for a partial person. There is nothing I would like more than to witness the future unfolding in a manner benefiting both. The onus is on us to ensure it occurs.

The spirit required to meet this onus exists within everyone. Although societal pressures divert our attention, I believe in its heart of hearts humankind wants earnestly to revivify its "Mother."

The spirit is verified intermittently throughout the day whenever acts of kindness and gratitude are performed. We are more selfless and honorable than we think, but the restraints imposed on us are tremendous. Life is a constant interplay between the "light" and the "dark"; deny the existence of opposites and the changes they effect, and you deny reality. It's not a question whether we are honorable but rather to what extent it flourishes.

This book has an ideal cast to it, but it is not one of those travel guides promoting a journey to enduring tranquility. I am not so naïve as to believe anyone can experience it on a consistent basis. I would be more than grateful if you interpreted what you find herein as an effort to unravel some of those individual characteristics that infringe upon one's chances for appreciating a more fulfilling life.

Lawrence K. Zeisler

Some people say one shouldn't write what they can't live. If such a demand had been placed upon me, I'd still be mired in the formative stages of the introduction. Sometimes the pen assumes a life of its own, and I can only surmise that during those inspired periods, it is answering an inner calling beyond the limitations of daily experience. Should I have resisted conveying what is felt to be the potential innate to us all because my actions can't always keep pace with my thoughts? Should I have ignored the spirit and shared with you a watered-down version of that potential?

I've found that any search for meaning will reach frustration if not accompanied by an acknowledgment of something exceeding the ken of rational thought; at some point, the quester must defer to the ineffable. You will discover in these pages a rich, reverential undertone but not in the conventional sense. Once I shed my Christian shackles my true spirituality was unearthed—one whose self-evidence is reflected in all natural phenomena. You can find that faith occupying the space between every line. It played the role of Muse during periods when the words flowed like spring meltwater, and it exhorted me to persevere through roadblocks so intense it would have been beyond the power of Aladdin's lamp to conjure concepts that I was wishing to find. More than anything else, the book is an act of thanks to this faith that saw me through to the end.

Sincerely,

Lawrence K. Zeisler

Preface

IN GENERAL, AMERICANS ARE TOLERANT. WHILE OUT IN public, I rarely encounter acts of hostility or blatant anger, which is commendable considering the stress-filled and politically charged environment in which we live.

We toe the line primarily because our ethics and laws exist within a framework of relative comfort, amusement, and safety. Although the livelihoods of a sizable majority of the citizenry meet the basic material needs (an admittedly conditional inference) placed upon them by society for survival, most strive to enhance their quality of life. The American Dream, after all, is to grab for the gusto.

The populace once routinely lived within its means, and the available goods and services complemented a simpler lifestyle. Extravagance was little more than a word in those days. By the sweat of their brows, hardened individuals built a sturdy foundation for the new and emerging nation.

It wouldn't be far-fetched to suggest that the phrase "living within one's means" went out with the gold standard. In this day and age, many people don't know their true financial worth and overspend with abandon. It is even more perplexing to try to determine life's basic necessities. This is because technology and its enabler, contemporary capitalism, have taken on lives of their own. We now play by their rules, and they want nothing more than to relieve us of our hard-earned cash. The entertainment, electronic, automotive, athletic, toy, pharmaceutical, financial, fashion industries,

Lawrence K. Zeisler

etc., incessantly solicit citizens for funds and shower them with reasons why their current living standard is subpar.

Do we need as much as they say we do? Of course not, but our pursuit of their expectations is what makes the commercial world go round. It's sad that so many of their offerings are of questionable value. Perhaps worse, the seeds of discontentment are being endlessly sown.

The list of life's requirements—taxes, loans, insurance premiums, unceasing bills, etc.—contribute to the discord and growing anxiety. Add to the mix the sense of powerlessness the individual feels in the face of fathomless bureaucracies and untold special interests. These factors, combined with the resolute campaign by product advertising to ensure our knee-jerk need to better ourselves materially runs strong, make for a mind-set that makes it hard to think of little more than self and family. Lord knows we don't need the added weight of the world on our shoulders—or do we?

Because this book deals primarily with our relationship to nature, the previous question pertains to the natural world. It is felt here that concern for the earth should be weightless, an innate, underlying constant amid the tumult, no more a burden than love of home and hearth. In truth, they are one and the same. The earth's interest should be as integral as our own self-interest. Sadly, not enough people realize this.

A good part of the responsibility for such a fundamental oversight will be placed at the foot of arguably the most fundamental institution known to Western peoples: their religion. Our major religion, Christianity, has failed to implant a love for the earth. Such a love should be seared into our souls. It's not. A sizable portion of the text will be dedicated to discussion of this matter.

The history of the environmental movement in the United States can trace its lineage to the establishment of Yellowstone National Park. In 1892, the Sierra Club was founded and environmental pioneer John Muir elected its first president. At the turn of the twentieth century, the "conservationist president" Theodore Roosevelt infused the cause with a serious jolt of passion, dedicating approximately 230 million acres of public land for the benefit of all Americans. In his Confession of Faith Speech on August 6, 1912, he said: "There can be no greater issue than that of conservation in this country."

Rachel Carson's landmark book *Silent Spring* was considered a key turning point in the early sixties, delivering an unprecedented earth consciousness to the American psyche. It dealt mainly with our careless use of synthetic pesticides and influenced the nation to implement laws mandating stricter use of the chemicals. The establishment of a nationwide ban on DDT was perhaps the most noteworthy consequence of the book.

In 1968, the Apollo 8 astronauts, photographing future lunar landing spots while orbiting the moon, snapped the historic Earthrise image that portrayed our vital and vibrant world enveloped in a smothering, lifeless vacuum. It provided stark, visual proof of the gleaming oasis we call home, and people took notice. Nature photographer Galen Rowell labeled it "the most influential environmental photograph ever taken."

These two key events, along with a growing litany of pollution-related episodes, were instrumental in the creation of Earth Day in 1970 by US Senator Gaylord Nelson from Wisconsin. A grassroots environmental movement was set in motion that played an active role leading up to President

Nixon's formation of the U.S. Environmental Protection Agency (EPA) in 1970—an agency that enjoyed strong bipartisan support. Important revisions to the Clean Air and Clean Water Acts were authorized, and the Endangered Species Act soon followed. It appeared as if we were headed in the right direction. By the end of the 1970s, polls indicated the public still harbored a decent degree of enthusiasm.

I began writing back in the eighties, largely in response to President Reagan's cavalier attitude toward the plight of the natural world with its accompanying breakdown of national concern. In 1986 he had the 32 solar panels President Carter had installed on the West Wing roof of the White House removed and also dramatically cut funding for the Energy Department's research and development in the area of renewable energy. His first secretary of the interior, James Watt, proved to be an environmental disaster and resigned in shame in 1983. Ditto for his first EPA administrator, Anne M. Gorsuch, whose counteragency policies resemble Scott Pruitt's, who just left the post drenched in shame as well. It looks like his acting replacement, ex-coal lobbyist Andrew Wheeler, will carry on their dark legacies. In this regard, the new boss is the same as the old boss, just less overtly obnoxious.

The warming effect that carbon dioxide (CO_2) gas placed on the climate was gaining credence in scientific circles by the 1960s. In 1988, the director of NASA's Institute for Space Studies in Manhattan, Dr. James Hansen, testifying before the Senate Energy and Natural Resources Committee, brought the matter to widespread attention, warning of a direct correlation between the greenhouse effect and global warming. His prescient plea went largely ignored.

Global warming emerged as a relatively hot topic in the nineties when President Clinton included it in the national discussion, but efforts to deal with it sputtered along, thanks in large part to the Republican Congress. The Kyoto Protocol, the first earnest international attempt at cutting emissions, is seen as a mixed bag. The fact that the world's largest CO_2 emitter, the United States, signed on but failed to participate was a major disappointment. The next effort in Copenhagen fell flat.

At the turn of the century, I felt optimistic that common sense would win the day and the country would wake up to the climate crisis. After all, reality was smacking us in the face. Al Gore's sobering 2006 film *An Inconvenient Truth* proved in no uncertain terms the harsh reality that humankind's burning of fossil fuels was directly contributing to the predicament.

Boy, was I wrong. Despite record warmth, intensifying natural disasters such as desert expansion, drought, and increased flooding, not to mention pleas for sanity from our European allies, President Bush turned his eye to what he deemed more pressing matters such as the invasion of a country not responsible for the tragedy of September 11, 2001. One can only fantasize how different things would be had Mr. Gore assumed his rightful, popularly elected place. Oh well, you know what they say about wishes.

The Paris Agreement, recently signed by 196 nations, is a promising step to a worldwide low-carbon future. President Obama endorsed the agreement without Senate ratification, showing the world that the United States was serious about taking on the problem. Not so with non-popularly elected Donald Trump, who openly campaigned against the deal.

Perhaps you detect a pattern, a seesaw of political wills

Lawrence K. Zeisler

that makes it difficult to maintain any sort of cultural consistency. The two major parties each have their version of what constitutes progress. Never in American history have the distinctions been so stark with the possible exception of the Civil War era. Sadly, one party harbors ideas that are often rooted in the past. Despite the fact about 97 percent of climate scientists say climate change is real and that human activity is the primary cause, a large segment of the Republican Party establishment espouses views about the catastrophe that conjure a sense of déjà vu, making me feel like I'm back in the eighties. Whenever it appears the country is serious about embracing the science and acting in a mature manner, the naysayers gain power and pander to Big Energy and/or their own selfish, shortsighted reasoning. Or perhaps plain ignorance. This book is a release of pent-up aggravation over what could have been.

The state in which I live, Pennsylvania, is experiencing a $2 billion budget deficit. Much of that total could be alleviated if fracking-friendly legislators in the Republican-controlled House didn't continually oppose imposition of a severance tax based on the volume of natural gas extracted, which every other major natural gas-producing state does. Could it be that legislative action is stalled because since 2010, the drillers and their associates have contributed $46.6 billion to lobbying and $14.5 million to high-priority campaign contributions to influential committee members and legislative authorities?

Industrial and commercial facilities across the country are discharging pollutants into our waterways, some vastly exceeding the amount permitted under the Clean Water Act. Once again in Pennsylvania, almost twenty thousand miles of streams and rivers are deemed unsafe for swimming and fishing. According to a report recently issued by the statewide environmental advocacy organization PennEnvironment, EPA data reveal that of the thousands of noncompliant violators, less than half faced federal or state prosecution, and most of those that did received nothing worse than warning notices. After all this time and with all we know, it's startling to hear that enforcement of the Clean Water Act is eroding.

So here we are. Why is it so numbingly apparent that the current president is dead set on undoing the good President Obama has done to save the planet? Maybe because he has polluted his cabinet and environmental agencies with names that compose an oxymoron when placed beside their respective posts. Maybe because he has made outlandish statements on the subject. Maybe because he doesn't like the man. Maybe because it seems as if the bottom line is all that matters to him unless it's something important to his agenda like the frickin' border wall that would spawn an environmental nightmare. The spinning wheel goes round and round.

A recent Yale poll has reported that Americans are increasingly concerned about climate change. A record 73 percent agree there is solid evidence of global warming, and roughly the same number say it is "personally important" to them. Sixty-two percent of respondents ascribe rising temperatures primarily to human activity and about 65% believe it is affecting weather in the United States. What does the remainder believe is responsible for the striking uptick in hurricanes, wildfires, heat waves, droughts, tornadoes, and "one hundred year" floods?

The poll represents a marked turnaround. As a voting topic in 2016, climate change ranked near the bottom in terms of matters of importance. In the 2018 midterm elections, only 29 percent of major televised debates referenced it. Most tellingly the man, not shy about his disbelief, was put in office in 2016, and his party of "what me worry" when it comes to the climate easily retained control of both congressional chambers that year. His election alone proved that human suffering and increasing wildlife extinctions were not enough of a priority to sway the vote.

But that was then. It's encouraging to note that 2018's blue wave produced a refreshing collection of new faces in the House of Representatives, some of whom are prioritizing the issue. Their ambitious and long-overdue "Green New Deal" proposal calls for a federal infrastructure and jobs plan geared toward vigorously curtailing our country's production of greenhouse gas emissions, funding renewable technology and energy-efficiency efforts with the goal of becoming a net-zero carbon economy, and confronting the problem of increasing income inequality. It is beginning to gain traction. A recent survey, one of the first to use "Green New Deal", found the vast majority of citizens questioned were in favor of the idea in principle, though most had never heard of it. The concept of earth first might finally be resonating.

The policy faces challenges. For one, you have the runaway national debt, thanks in good measure to Republican tax cuts. Reconfiguring the tax code by increasing the rates on high-income earners and corporations, implementing a progressive estate tax, and raising the capital gains tax on the wealthy, would redress the unfairness inherent in those cuts and provide much-needed revenue for the Green New Deal and other initiatives vital to our nation's welfare.

The traditionally time-consuming legislative mechanisms involved in vetting a proposition of the magnitude of the

Green New Deal are worrisome, especially when considering the ticking climatic time bomb under discussion. Support could weaken if deliberation over the policy takes on a partisan aspect, which seems all but certain. Many Republican constituents are not aware that the idea is being spearheaded by a cadre of progressive members of Congress. One of its premier champions, the newly appointed congressional representative from New York, Alexandria Ocasio-Cortez, campaigned on a Democratic Socialist platform. Studies have revealed that Americans are less apt to back policies initiated by the opposition party. Despite these obstacles, the findings represent a positive shift in public opinion.

So why did it take so long? For close to a decade, the concept of a Green New Deal was barely mentioned in the political discourse. *The New York Times* columnist Thomas Friedman coined the phrase in 2007. His impassioned advocacy to tax CO_2 emissions, incentivize wind and solar energy projects, and end fossil fuel subsidies gained a foothold in the mainstream for a short while, but by 2010, austerity politics put the discussion of a Green New Deal to rest.

The economy usually takes top honors among matters of importance to voters. The Green New Deal survey stressed qualities that appealed to parties across the political spectrum in this regard such as job creation and the promise of a more robust economy. The economic factor coupled with gut-wrenching reality—perhaps we finally experienced a natural disaster or doomsday report too far—and a youthful epiphany that forecasts a future up in smoke all influence the final analysis.

Hey, I'm not complaining, just peeved about the decades-long climate delay. Will it maintain the momen-

Lawrence K. Zeisler

tum necessary for a full-blown surge? It's time to dismount the seesaw and save the planet. An exploration into "why" might shed some revelatory light on the matter, hinder the prospect of a relapse, and hopefully contribute to Trump's dismissal in 2020.

The phrase "every little bit helps" is often referenced in discussions about life improvements. Regarding the present planetary debacle, "every major step is crucial" would be more apropos. One step would be the imposition of a progressive national carbon tax requiring industry to pay for emitting greenhouse gases. A sizeable majority of Americans support one if they could be guaranteed the money would be used for environmental restoration projects and/or renewable-energy research and development or public-transit upgrades. Yet only a third of respondents to a recent Reuters poll said they would be willing to pay an added $100 a year in taxes to help the cause.

Jacques Cousteau said, "People protect what they love." We need to honestly ask ourselves if the earth is worthy of protection despite the cost.

Another spinning wheel example reflects an apathetic tone to the problem. Now that gas prices have fallen, the purchase of less fuel-efficient SUVs and large pickup trucks is once again increasing, and too many hybrids lay fallow in car lots, accounting for about 2 percent of passenger car sales in the United States. Not long ago, when fuel prices were higher, economy cars were in demand. This phenomenon has played out since the first Arab oil embargo of 1973. Apparently, doing right by the planet takes a back seat in the fickle minds of many. This is problematic, considering that the transportation sector is the largest source of greenhouse gas emissions in the United States, the majority of that pollution coming from personal vehicles.

Everyone should ponder the true meaning of value. If they did, they'd probably agree that preserving the oceans is more important than purchasing a fully loaded Ford Explorer. One could downsize to a less expensive crossover (or better yet a smaller sedan or hybrid vehicle), contribute a slight portion of the money saved to humanitarian or environmental causes, and still drive in lavish comfort.

Although sublimating values would involve restructuring of priorities, removing the material excess would result in a cleaner and better life, spiritually and physically. I don't mean to preach, but perhaps we should take a positive page from the Good Book. The story of Jesus is one of sacrifice, and he frequently spoke of self-denial. His interpretations of both concepts are galaxies removed from ours.

Nothing is more satisfying than to sacrifice something of yourself for the sake of others. Nothing is more critical to life than the resurrection of the planet. To give is indeed better than to receive. We have the power and the know-how to slow and ultimately reverse the world's decline. All that's needed is the will.

I Pledge Allegiance to the Earth can be termed a study in polemics, and make waves it does, for it takes a swan dive (better yet, performs a cannonball) into the waters of some of our foremost institutions. Its value lies in its ability to provoke reaction and encourage introspection. Consider it a swift kick in the cerebral cortex. To recite Irish poet Brendan Kennelly, "If you want to serve your age, betray it."

There is a scene in John Steinbeck's novel *East of Eden* where upon completion of a discussion about the biblical story of Cain and Abel, a character named Samuel is visibly upset that his friend has introduced ideas that have shaken his worldview. After acknowledging that he needs time to ponder the matter, Samuel exclaims, "Your damned bitch is having pups in my brain already." Here's hoping that this book breeds like sentiment.

Conformists will find little solace in its words. Hell, who am I kidding? They won't find the book, period, but the contents will entice the discontented—those who question when all seems right with the world, are skeptical about the veracity of "feel-good" politicians and conspiracy-filled nonsense (mostly from the right), grow weary of the divisive rhetoric issuing from evangelical Christian pulpits, watch in disbelief as social media waxes ever more sensational, and shudder while bevies of ultraconservative news show hosts liberally pontificate with cockbird-like confidence. They cringe at the ability of mounting profits to beguile and nourish complacency toward all things that don't enrich coffers. Amid all the hoopla, they perceive a disturbance within the fabric of the collective soul.

I debated pulling my punches to make the book more marketable. I knew the effort was in vain when the pen lay inert on the table. I give no quarter, I ask for none. I'm reminded of a phrase that a friend is fond of reciting: "Tell a man what he wants to hear, and he'll pat you on the back. Tell him the truth, and he'll punch you in the nose." I'm not claiming that every word herein represents the unalterable truth, but their controversial nature is such that I've prepared myself for a beating.

Temperamental readers might brand me unpatriotic. They would probably not put much stock in the fact that the flag we salute blows on wind currents that circumnavigate the globe. It is likely that their worldview would founder in deep waters, and that they would bid adieu to the winds as they departed our shoreline, paying no heed to their life-sustaining worldwide journey. It is our duty, as it is all earth's peoples, to ensure that those breezes cleanse, not defile, humanity's collective face. If I softened my stance, I'd be forced to brand myself a traitor to all who inhabit this wondrous planet. Feel obliged to interpret my message as an act of disloyalty to whatever contributes to one's ignorance of the true nature of the global crisis unfolding before us.

The Rev. Dr. Martin Luther King Jr. stated, "Our lives begin to end the day we become silent about things that matter." Critics will hurl a plethora of adjectives at these pages, but *silent* won't be one of them.

By now you have probably ascertained a sense of frustration, a condition that owes its intensity to a deep-rooted and pervasive angst. Am I the only one who breaks into a cold sweat while weathering deep-winter warm spells, sensing something unusual about the swarms of insects buzzing overhead and the fresh roadkill that should be safely sequestered in peaceful hibernation? Why can't I immerse myself in the comfort like the scantily clad souls all around, cheerfully soaking it in? Am I strange for feeling irritated while listening to the local weather forecaster proudly announcing the springtime temperatures or when viewing a newspaper photo of a jogger trotting along an idyllic public trail? Doesn't anyone else imagine the pain and suffering inflicted upon the innocent life the world over due in no small part to the abnormal warmth visiting its plague on the planet? Forgive me for sounding like a wet noodle. On second thought, don't.

Many of today's trends bode ill for the future of wildness. To love something, it helps if one can feel it, embrace it.

Lawrence K. Zeisler

There are too many distractions, too much time spent away from the simple, natural things. Those fortunate enough to live near forests and streams are often engulfed by the tide of electronic and mechanical gadgetry, and residents of expansive housing developments can hardly be faulted for their inability to freely commune with nature. The artificial world is gaining a wider audience at the natural one's expense. It was particularly disconcerting to hear a radio personality recount that youths were busy building virtual snowmen on their computers and not outside.

Interacting with nature can present challenges that, when faced, uncover hidden strengths. The aim of the Outward Bound program is personal growth, and it encourages an individual's social skills by offering demanding open-air activities. During a recent event, students from a Philadelphia city school were taken out of their element and introduced to a series of outdoor tests, some requiring teamwork. Upon completion, nearly every one of them said they benefited, citing better feelings of self-confidence and making strides in communication with and compassion for their fellows. It instilled a newfound sense of perseverance.

One doesn't have to physically behold something to relate to it. Though not as inspiring as an actual encounter, our extraordinary minds afford us the opportunity to visualize things and respond with emotion. We've all seen provocative footage at the movies and on television and browsed photos online and in magazines that illustrate life's marvels. Only the most devout atheist would be unable to perceive a spark of divinity when witnessing cinematic depictions of the sun's rays piercing the canopy of a stand of giant redwoods. It would be a cold heart indeed that felt no sympathy while observing accounts of starving children.

> *I saw a fox in the morning light,*
> *watched it bound amid clovered fields,*
> *bob and weave to the wood wind's song.*
> *I saw it lick the warmth of a sunlit daisy,*
> *lingering long enough to catch a perfumed scent,*
> *and, in a twinkling, leap in sun-dappled frenzy,*
> *seeking to match a butterfly's flutter;*
> *then in elfin whimsy, spring into a blurry tailspin,*
> *stopping only when claiming a furry prize.*
> *As I lay in twilight's lengthening shadows,*
> *I saw a fox in the morning light.*

Something does not have to be in the backyard to be appreciated. I may never witness a bobcat in the wild, but knowing it's haunting scream pierces the still night air is drama enough.

I had the good fortune to view a video taken by a woman paddleboarding with friends at Deception Pass, Washington. It portrayed a pod of orcas, an endangered population inhabiting Pacific Northwest waters, swimming close by. The footage was so poignant you could almost feel the rush of condensed air and surface spray propelled skyward from their blowholes. The loud exhalation created by their mammoth lungs bespoke power but also emphasized the fragility of the great creatures whose beating hearts, like ours, require the flow of oxygen-rich blood to sustain their

Lawrence K. Zeisler

complex physiology. These factors, along with the overall beauty and harmony of the encounter between humans and mighty carnivores, evoked the spirituality that impregnates life's common thread. It left me weeping with joy.

The joy was mingled with sadness upon remembering that two-thirds of orca pregnancies experienced by this threatened group failed between 2007 and 2014 because of nutritional stress due to plummeting numbers of Chinook salmon as well as toxic pollution and intrusions from boats. The only calf born in the last three years died shortly after birth.

Despite all that has been written, every day I am made aware of the goodness that underlies humanity. I see it evidenced in every act of thoughtfulness, every job well done. I see it in corporate drawing rooms and small independent businesses where men and women strive to develop new energy-saving devices and in research facilities where cures to aid the suffering originate. I see it manifested in sensible and caring legislative practices such as the recently passed BUILD Act that will promote economic growth in developing countries, advance global stability, and open opportunities for businesses abroad. I see it in state capitals where lawmakers are adopting policies to tackle a warming earth. I see it in the army of young enthusiasts affiliated with the climate justice group the "Sunrise Movement" whose mission is to bring climate change to the forefront of public and private life while seeking support for the Green New Deal. It moves those corporations that voluntarily reduce carbon emissions and permeates the labs where scientists and technicians work to unlock the secrets of microbes to further ethically based biotechnical advances. I see it whenever someone forfeits their time to help a friend and in those who do the same for strangers. I see it in something as commonplace as a warm smile or handshake. Most of all, I see in the artless expressions of little children the glorious possibilities that one day may—no, must—mantle the earth. I play the devil's advocate to promote a better comprehension of the forces arrayed against those possibilities.

> *A human being is a part of a whole, called by us universe, a part limited in time and space. He expresses himself, his thoughts and feelings as something separated from the rest…. a kind of optical delusion of his consciousness. This delusion is a kind of prison for us, restricting us to our personal desires and to affection for a few persons nearest to us. Our task must be to free ourselves from this prison by widening our circle of compassion to embrace all living creatures and the whole of nature in its beauty.*

> —ALBERT EINSTEIN

> *The aspect of Nature is devout. Like the figure of Jesus, she stands with bended head, and hands folded upon the breast. The happiest man is he who learns from nature the lesson of worship … It is the organ through which the universal spirit speaks to the individual, and strives to lead back the individual to it.*

> —RALPH WALDO EMERSON

Lawrence K. Zeisler

Introduction

ADAM AND EVE ENJOYED AN EDENIC COEXISTENCE WITH their fellow creatures; both humans and animals having been provided plants and fruit for food. This idyllic scenario found in the second chapter of the book of Genesis met an abrupt fate in the third, culminating in Adam and Eve's punishment and forceful expulsion from the Garden by an irate God. I find the above account difficult to square with the depiction of the sixth day of creation described in the first chapter which ends with a contented God blessing his freshly formed male and female human achievements and instructing them to subdue the earth and gain dominion over all living things. A dominance reinforced after the Flood when the Lord declared to Noah and his sons that all creatures will now be candidates for consumption, existing in fear and dread of humankind.

Despite the Bible's frequent referrals to God's connection with all life, the inherent unity of humans with the earth's creatures and the earth itself had been all but neglected until recently by people who adhere to the Christian faith. To my knowledge, one's treatment of the earth was never a serious factor to consider during the quest for virtue.

There is a good chance that from the outset, nature may have been shunned by the early biblical writers, being representative of the milieu where sin and temptation abounded. This is first evidenced in the generally held notion that the devil, in the guise of a serpent, corrupted God's children with the original, world-altering temptation.

The overlapping of the physical with the mental—temptations or earthly desires—could have occurred because of the competition early Judaism and Christianity experienced with the established nature-based religions in their midst. There are numerous references in the Old Testament to pagan ritual and the worship of false idols. The fact that God's people sometimes reverted to such practices must have been disconcerting to those penning the sacred manuscripts. If this were so, it's not hard to deduce how the material earth would have been cast in a regrettable role. If the rain contained a pagan spirit, it and that spirit were partners in crime. Better to look away from the earth lest the temptation to find an elemental god again arise. This factor most likely contributed to an atmosphere in which it was difficult to behold nature with esteem.

Apparently the authors reasoned that only a god in unmistakable control of nature, and any spirits or deities believed existing therein, would have the capacity to remedy the problems they faced. God could not merely be responsible for nature's existence; he must have jurisdiction over it. His omnipotence had to be unquestioned; power and control were matters of faith. When God's creation of the natural elements is detailed in the Old Testament, it is voiced with deference, usually coupled with the acknowledgment of his authority over those forces and proclaiming his glory. These are often associated with intimations (or outright declarations) as to why one should fear and/or respect his might. Reverence for mastery of the natural world, in conjunction with disdain for anything pagan, apparently overshadowed realization of the peace and harmony essential to an indwelling love of nature.

One thing is certain: the information in the Old Testament writings dealing with God and nature left no visible imprint on Jesus. The ordained son had little time for his father's nonhuman achievements, making one question the effectiveness of their impact.

Though the Incarnation represents God's descent to earth, the popular notion is that he exists "up there." If it is true that we are all of one flesh and that flesh is of Christ, it is also true that many espousing this will argue that we will not officially make his acquaintance until after physical death. As understood by many, the final synthesis will occur in a dimension beyond the boundaries of earth and death or on an earth laid low by the ravages of Armageddon, if one interprets the book of Revelation literally.

Most Christians comprehend God only with the aid of a descriptive set of passages. In effect, their convictions are based upon those words. Isn't it said that if one is not in accordance with the Word, their faith is in vain? To them, the Word is God.

We express our thoughts and share ideas with words. They inform and instruct us about life, but words unsubstantiated by proof can take on a life of their own, superseding reality. For instance, they tell us of a place where death, sorrow, and pain do not exist. They demand that the faithful concentrate on the miraculous elements incorporated in Jesus's life, death, and resurrection, and they relate a history devoid of evolution. The danger is that when the supernatural is glorified, it can steal the show, often ranking above Jesus's earthly message. Would the zealots be so concerned about what Jesus would do if the everlasting promise of the resurrection was removed? What about nature, which is physical reality? To those mesmerized by these appealing mental pictures, nature might seem commonplace at best.

Heaven's otherworldly location further jeopardizes one's chance for feeling true affinity with the earth. The problem is compounded when it is considered that God's home was made distant in part to insulate him from the place where evil lurks.

These assertions stand out in bold relief when compared with Far Eastern and various indigenous cultures whose spiritual experiences are often realized during silent, palpable communication with the physical world, unencumbered by liturgy and dogma.

Evangelicals are the least environmental of committed Christians in the United States; many view climate change as a Leftist phenomenon lumped in with the overall liberal agenda. Perhaps that's why the planet's problems regularly fly below their theological radar. It's no coincidence that Donald Trump received a higher percentage of their votes than any other president. After nearly two years of exposed marital affairs, outright lies, and antagonism, most of them still approve, recognizing him as God's imperfect agent who is making America great again.

Thankfully, growing numbers of Christians are acknowledging the earth's plight. The National Council of Churches has described stewardship of the earth as a moral value. In 1991, the United States Conference of Catholic Bishops (USCCB) released a statement noting that environmental ethics are an integral part of Catholic teaching. Pope Francis, God bless him, frequently pontificates on the earth's behalf. It seems like just yesterday that the earth's saving grace was going to have to come principally from without our houses of stained glass.

Can this religious awareness reverse the effects of the

uneasy relationship Christianity has shared with the natural world? Has it taken on new meaning in sermons and assumed an equal space among the prominent social issues? Most importantly, does it have the power to go beyond mere words and sufficiently implant a newfound passion into the hearts, minds, and souls of the bulk of the faithful? Perhaps I should say awaken it, for it is believed here that the desire to do right by the earth dwells within each of us. There are no easy answers to these questions, but they need to be seriously entertained; the demons that have stood between the Christian God and his creation must be exorcised. Those who would evade this truth by using a soft-sell approach risk the peril of undermining the movement's potential. We must get to the heart of the matter; the reasons should be explored.

It's difficult to "green" a religion that makes so little mention of the natural world's sanctity, especially in the New Testament. This is made doubly difficult when the adherents take its words literally. It's hard to read between the lines to find an environmental implication if the words composing those lines are devoid of any reference to nature. The problem is complicated when he who is speaking those words is unquestionably omniscient and beyond reproach. Christ's evident compassion centered exclusively on humankind. If the Word is the way, it is hard to find value in that which is not divulged.

In this light, I would like to offer two quotes: the first by Bucknell University professor of religion Mary Evelyn Tucker and the second by environmentalist Aldo Leopold.

We need to underscore the dark side of religious traditions as well as their lateness in awakening to the environmental crisis. In addition, we should note the ever-present gap between ideal principles and real practices as well as the inevitable disjunction between modern environmental problems and traditional religious resources.[1]

As recently as the mid-twentieth century, Aldo Leopold wrote:

No important change in ethics was ever accomplished without an internal change in our intellectual emphasis, loyalties, affections, and convictions. The proof that conservation has not yet touched these foundations of conduct lies in the fact that philosophy and religion have not yet heard of it.[2]

Professor Tucker mentioned the dark side of religion. It doesn't get much darker than this. I am referring to a disturbing belief held by a politically powerful segment of the Christian Right: the notion that the apocalypse will play out on earth. According to their literal interpretation of the biblical narrative, environmental ruination is seen as God's will and will hasten the arrival of the rapture—their divinely inspired rescue from a crumbling earth—while the rest of unbelieving humanity is subjected to seven dreadful years of misery. At the end of the seven years, Jesus will return and begin the Millennium, ruling over a pristine planet where the faithful will enjoy one thousand years of prosperity. Intelligent people are willing to trade reality for what they perceive as truth. This isn't so, is it? Will someone please pinch me? It is apparent that numbers of Christian adherents are comfortable languishing in their ignorance, choosing to cling to beliefs written by those whose world-

Lawrence K. Zeisler

view was confined to a primitive sphere. Talk about the power of words! If this wasn't accepted as gospel, it could rank as a conspiracy theory extraordinaire.

Let me get this straight: This group of primarily evangelical Christians would turn a negligent eye to their Lord's creation, let it fall into ruin, and hope he materializes and not only forgives them but performs the task of environmental reclamation as well. The institution of an earth ethic would constitute a restructuring of their emotional and financial priorities. Not doing so gives them less to worry about. Do they have the wherewithal to exhume the light buried deep in their souls?

Environmental detachment permits the justification of deregulatory policies that give businesses greater freedom to expand while endangering our well-being. Laissez-faire economics is not suitable for this day and age. Playing fast and loose with planet earth got us into this mess. The profit motive, when left to its own devices, can lead us astray, often condoning wasteful and frivolous, even destructive impulses. The free market economy requires sensible (I stress sensible) adult governmental supervision from state and federal executive and legislative branches. Today's harsh realities must be met by pragmatism infused with reason and empathy for us and our world. While some members of the private enterprise community display sensitivity to the climate crisis and act accordingly, the rate and range of the overall response needs a firm kick in the hindquarters. The twenty-first century can afford nothing less; there is too much at stake. How often has the phrase "better late than never" been spoken one too many times as it applies to environmental ruination?

Waiting for the free market reaction to an ongoing

crisis, environmental or otherwise, can be an exercise in frustration. Sometimes careless and/or insensitive practices proceed unhindered until a public backlash or competitive threat is encountered, which often comes at the expense of valuable time, and pain.

Twenty some odd years ago the Big Three automakers, Honda, Toyota, and Nissan manufactured about 5,000 roadworthy electric cars in response to California's 1990 zero emissions vehicle (ZEV) mandate which specified that in order to sell gasoline powered vehicles in the state electric vehicle (EV) offerings would be required. Granted, as is the case with any emerging technology there were EV drawbacks, such as problems with parts suppliers and limited driving range, but battery improvements were in the works, and continued fine-tuning of the vehicles and subsequent mass production would have reduced costs and certainly resulted in their being a common sight on today's roads. However, faced with an auto-industry suit in 2002 and persistent pressure from the oil industry, California rescinded the mandate and that period's nascent push for broad-based electric auto technology went the way of the Carolina parakeet. Some motives behind the actions may have been short-term developmental costs and worry about future loss of revenues by automakers (EVs need no tune-ups and little maintenance) and big oil's fear of forfeiting their stranglehold on transportation fuel.

California, thirteen other states and the District of Columbia, comprising about one-third of the national vehicle market, are determined to enforce the Obama-era's stricter mileage and emissions standards even if the President weakens them as planned, which could split the United

Lawrence K. Zeisler

States auto market, saddling it with regulatory uncertainty. Faced with the dilemma of having to manufacture two different lineups of autos, Ford Motor Company, Volkswagen of America, BMW and Honda secretly assembled with the California Air Resources Board and agreed to rules that are moderately less restrictive than the Obama regulations, ones that can be applied to all the vehicles they sell nationwide; by 2026 the average fuel economy requirement would be about 50 miles per gallon instead of 54.5 mpg by 2025. To achieve this threshold numerous electric vehicles will be launched. Additional auto manufacturers are expected to jump on board, heightening the probability that California will be seen more favorably than the Trump administration in the likely court battles ahead. Like Washington Irving's folktale of Rip Van Winkle, the market awoke after a twenty-year slumber.

It's been known for decades that plastic waste has been clogging landfills and oceans. General negligence by industry proved more profitable than dedicating the necessary resources to remedy the problem.

In the United States only about ten percent of plastics are recycled. On top of this, the traditional recycling processes can't break down many of plastics' various resins and contaminants, the outcome being either landfill disposal or fabrication of "impure" derivative products with limited applications.

Consumers are becoming aware of the devastation and are putting pressure on the industry by rejecting the use of plastics whenever possible. Suddenly petrochemical companies have received an infusion of brain matter and are working on answers to the recycling dilemma. They are experimenting with ways to chemically reduce the substances to their molecular level, developing clean, undiluted resins that can be reused as raw materials for new products, which when utilized would diminish the necessity for freshly pumped oil used for plastics production. The costs of implementing the improvements are considerable but the potential upside in market opportunity, not to mention the environmental and societal benefits, definitely justifies the investment.

The same basic premise could be applied to the push by some oil companies, consumer products manufacturers and automakers for a U.S. tax on carbon dioxide emissions, which puts them at odds with various trade associations and other groups including the U.S. Chamber of Commerce, National Association of Manufacturers, and American Petroleum Institute. This represents a sea change in attitude, especially from the fossil fuel and auto industries, that historically have fought environmental efforts which threatened their bottom lines. The long overdue shift has occurred largely in response to mounting pressure from shareholders, young people, and those most impacted by climate disasters, principally citizens living in coastal regions. The initiative would benefit business in two major ways: protection from climate-related lawsuits involving former legal emissions, and freedom from various federal regulations related to greenhouse gas emissions. It is viewed by its promoters as a favorable alternative to the more combative and demanding Green New Deal.

It is customary to lay the blame for environmental degradation on misused applications of science and technology, but the human-centric aspect pervading Judeo-Christian thought cannot be ignored. This characteristic is expressed in the belief that only humans are created in God's image and are uniquely capable of meriting his divine grace. It also underlies the affirmation that the proper path to perfec-

Lawrence K. Zeisler

tion leads toward the spiritual and away from the worldly. Though Christianity likes to assure us that God touches inhuman things, it does not want us to focus on them while searching for him. Both the Old Testament God and Jesus Christ demand our undivided attention.

So is it happenstance that Western culture, which heralded the chaos that threatens earth's environment, grew to maturity worshipping the Christian God? I think not, for the religion possesses qualities that weaken its power to act as a deterrent to the destructive capacity of human endeavor. It could be argued that said qualities have inadvertently aided and abetted that destruction by providing our machinations with a springboard from which to proceed largely irrespective of the constraints imposed by a reverence for the natural order. One must question if there are enough spiritual safeguards contained in its design.

The safeguards apparently were not enmeshed in the Protestant work ethic, which determined that worldly success could be interpreted as an indication of eternal salvation and traces its origins to the Reformation in sixteenth-century Europe. Many noted thinkers have detected the connection between Protestantism and the growth of modern commercialism. The emergent industrial capitalism in the late eighteenth century, with its emphasis on factories and mass production, was based on processes that indiscriminately used natural forces and materials during production. The blatant disregard for the consequences of manufacturing, spurred by the profit motive's incessant prodding, carelessly polluted cities and the surrounding countryside, expanding the spiritual alienation from nature.

Have you ever thought about why the advanced cultures of China and India, before contact with the West, didn't develop technologies that flagrantly exploit the environment? The primary reason is that their religions and traditions conform to nature, firmly embracing her. Their creative efforts reflected a consideration for the natural system's parameters.

The Isha Upanishad, one of the ancient texts that contain some of the central tenets of Hinduism states: "The whole universe together with its creatures belongs to nature. Let no one species encroach over the rights and privilege of other species. One can enjoy the bounties of nature, by giving up greed." In other words, don't carelessly exploit nature.

Not so with Western Man; "mold and control" has been his mantra. Is it any wonder why the phrase "playing God" is so firmly established in the lexicon? In our rush to recreate the Creation, we have assumed the father's mantle. Like the supernatural feats highlighted in the Old and New Testaments, science is engaged in the manipulation and rearranging of matter and fervently committed to exceeding nature's limitations. Historically, and thankfully to a lesser extent today, an inadequate regard for God's effort has been displayed. He must shoulder some of the responsibility for the recklessness (or, I should say, the scribes playing his part two to three millennia ago).

The above mantra excited those "sportsmen" responsible for shooting and torching the passenger pigeon into extinction, once numbering in the billions in North America and whose flocks sometimes took hours to fly over a single locale. The same callous indifference applies to the grizzly bear, mountain lion, wolf, and plains bison (which were all but extirpated in the lower forty-eight states) because their freedom was considered threatening to our way of life. In the case of the bison, pursuit of short-term economic gain and a concerted effort to marginalize the Native American way of life accelerated the killing. It meant nothing that they had endured millions of years of evolution and were a magnificent symbol of our natural heritage. This attitude didn't apply only to specific life forms; whole ecological systems were destroyed to make room for progress. Most of the great swamps of the southeastern United States, those biological treasure troves, have been drained or otherwise despoiled.

If the true spirit of Christianity was adhered to by considerably more than just a chosen few, the urge to write this book would never have materialized. In other words, if this world were composed of the saintly, it would be virtually pollution free. Despite Christianity's historical failure to acknowledge the worthiness of nature, the saints lived environmentally sound lives. It seems that the holy do justice to nature naturally. Is this proof that God and nature are one?

In describing the Holy Fathers, Thomas à Kempis, the renowned medieval master of the spiritual life, wrote:

They often forgot even their bodily needs in the great sweetness of contemplation. They renounced all riches, dignities, honours, friends and kindred; they desired to possess nothing in this world. Scarcely would they take the necessities of life, and only with reluctance would they provide for the needs of the body. Thus, though destitute of earthly goods, they were abundantly rich in grace and all the virtues. Outwardly they were poor, but inwardly they were refreshed with grace and heavenly consolation. They were strangers to the world, but to God they were dear and familiar friends.[3]

Alas, the bulk of humanity is not saintly. Although I hear

Jesus's name used repeatedly, few endeavor to seriously emulate his or the saints' lifestyles. In all fairness, the cards are stacked against them, for today's standards make it difficult to follow a saintly path.

Throughout history, a miniscule number of Christians have achieved an exalted state. Included in the immense stockpile of those who haven't are most of the privileged inhabitants that have resided within the Vatican's consecrated walls. Verily, the medieval Church that accumulated vast power fell prey to corruption and excess. It appears that for most people, their faith is not strong enough to encourage them to renounce "worldly" ways.

I put worldly in quotation marks because I feel the term does an injustice to nature. It does not adequately disengage the streams, forests, and mountains from the human weaknesses that cloud one's perception of the truth. It is true that while undergoing their trials the saints concentrated on the spiritual and ignored the material, but this is not meant to imply that they looked upon the earth with disdain. There is evidence that once sainthood was achieved, they felt concord with the natural world. It's a shame they often realized this only after intense personal struggle.

The effort to conform to Christ works best for those who are willing to devote themselves unconditionally to him, which is possible only for the stout of heart. The majority of present-day attempts are fragmented, and while they can yield positive results, there are dangers. Many aspirants have a tendency to blow their progress far out of proportion to its real worth, bestowing upon their mediocre performance a false sense of grandeur. This penchant for illusion is widespread and preempts one from fulfilling the requirements necessary for a deeper understanding of and adherence to

Lawrence K. Zeisler

what it takes to be a true Christian.

When referring to the religious, I am speaking of leaders and followers, of whom the flock is legion, and not the holy ones, like Mother Teresa, who undoubtedly spent long hours agonizing over their personal frailties. Those truly sincere in their pursuit of spiritual nourishment must face themselves with strength and courage, for uprooting one's self-centered nature entails considerable suffering and repudiation of material things. Most people don't have the time or integrity to commit to such rigorous mental and physical discipline.

The saints prospered in love. By virtue of that love, they treated the earth with dignity, while those of marginal faith are often too busy attending to selfish interests that they hope will reap them reward here and in the hereafter. Jesus's words moved the saints. They have not had sufficient impact on most of the less than saintly to elicit serious sacrificial urges, and without the commitment to sacrifice, those words have limited meaning.

Jesus needs help. Despite centuries to work with, religion has failed to confer elevated virtue. Perhaps most glaring has been its inability to rein in the selfishness festering in the bowels of capitalism. Selfishness with its attendant greed, not the institution itself, tarnishes the workings of the souls of those members of the capitalist class that prioritize profit at the expense of the social good, environment and natural resources. Augmenting his message with definitive evidence of something beyond our ken might encourage people to act in a sound manner. The earth's existence provides the most solid proof of a divine presence.

It is no accident that paying the earth lip service endangers some basic virtues. Conversely, if one truly regarded the earth, virtue would come easier, and vice would suffer. Surely greed would not be so rampant if we showed greater esteem for all life and sincerely cared about its fouled beauty. Would vanity be so pervasive if we focused on the earth's appearance to the extent we do the image in the mirror? Even envy and jealousy would diminish if our attention was diverted from what we feel to be our shortcomings to the earth's escalating catalog of deficiencies. Reverence and compassion for the outside world confers in one a sense of humility, which reins in self-importance and moderates the tendency to devise selfish needs originating within. This principle also applies to humanitarian causes. For example, the idealistic young people serving in AmeriCorps volunteer programs have less time for self-centered interests while engaged in public service.

Hence, the same forces that undermine our love of the Creator urge us to lay waste to or ignore the Creation. Industrial polluter and roadside litterbug alike lack a fundamental respect for the spiritual. We can no longer afford to act with our heads in the clouds. Only our undivided attention will save the earth and ourselves from excessive suffering.

Forces that divide our attention are at work, and they compose the ego. To simplify matters, and in defiance of the psychoanalytic theory of personality, the ego as defined here is that portion of the personality that divides "I" from everything else because of its penchant for ideas that fail to see interrelationships. Despite the hackles that will be raised in the psychiatric field, the consciousness will be split in two, distinguishing the ego from the intellect. The intellect will be referred to as the natural faculty of perception and memory retention and the ego as one's cultivated, often contentious, means of

Lawrence K. Zeisler

awareness and home to prejudice and vice.

The ego is uncooperative by nature, quick to judgment and offended when criticized, resistant to personal improvement, and reliant upon prejudiced thoughts for guidance. It has a knack for persuading the individual that the concepts it forms are indispensable to understanding, but it limits comprehension by diverting attention from other crucial details. It is the source of the narrow-minded outlook. Hence, its attempts at securing stability and peace of mind are at risk of failure because it is isolated and rigid, whereas life is interdependent and always changing. When Adam and Eve fell from grace, their egos were born. The fruit they tasted held the knowledge of their unconformity with God and nature.

Whether consciously or subconsciously, the ego excuses mental impurities and convinces one that he or she is as pure as the driven snow. Whenever one perceives the truth of a given matter, it is the intellect, not the ego, that has done so.

While it is true that America's lands, waters, and skies have been the beneficiaries of environmental research and action unheard of thirty years ago, our sensitivity toward the earth could stand further refinement. Can you state that you are strongly troubled that bird populations in Europe and the United States are in decline due to acid rain? A team of Cornell scientists has discovered that tree loss, also a consequence of acid rain, is likely not the only reason. They have determined that the rain's acids deplete soil calcium, which reduces the populations of calcium-rich prey, such as snails and millipedes, that are vital to egg formation and nestling growth. Are you disturbed that sixteen of the last seventeen years have been the warmest globally since records have been kept, which is interfering with natural cycles? The chimney swifts in my region have been returning from their winter havens earlier than usual for some time. Have you wondered how hibernation's deep sleep will be affected? Will animals make more trips to the surface during warm periods? Will the food they depend upon be available? Did the American toad I saw on the road in my native Pennsylvania last January make it across, and if so, what were its chances of survival? How severe will the shock to plant buds be when a midwinter's warmth is snapped by a blast of arctic air? It's been held for some time that disrupted blooming cycles would be an early indication of a global warming trend. A father and son research team in England has proven that hundreds of wild plants are flowering at least six weeks earlier than they did a decade ago. This puts them in direct competition with species with which they are not accustomed to sharing the day. For some, extinction could be the result.

Will plants and pollinators, whose symbiotic relationships have evolved over millennia, respond identically to random temperature changes? The climate atop the crests of the Great Smoky Mountains is comparable to that of southern Canada. Hence, much of the flora and fauna inhabiting the high elevations originally hailed from points north. Numbers of species "trapped" along the ridges, especially plants and trees, will probably be unable to acclimate to warmer temperatures and eventually submit to their torrid touch. The Pennsylvania Department of Conservation and Natural Resources (DCNR) points out that winter temperatures in the Northeastern United States have risen 1.3 degrees Fahrenheit per decade from 1970-2000. It states that higher temperatures, coupled with wetter conditions, will likely place iconic tree species such as the American mountain ash, eastern white pine, mountain maple, American beech, quaking aspen, balsam fir, and various birches in jeopardy. The emerald ash borer and Hemlock woolly adelgid, both invasive pests native to Asia, are decimating host trees in the region and widening their zones of operation due to warming.

A study by researchers from Scripps Institution of Oceanography at the University of California-San Diego and Princeton University, using state-of-the-art measuring techniques, reveals that the earth's oceans have retained more heat over the last twenty-five years than was estimated. This is a concern since they absorb the lion's share of greenhouse gas emissions—much more than the atmosphere. The unexpected rise in temperature suggests that the earth is more sensitive to fossil-fuel burning than thought and that the waters are losing their capacity to sequester the gases.

The Arctic summer ice pack has decreased in thickness by about 40 percent over the last thirty years. If this trend continues, it will be virtually gone by 2100, severely compromising the existence of species including polar bears. Some bears already have a noticeably reduced stature because of the restrictions the changing environment has placed upon their hunting. A recent study conducted by a group of eighty scientists from forty-two institutions states that Antarctica, the earth's largest ice sheet harboring between 60–90 percent of the world's fresh water, has lost almost three trillion tons of ice from 1992 to the present, with 40 percent disappearing in the last five years. Particularly vulnerable is the western part of the continent, where warmer ocean water is melting two massive glaciers from below. The fear is that if left unchecked, the entire region will be transformed into a new sea. The resultant sea level rise would threaten low-lying cities. Some American coastal communities, especially in New Jersey and Florida, are already encountering increased instances of "sunny-day flooding"—tidal flooding that occurs without a storm.

Marine experts posit that by 2050, plastic waste in the oceans is expected to outweigh the fish. It is estimated that eight million tons enter the water every year. The largest of the five offshore plastic collection heaps, the Great Pacific Garbage Patch, encompasses a surface area twice the size of Texas. Calculations put as many as one million seabird deaths, as well as 100,000 marine mammal fatalities occurring yearly because of plastics and discarded fishing gear. An increasing number of whales washed ashore are found to have ingested copious quantities of material. An autopsy of a pilot whale, following an attempted rescue, revealed seventeen pounds of plastic clogging its stomach, most likely preventing it from digesting food. It vomited five plastic bags during the rescue effort. Sixty-four pounds of net segments, rope, polypropylene sacks, plastic bags, and other unnatural debris were found inside a thirty-three-foot sperm whale found dead on a Spanish beach.

Chemicals in plastics consumed by ocean life are working their way up the food chain. A recent Austrian study revealed plastic particles called microplastics in human stool, suggesting a possible widespread incidence in the food we eat. Sustained ocean temperatures of 86 degrees or above can cause the deterioration and death of living coral reefs; this phenomenon, "coral bleaching," is on the increase. Families that once fished Bolivia's Lake Poopo do so no longer because it has dried up. Valuable species of shellfish are declining along the East Coast because of degraded habitat induced by a warming environment. The famed ponies that have lived on Chincoteague Island, Virginia, for centuries are succumbing to a potentially fatal fungus-like infectious malady associated with subtropical regions, sometimes referred to as swamp cancer. Officials speculate that milder temperatures will exacerbate their plight.

An in-depth assessment performed by scientists from thirteen federal agencies concluded that unless fossil fuel use is dramatically reduced, the world will face calamitous, potentially irreversible climate change. Another study states that if global warming proceeds on its current path, by this century's end about one-sixth of oceanic sea life will be lost. Do you care enough?

Public response in recycling, farmland conservation, open space initiatives, and wetlands protection has been favorable. The retinue of laws and controls that have been implemented to induce industry to clean things up are essential, but as long as dependence is placed primarily on government to police the earth's fate, the pendulum will swing too inconsistently. Regulations enacted to control pollution can and have been erased with the swipe of a presidential pen. Even the EPA, whose job it is to enforce measures around clean air and water, has engaged in willful dereliction of duty thanks to the circus ringmaster in the White House and his handpicked retinue of clowns.

I look forward to the day when the regulations, as important as their enforcement, are replaced by passionate concern. The fact that a growing number of corporations are assuming responsibility for their actions is proof that our commitment to the environment is expanding. Major US retailers Walmart and Target are endeavoring to cut their carbon footprint and, to this end, are demanding that suppliers make efforts to do likewise. Farmers, wastewater plants, and cities and towns around the Chesapeake Bay are instituting measures that have improved conditions in our largest and historically super productive estuary, though there is a long way to go. Tough enforcement of the Clean Air Act over the years has prodded factories, power plants, and states along its margins to address the damaging effects of air pollution.

A group of lawmakers in the House of Representatives recently introduced the first bipartisan climate bill in nearly a decade. Called the Energy Innovation and Carbon Dividend Act, it would place a fee on carbon pollution emitted from burning fossil fuels, the rate increasing yearly. Besides the obvious environmental benefits attending the incentive to create technological advances in and use of clean energy, the legislation asserts that 100 percent of the revenue be disbursed among households in the form of a monthly "carbon dividend." If enacted, it is estimated the policy would reduce America's emissions by about 40 percent in the next twelve years, add 2.1 million jobs in the next decade, and prevent thousands of annual pollution-related deaths. The reported rollback of some environmental regulations incorporated in the proposal looks like a giveaway to polluters, though the safeguards can kick back in after ten years if emissions targets aren't achieved.

Some sports enterprises are stepping to the forefront. Lincoln Financial Field, home of the Philadelphia Eagles, just announced that it received a prestigious award from Leadership in Energy and Environmental Design (LEED), the internationally recognized green building certification system. The stadium currently generates 4 megawatts of power from 11,108 solar panels and 14 wind turbines, accounting for one-third of its annual electrical demand. The purchase of credits from sources that use renewable energy constitutes the remaining balance, making it 100 percent reliant on clean energy. It incorporates onsite bio-digesters that decompose food remains, contributing to four thousand tons of yearly waste removal that would otherwise be destined for landfills. The complex has done away with plastic straws, substituting them with ones made from renewable, compostable resources. Pocono Raceway in Long Pond, Pennsylvania, has installed a solar farm that provides the track's energy requirements and offsets the 28,838 metric tons of CO_2 released yearly during its competition events; any surplus energy is diverted to the grid where it serves local homes and businesses. It has also instituted a serious recycling program.

Landis Sewage Authority (LSA), a water treatment plant in Vineland, New Jersey, epitomizes a holistic approach to water resource administration and develops more power than it consumes with a combination of earth-friendly technologies. Its executive director, Dennis Palmer, aims to attain a near-zero carbon footprint and to recycle or reuse all the by-products resulting from sewage treatment. In addition to a forty-acre solar array and onsite wind turbine, a combined heat and power system uses microorganisms to break down the plant's sludge in a bio-digester, producing methane gas. The gas is captured and piped to a generator, making electricity and hot water. A recently constructed waste receiving station accepts liquid food waste, cooking fats, oil, and grease trucked in from surrounding restaurants, fast-food establishments, convenience stores, and homes. After passing through a grinder, the waste is mixed, heated, and pumped into an anaerobic (oxygen-free) digester, where the methane gas generated is converted to energy in an environmentally sound way.

The one hundred and fifty acres of pines and cedars maintained by the LSA forestry program remove CO_2 from the air. The habitat restoration project, managed in conjunction with various environmental organizations, provides refuge for a variety of indigenous plant and animal species, including a rare at-risk native flower called the swamp pink. Its four hundred-acre farm uses converted wastewater biosolids, rich in phosphorus and nitrogen, as an organic fertilizer for the hay and straw it grows and sells to horse farms and landscapers. Feed corn for cattle and chickens is harvested, and gross sales of over $100,000 are realized per year. Unlike most treatment plants that discharge treated wastewater into streams or rivers, LSA returns rigorously decontaminated effluent onto its property via spray irrigation and into infiltration basins where it percolates through the ground and contributes to recharging the aquifer. All in all, it is a sustainable and profitable venture. Other water treatment facilities have taken notice and are making strides in sustainability. Additionally, in 2016, LSA hosted three young African leaders, offering them academic and networking assistance and hands-on training that can be implemented upon returning home.

Nine states in the Northeast and Mid-Atlantic region, along with the District of Columbia, revealed that they will partake in a new "cap and invest" program to decrease emissions from cars, trucks, and buses and will upgrade the rail systems. The result will be a transportation network that is cleaner, more reliable, and more affordable. A major goal is to provide underserved regions with improved access to public transit.

For some, the primary motivations are market advantage, threats of permit violations, and profits, which is still cause for excitement. Those displaying empathy proceed from a stronger and more enduring foundation, which is evidently the case with Mr. Palmer. In the end, nothing short of a fundamental shift to an earth-first national ethos will ensure that we elect officials who sustain the commitment to proper planetary management.

For serious environmental revitalization to occur, sacrifices will be required. To a mind (or ego) accustomed to the plethora of luxuries in modern households, this request sounds sacrilegious, yet history has proven that humans can do with far less than is offered today. The rebuttal to this claim would mention the multitude of discomforts Americans endured as recently as fifty years ago or even yesterday if one chooses to swallow the hedonistic demands of product advertising. Conversely, an early-twentieth-century inhabitant, peering into a crystal ball, would be shocked by the magnitude of today's abundance.

Before you slam this book shut, please understand that I don't advocate a return to the Stone Age. Many of today's appliances are wondrous assets, but we don't need as much as we think we do. Although the United States represents less than 5 percent of the world population, it produces 14–15 percent of greenhouse gas emissions and consumes nearly 20 percent of the world's energy. A recent UN report stated that a person living in the industrialized world uses more resources in their lifetime than five to thirty people in developing countries. Not surprisingly, the average European uses about one-half the energy of their American counterpart without compromising their living standard. They know how to buy "smart" and engage in less energy-demanding activities. The statistics will dramatically shift as the standard of living in emerging nations improves and their citizens surrender to materialism's spell. China and India are making their consumptive presences felt. China now holds the dubious distinction of top national greenhouse gas emitter, though we track by far the largest per-capita carbon footprint. However, both Asian countries realize the virtues of renewable energy and are forecast to be two of the world's most dynamic solar markets over the next decade and beyond. China has announced it will invest $360 billion in clean energy in the upcoming three years and is promoting an aggressive timetable to end production and sales of gas and diesel cars, replacing them with zero-emission vehicles. It is currently the largest market for electric vehicles. The government has subsidized charging stations (by the end of 2016, the country had about three hundred thousand) to expedite the process. In Europe, a consortium of automakers engaged in a joint venture based in Munich called Ionity, whose goal is to boost electric car sales, is planning to have four hundred "ultra-fast" electric car charging stations in place across Europe by 2020.

The International Energy Agency predicts that renewable energy will account for roughly a quarter of global electricity generation by 2020. While great strides are being made in this arena, it is estimated that global energy demand will increase by 28 percent in the present generation. Consequently, although the clean stuff's deployment is expanding, the net amount coming from hydrocarbon production is also rising, providing more reason to promote responsible energy practices. It should be noted that despite its renewable push China continues to build coal plants it had planned to cancel, while subsidizing a pollution-heavy infrastructure across the globe.

Lawrence K. Zeisler

It used to puzzle me that people who worked and played under the auspices of a loving God could be so insensitive to the deterioration they wrought upon his work. An intrinsic part of the answer is now apparent: acts of grace, such as charity and compassion, were directed at human relationships to the exclusion of the environment. Thank goodness that appears to be changing.

There are those who will label me a nonbeliever upon reading these words. My response is that never, during my mature years, have I contemplated natural things with anything less than profound admiration and gratitude for the common hand responsible for their existence. I can only extend my sympathy to those who separate the dancer from the dance.

The Truth Is Out There: Don't Fight It

As is the atom, so is the universe.
As is the human body, so is the cosmic body.

—The Upanishads

There is undoubtedly a presence exceeding humankind's mental capacity. The Christian calls it God, gives it a human face and voice, and hopes death will illuminate the path to eternal unification. The scientist chooses to officially ignore it while striving to unravel its mysteries.

If in the beginning there was God, from whence did he come? Did he just materialize? Saying he preceded existence only takes us back a step, but a step to what, nonexistence? If on the other hand, he was responsible for nothing or nothingness, wouldn't he have forfeited his own being while making it happen? How can something be part of nothing? What came first, the chicken or the egg? Perhaps neither one did. If this sounds ludicrous to you, go to the head of the class.

Questioning is useless when using our limited awareness as a filter. Ideas like Big Bang, first and beginning, even something, nothing, and imagine are irrelevant. The answer, if obtainable at all, lies beyond time's constricting perspective, perhaps in a different reality or dimension, maybe in a remote, untapped portion of the brain. It is conceivable that death is the key to unlocking the door to revelation. No word, concept, or belief system can clothe the sheer nakedness of our impotence regarding this issue. All must yield to this undefinable Truth.

As a lad, I occasionally reached wit's end trying to locate a crack in the cosmic riddle. Naivety ultimately capitulated to reason and awe. The Truth is humbling and is the source of my faith. The naturalist (the belief that nature alone exists) might state that faith is grounded in ignorance, to which I heartily concur: pure, unadulterated ignorance that makes no claim to understanding. You know what? I don't feel any the dumber for it. A faith whose strength resides in the assuredness of the Truth's indisputable and pervasive essence: despite its fathomless nature, it's munificence is evident to the senses.

At times, when stepping outside, the natural world embraces me in a personal manner. I owe this kinship to a sense that something is in the air: a soothing, binding influence imparting security and belonging. The sensation is paradoxical, for it leaves me feeling sheltered yet exposed. As to the question of its being conscious of me, I haven't the slightest clue. I can only reply that the experience doesn't make me self-conscious in the least. It's as if a veil has been lifted, and I see that which has been around me all along. If I had to choose one word

Lawrence K. Zeisler

to describe this state, it would be liberation.

This feeling is bound to a heightened realization of a universal interconnectedness. When I envision our beautiful planet, I no longer picture it as a shining beacon spinning alone in the darkness. This enables my gaze to pierce the comforting aura of the clouds and deep-blue sky and run with the expansive freedom of the cosmos. When one realizes that we are the stuff of the stars and bonded with all of reality by a unifying, incomprehensible force, the cold reaches of the universe become bathed in a warmth that penetrates the protective atmosphere and fills the soul with peace. There is a void beyond the farthest outposts of rational thought. The Truth fills the void; there is nothing more sensible.

The faith spoken of here does not challenge the scientific method or hinder its progress. Divine recognition is different from divine intervention. Because it is independent of the stifling interposition of strict biblical concepts, belief in the Truth is no threat to science. Science is not deterred in any way when acknowledging that its findings are helping to shed light on that which formed the earth. We know too much and have come too far to need to cling to the outdated notion that faith encumbers scientific curiosity. By precipitating a more penetrating gratitude for life, its inclusion might curb scientific subservience to those aspects of industry that put profit ahead of human and environmental health and encourage commitment to more practical and harmonious, but no less intellectually demanding, endeavors that will confront us the remainder of our creative lives.

If the inspiration demanded for the advancement of "negative emission" technologies—designed to remove CO2 from the atmosphere as well as its discharge from fossil-fuel burning power plants and its safe storage underground—

ushers from a source much more profound than that which only enriches the investment portfolio, the pursuit of their application will be tackled in earnest. If proven viable and used with concurrent efforts to mitigate greenhouse gas emissions, various pursuits will go a long way in curtailing global warming. Since protracted scientific undertakings require a steady infusion of funds, it's incumbent upon governments to enact policies that incentivize businesses to research, develop, and use the urgently needed technologies. Regrettably, many of those striding the hallowed corridors of American power could use a generous sprinkling of reverence for that which provides them the breath of life.

Science, for all its rigorous discipline, bases existence on the roll of the dice. From an evolutionary standpoint, it puts its faith in chance. Devoid of the Truth, evolution has no purpose, meaning that utter accident determined the supremely effective system directing life's course. If so, it would be hard to disprove that we've been extremely lucky not just with the manner in which life evolved but also with the mix of chemicals constituting the earth and atmosphere.

There is no doubt that flora and fauna mutate and develop in response to environmental conditions, but it is not unreasonable to assume something could have drafted the general course evolution would follow or at least set the parameters by which the process would abide. Natural selection's essential quality, its randomness, works too well. Some may view the paradoxical quality inherent in that statement as a serious challenge to this argument's veracity; randomness, after all, connotes disorder. However, it could be interpreted instead as further proof of the discussion's overall premise, which is that the Truth reserves the right to transcend all attempts to logically make sense of it. The conventional definition of

Lawrence K. Zeisler

"random" would not apply, nor would the concept appear illogical, if seen in the context of a greater order.

There are still the questions of how the ingredients composing the environment originated and combined in a way to make life possible. Scientists are strenuously pursuing what conditions and materials produced life from nonliving matter. Even if the struggle bears fruit, good luck with determining the origin of nonliving matter.

To not realize the Truth is to be cosmically parentless as an individual, species, and world. Realize it, and one's quest for knowledge, as well as daily life, is undertaken with greater affection. Anyone standing before a majestic, snow-capped mountain will be overcome by the grandeur. Not everyone will be conscious of the fact that its glaciers and snowfields are crucial sources of freshwater, but only the spiritually aware will feel the inherent consolation contained in the confidence that something beyond our comprehension provided for the beauty and function and that all worldly phenomena are cut from a common cosmic cloth.

Christians will question me, citing that God represents the solution to the conundrum. What they will not tell me is that their deliverance began on the opening line of the Bible. "In the beginning" places the Truth squarely in the human realm—in time. In three words, its mystery is breached, setting the stage for the personification of the unknown.

God communicates with us throughout the Old and New Testaments, advocating a lengthy list of laws and rules to follow while displaying an array of human traits. The Old Testament God stresses his predominance and tells us to put none before him while demanding unquestioned obedience. Jesus forgoes the autocratic approach but discloses that failure to comply with some of his guidelines could land one in hell. Thanks to the written word, we have a vivid description of an all-knowing, centralized power not only solely responsible for existence but also in strict, current management of the cosmos. It's not difficult to deduce how such knowledge and preferential treatment could breed a sense of privilege and superiority.

This notion underpins Christian belief. It must be a boon to one's comfort and assurance to think the one true God took the time to consider their welfare. The more committed among them cling to this trust with passion and look upon nonbelievers with emotions ranging from mercy and tolerance to pity and, within the ranks of the overly judgmental, disdain.

It is an honor to be the only species capable of contemplating the grandeur of creation. In theology, this faculty is fundamental to enjoying God's exclusive gift to humanity: divine grace. It is taught that his grace is instrumental in orchestrating virtuous deeds and revealing the strength needed to face life's trials, as well as withstanding temptation, and is increasingly exhibited through good works and acts of faith. It has been an uplifting influence in the lives of those committed to spiritual growth and a key to unlocking the door to the innocence or lack of guile that awards the truly penitent. Alas, legions of the faithful fail to adequately implement its divine support to their advantage while seeking their own salvation. In the case of shallow-minded individuals, this species-specific blessing could help to bolster the notion of anthropocentrism, or human supremacy, that is the root of our problematic actions within the ecosphere.

Jesus's words radiate with beauty, but their allure can be hypnotic. To some followers, the desire to personally embrace them is overwhelming and often validates thoughts and conduct that don't reflect the depth of their intended

Lawrence K. Zeisler

meaning. Ironically, his premiere promise exacerbates the problem. Nothing fans the flames of self-deception like basing one's immortal fate on the integrity of their mortal performance. If one needs to believe something badly enough, the imagination can grant the wish. There are no shortcuts to God, but those who are convinced of their own righteousness have already booked one-way flights.

Many believers will scoff and call me misguided. I reply, "The mind, not God, works in strange ways." Folks often see what they want to see, perceive it as truth, and ignore the rest.

If exercised improperly, faith is headstrong and closed minded. The devout souls not held hostage by the portions of the Bible that betray its archaic roots must realize the evidence of evolution. They assuredly comprehend the validity of geologic science and that the earth is not ten thousand years old. Believing God set the evolutionary process in motion while supporting those in political power who would interrupt and endanger its momentum by turning a heedless eye to planetary destruction is not only tragic but possibly blasphemous.

The Christian religion is based on an era when life was full of mystery and the sources of physical and mental suffering were largely unknown. In those days, demons and evil spirits were the root cause of numerous afflictions, and resignation and hope played principal roles—first lines of defense against the incomprehensible natural, and supernatural, forces all around.

Science is slowly unmasking the divine majesty's secrets. It is not challenging or interfering in any way with God, but it is lifting the veil of ignorance that shackles a good portion of the Christian faith by allowing us to peer at the genius inherent in the handiwork we should be honored to observe and make every effort to nurse back to health. Its revelations are removing the unknown from one-half of the eternal equation, providing a source of enlightenment and supplying tools to better manage our fate, of which suffering is part.

Deference for the wondrous natural system brings one closer to the Truth or, for the Christian, God. An understanding of the earth's complex physical puzzle, with the resultant familiarity and comfort it evokes, enhances an awed respect for the unexplainable. Had the author or authors of the book of Genesis been privy to today's knowledge, there is little doubt the Creation story would have incorporated the evolutionary process.

When the Bible narrative was written, nature was not endangered, but her worship was viewed as a danger to order and law. Seeking to deliver the people from the bondage of their animal lusts, its authors focused on a spiritual plane existing above nature. In the process, she was all but overlooked, and humanity's roots withered and dried. Law and order were firmly established, while nature's gods have long vanished. She is now in harm's way because of us.

Christians yearn for familiarity with their Lord but are not overly concerned about attaining intimacy with the product of his hands. They put more emphasis upon the authenticity of the written accounts of Christ's miracles, in which they have a vested interest, than the living proof of God's existence. They might mention the miracle of human birth or marvel at the accomplishments of modern medicine or the latest technological achievement but overlook the sublime quality of a sparkling stream. This criticism does not apply to every Christian, but until the evidence decisively proves otherwise, I will not deviate from the contention that, in general, it is pertinent. Many will feel unjustly insulted. If these fine people were to search their souls, would they be able to hear God's voice in a hawk's shrill call or detect his breath on a cool autumn breeze? Can they sense divinity in the blood pulsing through a blue whale's massive arteries? It's time to concentrate on worshipping the miracle of life.

This paragraph applies to Christians, naturalists, and anyone else willing to listen. What's wrong with accepting our place by graciously deferring to the Truth? Facing its existence is not akin to giving up. To the contrary, a humble recognition of it clarifies the vision by deflating swelled self-importance and brings into sharper focus our commonality with one another and all living things. Our true potential would be better served if we pursued knowledge and brotherhood with reverence for the universal unknown we are all beholden to, the concrete proof of which lies in front of our faces. We may not be able to put a finger on it, but it's fingerprint is everywhere. Those employed in the service of technological progress should be mindful of this fact. There is no doubt that life would be the beneficiary, and there is little question that acknowledging the Truth would dispel many of the obstacles standing between science and faith by freeing God from the suffocating demands imposed by words and the beliefs they foster.

The words *God* and *Creator* will often be used in the ensuing text. Bear in mind they are shackled to and limited by the mental images they invoke, mere frames of reference that only hint at that which defies the imagination. Discussions specifying the Judeo-Christian God should be interpreted in the context of the biblical tradition.

Please understand that no disrespect is being leveled at said God. How can one not be awestruck by the monumental reverence bestowed upon him by so many for so long? You will find random employment of the term throughout these pages out of consideration for those multitudes and for convenience. Its familiar ring adds a personal quality to any point under discussion.

Lawrence K. Zeisler

Chapter 1

"In pushing other species to extinction, humanity
is busy sawing off the limb on which it perches."

—Paul R. Ehrlich

A ny true artist's work is a labor of love, the product of a soul search demanding ample expenditures of energy. Just as a painting, literary work, or musical composition reflects one's inner urges and drives, so too must the earth and all upon it be the manifestation of that which is responsible for its existence. A conservative estimate cites eight million species inhabiting the planet. That number alone should move any person of faith to the earth's cause.

When humans entered the scene, the earth was in the midst of a prodigious biological flowering. It is reckoned that since then, plant and animal extinctions have been accelerating at an alarming rate with a grossly disproportionate share transpiring in the last three hundred years. We are experiencing the most dramatic case of species mortality since the end of the Cretaceous Era, about sixty-five million years ago, one thousand times faster than what is considered natural. The World Wildlife Fund calculates that the global population of vertebrates (mammals, birds, reptiles, amphibians, and fish) has decreased by about 58 percent from 1970–2012. A Intergovernmental Panel on Climate Change report states that if the average global temperature rises by 3.5 degrees Celsius, 40–70 percent of animal and plant species will be in danger of extinction. *Scientific American* magazine asserts we are losing more than one hundred species per day in the tropical rainforests, which are vanishing at the rate of about eighty thousand acres daily with another eighty thousand acres being degraded. The world's rainforests are responsible for roughly 20 percent of the total oxygen produced each year and play key roles in moderating climate and carbon absorption. These regions are by far the most prolific on earth, housing at least one-half of its flora and fauna. Their topmost level, the canopy, may be the richest biological storehouse in the world; a 2.5-acre area could shelter as many as forty thousand different insect species.

An avuncular researcher from the University of Tennessee, Pimm is not merely being theatrical. Based on his and his colleagues' calculations, some 50 percent of the world's flora and fauna could be on a path to extinction within a hundred years. And everything is affected: fish, birds, insects, plants, and mammals. By Pimm's count, 11 percent of birds or 1,100 species out of the world's nearly 10,000, are on the edge of extinction; it's doubtful that the majority of these 1,100 will live much beyond the end of the next century. The picture is not pretty for plants either. A team of respected botanists recently reported that one in eight plants is at risk of becoming extinct. "It's not just species on islands are in rainforests or just birds or big charismatic mammals," says Pimm. "It's everything and it's everywhere. It's here in this national park. It is a worldwide epidemic of extinctions.[1]

Lawrence K. Zeisler

Under normal conditions diverse ecological communities are more resilient and better able to stand against stresses imposed from without. We have introduced a vast cocktail of pollutants and pesticides that threaten these communities by weakening plant and animal immune systems, making them more vulnerable to microbial and fungal infections and less able to counter the devastation of climate change, exotic species invasions, habitat loss, chemical spills, and other sources. Individual species do not live in a vacuum but are bound to those around them in a complex ecological web, all contributing to a sustainable whole. This interdependence, in conjunction with the drastic changes to the biosphere our activities have brought on, means extinction is likely to escalate exponentially in the coming years as increasing members of each network succumb and whole ecosystems unravel.

The noted natural historian and broadcaster Sir David Frederick Attenborough recently told Britain's Prince William at the annual meeting of the World Economic Forum in Davos, Switzerland, "We are one coherent ecosystem. It's not just a question of beauty, or interest, or wonder—the essential ingredient of human life is a healthy planet. We are destroying the natural world, and with it ourselves."

Plants and animals have undergone eons of transformation, adapting to alterations in their surroundings. For the process to work effectively, the alterations occur slowly. Climate change, exploding human population growth, and pollution poison matters by speeding the rate of environmental conversion. Those species that are immobile or confined to a specific habitat meet their fate when the landscape is adversely affected. Ones higher on the food chain are disadvantaged because they need more time to adapt. The polar bear's plight is the most notable. If the Arctic refuge it calls home continues its rate of melting, it will be unable to modify its lifestyle and most likely go extinct in the wild.

Simpler life forms reproduce quicker than more complex ones, which gives them a dramatic edge when facing environmental shock. The African elephant, whose daily nutrition requirement strains the local vegetation, gives birth once every four years, but it's not unusual for a female rabbit to produce thirty offspring a year. Farther down the chain, the common housefly is capable of laying 4–5 batches of 100–150 eggs during her adult life of 1–3 months.

On the bacterial level, reproduction occurs much faster, which enables them to change in response to external pressures. Superbugs or super bacteria arise because their accelerated generational rates allow them to genetically mutate and develop resistance to antibiotics.

Researchers conclude that about a third of the estimated sixty-three hundred documented species of amphibians are in danger of extinction, primarily because of human interference (largely contaminants). They agree that since 1979, over two hundred frog species have vanished. Aside from the importance of amphibians in the food web as insectivores and prey for higher animals, it is concurred that their susceptibility to environmental imbalance makes them bellwethers of environmental health by indicating subtle yet potentially drastic ecosystem changes. One is reminded of the canary in the coal mine allusion on a much more complex level.

One cannot assess what effect viewing a sharp-shinned hawk, tracking past the window on a snowy day, has on the soul. Nor can they measure the difference in value between a woods edge harboring a host of native songbirds versus the same one devoid of all but a couple of species. It is impossible to gauge the deficiency of compassion in a heart unmoved by environmental suffering. That gap in compassion may not be quantifiable, but there is little doubt that those feeling it are spiritually deficient. Unless diversity itself is considered sacred or at least inexorably linked to the sacred, species will disappear with alarming regularity.

You may argue that there have been previous mass extinctions, five on record, and that natural replacement of species has always refilled the diversity void. True, but much of the replacement fauna and flora will not duplicate those with which we are familiar. It's also true that unlike this one, previous extinctions were unavoidable. Human interference might not be as dramatic as the meteor and volcanoes thought to have laid low the dinosaurs, but when the smoke clears, it may be as devastating.

Large numbers of familiar medicines come directly from nature or from chemical formulas developed from natural substances. Rainforest plants have been used in the treatment of hypertension, rheumatoid arthritis, and Hodgkin's disease. The dreaded viper known as the Fer-De-Lance, which inhabits the tropical forests of South America, exudes a venom that causes a precipitous and often fatal drop in its victim's blood pressure. By isolating the chemical responsible for the reaction, researchers refined the design template for production of the synthetic chemical captopril, the first of drugs devised to combat hypertension known as ACE inhibitors. About a quarter of our pharmaceuticals are derived from rainforest sources whose surface we have barely scratched.

I was beginning to understand. That the tropical rainforest may well be nature's chief library of experience from which humanity can learn, not only how to do things but also what vast variety of things may be possible. And why the environmental crusader Norman Myers was moved to saying that doing away with it would be like burning the ancient library of Alexandria - that if present patterns of converting tropical rainforest persist, it may be the worst biological debacle since life's first emergence on the planet 3.6 billion years ago.[2]

Though the rainforests have been given the most press, organisms across the globe are yielding medicinal secrets. Some of the more notable substances that have been harvested are morphine, salicylic acid (from which aspirin is derived), and penicillin. A substance that combats breast and ovarian cancers, Taxol, can be traced to the bark of a yew tree native to the Pacific Coast. Another anticancer drug comes from a deep-sea sponge. A clot-dissolving compound in the vampire bat's saliva may one day be used to treat stroke victims. A material located in the liver and other soft tissues of certain sharks is the key component in the development of a cancer drug and a possible treatment for blindness in the elderly.

It has been calculated that elephants have a cancer mortality rate of 5 percent compared to 11–25 percent in humans. Research has revealed that the pachyderms have twenty copies of a tumor suppressor gene labeled TP53 (humans have one) that produces a protein, p53, that detects DNA-damaged cells and signals them to begin repair. If a cell cannot be restored, the protein triggers a process of

Lawrence K. Zeisler

cellular suicide known as apoptosis, preventing it from dividing and possibly developing into a tumor. However, tumors can spread if they find avenues around this genetically programmed self-destruction.

The elephant TP53 performs an added function: it activates a dormant, or dead, gene exclusive to the species called LIF6. The gene quickly kills an impaired cell that has avoided cellular repair or suicide, successfully nipping a possible cancer in the bud. The multiple copies of TP53 guarantee a more thorough search for unrestored DNA damage. Scientists believe the resurrected, now-functional LIF6 gene is a key to how the long-lived animals can survive countless cell divisions, each one carrying a minute risk of spawning a cancer-causing mutation, and aided their evolution over millions of years to such enormous proportions.

After subjecting human and elephant blood samples to radiation to induce DNA breakdown, it was determined that both human and animal displayed a similar rate of DNA repair, but far more elephant cells underwent apoptosis, which correlated with the larger number of TP53 genes activating the LIF6's specialized protein. The hope is that by studying this phenomenon further, devising drugs that mimic the gene could lead to a breakthrough in cancer prevention. At the least, it might enlighten us about something fundamental to cancer. It is suspected there are other ways elephants have evolved to battle the disease. The fact that their cells are similar to ours lends strength to the effort. Animal species lacking the LIF6 gene are protected from cancer in various ways. There is much untapped potential.

The venom of the Israeli deathstalker scorpion contains a peptide (mini-protein) called chlorotoxin that tends to naturally bind to tumors in the brain. Researchers in Seattle,

Washington, have been able to reengineer the venom and create a nonpoisonous version that when injected into the bloodstream attaches to only diseased cells. They have blended the clinging molecules with a florescent dye. This compound, known as "tumor paint," coats tumors; when hit with near-infrared light, it causes the cancer to become luminous, enabling surgeons to easily locate it.

Advanced by pediatric oncologist Dr. Jim Olson, tumor paint provides the means to precisely target malignant cells without damaging healthy tissue, so tumors are easier to remove. It could be FDA approved as early as 2019. Dr. Olson states that most man-made drugs cannot penetrate the protective membrane that wards off toxins surrounding the blood vessels in the brain (where the tumors exist), but the scorpion venom, aided by millions of years of evolution, has a means to circumvent the barrier and enter the brain. The technique has been tested in skin, prostate, breast, colon, and other cancers.

The hope is that surgeries will be supplanted by using a substance like tumor paint to deliver not just a dye but an anticancer drug expressly to a tumor. There are indications that other components of the venom might help to regulate insulin, increasing the possibility of a treatment for diabetes. Dr. Olson now specializes in studying proteins solely derived from nature for use in medical treatments. With so much untapped potential, the tragedy deepens when one learns that only about two million of the estimated eight million plant and animal species have been classified.

Donald Ingber, professor of bioengineering at the Harvard John A. Paulson School of Engineering and Applied Sciences and founding director of the Wyss Institute, states, "Nature has frequently already found elegant solutions to common problems; it's a matter of knowing where to look and recognizing a good idea when you see one."[3]

A field of science called biomimicry advocates technology should be used as a tool in the service of nature, the goal being to heal the troubled environment through implementing earth-friendly advances. Biomimicry recognizes nature as both teacher and benefactor, something traditional peoples have known for tens of thousands of years. Theirs is a sustainable view that says we must immerse ourselves in the study and understanding of natural processes and develop technologies based on the imitation and subsequent modification of those processes for the purpose of life enhancement. The premise is that nature has nurtured a time-proven system that renews itself with hardly a hint of inefficiency, waste, or pollution. The secret of survival surrounds us.

Biomimicry takes signals from efficient anatomical or structural designs found in nature and adapts them to a specific technological improvement. For example, termites use convection to create complex ventilation systems that keep their mounds cool on the hot African savannahs. An office complex designed in Zimbabwe by the engineering company Arup has a climate-control setup patterned after the natural cooling termite network, dramatically cutting down on the energy required for ventilation and resulting in substantial savings in air-conditioning expenses. Buildings play a huge part in humankind's total energy use, and finding creative ways to make them more sustainable is of the utmost necessity.

The *Stenocara* beetle, native to the Namib desert in Africa, harvests moisture from the morning fog through a series of nodes, or bumps, located on its back. The water runs off the nodes into passageways leading to its mouth. Biomimetic models based on this phenomenon are being developed to draw water from the air.

Kingfishers have a unique beak that allows them to exit a low-resistance medium (air) and enter a high-resistance medium (water) with minimal splashing. Japanese engineers researched the beak's specialized qualities and used it to address a problem plaguing their high-speed bullet trains. The loud noise generated by the displacement of air in front of the trains was problematic when exiting tunnels. The shock wave labeled "tunnel boom" disturbed nearby residents and wildlife, and the concussion was so intense that physical damage to the tunnel occasionally occurred. The engineers identified the train's nose as the culprit and refashioned it in the likeness of a kingfisher beak. The adaptation permitted the train to negotiate the pressure difference between the low-drag outside air to high-drag tunnel air much more effortlessly. The improvement contributed to a 10 percent increase in speed, 15 percent decrease in electrical use, and the cessation of tunnel boom in newer trains.

Hagfish, primitive eel-shaped fish, emit a defensive slime that expands into a gelatinous, elastic deterrent when released into seawater; its purpose is to clog the gills and mouths of predators. The slime, a natural and renewable material, is composed of mucus and thread-like fibers; it is lightweight, flexible, and, for its weight, stronger than steel. When the fibers are dried and stretched, they turn into a soft thread that can be converted into textile fibers. The thinking is that it could be woven into protective clothing, creating lightweight versions of body armor. It may one day displace petroleum-based materials like Kevlar and nylon. Benthic

Labs is working on developing a biodegradable polymer using natural filaments made by the hagfish that would have multiple civilian applications. Some eco-friendly fabrics of the future might be derived from fish slime.

Because it is difficult to breed hagfish in captivity, mass production of the slime must be replicated in the lab. The US Navy has come up with a synthetic version of the biomaterial that mimics its effects and is experimenting with ways to artificially enhance its expanding and clogging capabilities for field applications: blocking ballistics, jamming enemy boat propeller blades, firefighting, and even bottling it into a spray to protect divers from sharks. Fouling of ship hulls with organisms like barnacles and mollusks is an ongoing problem. The current deterrents are paints mixed with powdered copper that eventually leaches into the water and pollutes, injuring or killing sea life. The slime's unique properties hold promise as an antifouling agent.

Learning from nature is fascinating and seemingly endless. Researchers in Japan have developed a needle based on the bite of a mosquito. They discovered that the insect's mouth is structured to penetrate the skin in a painless, efficient way. Their engineering produced a product that works beautifully. Scientists in the United Kingdom studied the wood-boring wasps ability to drill into wood with delicate efficiency and fabricated a neuroprobe that is easier to maneuver, enabling surgeons to operate in a gentler and more controlled manner. Evologics analyzed the ability of dolphins to communicate via a network of frequency-regulating acoustics and parlayed the knowledge to invent a method of data transmission for a tsunami early-warning system.

Scientists Jeffery Karp of Harvard University and his Harvard/MIT colleague Robert Langer studied porcupine quills and created discs of medical tape infused with microscopic barbs based on their observations. The hope is that the breakthrough will prove effective in sealing surgical wounds. The same gentlemen used the physiology behind the gecko's ability to cling to vertical surfaces to invent a biocompatible medical adhesive bandage that adheres to the exterior of tissue. It is patterned after the fibers at the tips of the fingerlike projections on the lizard's feet. When coated with a thin layer of medical-grade, sugar-based glue, the tape is waterproof and seals tightly to internal organs. It could aid in repairing blood vessels and closing holes in the digestive system. Since it is biodegradable, it does not have to be removed; it dissolves after serving its purpose with no release of toxins, unlike many of today's adhesives that can harm cells and irritate tissue.

While on this sticky subject, scientists are working on other bio-inspired glues derived from the proteins found in marine animals such as oysters and mussels. These species produce natural, nontoxic cements that secure them in place, enabling them to better feed on microscopic prey while clinging to wave-washed rocks. An MIT research team engineered a hybrid product that fused naturally viscous mussel proteins with a biomimetic polymer, creating a new adhesive. The result was much stronger than the original mussel glue. Because of their maritime origin, shellfish-inspired adhesives would work well in the moist intrabody environment. Many current medical adhesives don't bind forcefully or very long to biological tissue when wet.

Lawrence K. Zeisler

The Dusky Arian slug covers itself in a mucus to stay moist. When combined with specialized proteins, it makes a glue that enables it to attach to a surface so effectively that predators often can't dislodge it. Influenced by the Dusky Arian, another Harvard research group formulated a family of glues using polymers that, like the proteins in the slug adhesive, create a powerful chemical bond with the tissue beneath. They incorporated a stretchable bio-material known as a hydrogel. After experiments on pig organs and simulating real-life applications, the glues not only adhered better than commercial medical adhesives, but their pliant character made them less brittle, allowing them to conform to and flex with the tissues, strong indicators of their potential.

It is likely that the medical adhesives under discussion will be safer, more attractive alternatives to staples, sutures, and screws that rend tissue and bone when inserted. If designed to supplant surgical meshes, particularly those involving hernia repair, many postsurgical complications might be alleviated.

The nonmedical applications are intriguing. Many items we buy such as computers use permanent glues to attach parts. Scientists the world over are working on bio-inspired alternatives that degrade when no longer needed, making dismantling and recycling of the items much easier. Glow-worm glue, which the creature uses to ensnare prey, could be used to devise an eco-friendly substitute for formaldehyde-based wood glues that can sicken people when exposed. In the aftermath of Hurricane Katrina, trailers providing refuge for victims started oozing formaldehyde from the adhesives in their panels. The shellfish-derived adhesives mentioned above proved superior to five of the strongest commercial glues when bonding polished aluminum, wood, and Teflon. It is hoped that the success achieved in controlled laboratory conditions will translate to real-world applications.

As attractive as it sounds, implementing a nature-based substitute is no easy task. Scientists must determine the ingredients in a natural substance and study how they combine before humans can mimic it. It must be tested on various materials prior to delivering a more effective version. Rigorous experimentation is required to measure the new material's efficacy and safety before possible deployment.

Only a miniscule portion of what nature has to offer humanity has been detailed, but the promise is endless. With the right commitment, we could be on our way to probing that promise's vast complex of inner workings and extract its fertile universe of blessings, paving the way to a healthy and enduring future.

Chapter 2

"It's not just the economy, stupid."

—Variation on a theme James Carville
coined and Bill Clinton exploited

The earth is a "closed system" meaning it produces everything required for the survival and growth of its inhabitants. A series of natural chemical cycles working in concert are fundamental to the system's sustainability. The carbon cycle is one. Carbon is essential to life. The carbon cycle is represented by the ceaseless interchange of carbon through its storage and release from the four primary reservoirs: the earth's crust (which houses fossil fuels), soils and plants, the atmosphere, and the oceans. Existence relies upon the cycle's proper functioning. There is a fixed amount of carbon within the environment, and when left to its natural devices, the planet retains a relatively stable relationship between ebb and flow.

Human enterprises such as fossil fuel burning, deforestation, and factory farming (which includes, among other things, dependency on cattle and relentless tillage) rupture the cycle by disturbing the balance of where the carbon is stored, expelling a disproportionate amount into the atmosphere. Climate change is a direct result of these and other anthropogenic (human-induced) disruptions.

About half of the world's forest cover has been leveled. According to the United Nations Food and Agriculture Organization, the earth's forest loss each year is an area about the size of the country of Panama. Ninety percent of native trees in America have been felled since the colonists arrived. Slowing the rate of destruction is important for numerous reasons, a predominant one being their ability to absorb and store carbon; one large tree can store up to 1.5 tons in its lifetime. In fact, one half of the weight of dried wood is carbon. When a tree dies a natural death, its carbon is taken up by the soil during decomposition or, after bonding with oxygen, is slowly emitted to the atmosphere as CO_2. During burning, the CO_2 release is instantaneous, and more potent greenhouse gases such as nitrogen dioxide and methane enter the atmosphere. Fortunately, milled wood used for construction continues to store the accumulated carbon.

Natural climate solutions to the greenhouse crisis are essential. Conserving and regenerating nature is of paramount importance for the sake of all planetary inhabitants. One relatively cheap and sure way is planting native trees to repopulate deforested land. The U.N. has issued a challenge to countries declaring they engage in widespread reforestation projects, setting the target of replanting an area larger than the nation of India by 2030. Some have taken up the gauntlet. The multicountry African Forest Landscape Restoration initiative plans to restore 247 million acres of damaged forests by 2030, China wants to generate forests comparable in size to Ireland, and Pakistan recently planted 1 billion trees. An international effort, Initiative 20x20, plans to replant 49 million acres in the Caribbean and Latin America by 2020. Grassroots restoration programs in some countries, most notably in Africa, enable rural communities to involve themselves in protecting and nurturing naturally established seedlings and resprouting trees, saving on costs by reducing the need for replanting and expensive external assistance. This restoration movement is growing and producing a generation of young activists.

Another reason to analyze our land-use practices is that the soil is a vast storehouse of carbon. Scientists say that soil harbors more carbon than the atmosphere and all terrestrial plant life combined. As the primary ingredient of organic matter, carbon plays a critical role in the fertility, structure, and water maintenance of soil. Plants absorb carbon from the air during photosynthesis and convert it into carbon compounds, some of which are used to furnish above-ground growth. In this way, it is transferred from one medium (the atmosphere) to another (plant material). A relatively small portion of the carbon is discharged back into the air as CO_2 during respiration. The excess enters the roots and feeds soil microbes that symbiotically aid the plant in acquiring nutrients released during the decomposition of organic material. When decomposition is complete, the remaining material called humus consists mainly of large, complex, carbon-based molecules. Most humus is so stable that if left undisturbed, its carbon can remain harbored for hundreds or thousands of years. Hence, these processes contribute to the soil's ability to act as a carbon sink or area of storage.

It is estimated that cultivated soils globally have been depleted of more than 50 percent of their stored carbon, most of which has been returned to the atmosphere as CO_2 via oxidation. Between one-quarter and one-third of the surplus CO_2 in the atmosphere has come from land-use practices over the last century, the majority from industrial agricultural operations. This release of billions of tons of carbon has added to global warming, and the deteriorated soils lose much of their vitality and ability to feed the growing worldwide population.

There is marvel enough in the way nature functions to infuse an "awake" person with a flush of reverence. Ah, the radiance of it all commands one to take notice. If form and function are life's bread, color has to be its butter. If our destructive activities, especially those contributing to climate change, are left unchecked, the oceans and lands will progressively lose diversity, resulting in a heartbreaking diminishment of planetary stability, color, and beauty. The species most able to adapt are often those that are more basic and mundane.

The oceans are already bearing witness to this tragic unraveling of species and splendor because of climate change's warming and acidifying of their waters. Coral bleaching, in which stressed corals excrete colorful symbiotic algae living in their tissues causing them to take on a blanched appearance and eventually die, is associated with increasing temperatures. In 2016, bleaching affected up to 90 percent of the Great Barrier Reef's coral and destroyed nearly 30 percent. The US National Marine Fisheries Service says that live coral has declined 50–80 percent over the last three decades in some areas of the reef system in the Florida Keys, the third largest in the world. This is just the beginning. Even if countries comply with the emissions reductions agreed to by the Paris Agreement, more than three-quarters of the world's coral reefs will experience annual bleaching before 2070, drastically reducing their chances for survival. Covering less than 1 percent of the earth's surface, coral reefs are home to at least one-quarter of all marine

Lawrence K. Zeisler

life and provide an estimated $375 billion of goods and services a year from tourism, fisheries, and coastal protection. Though not all forms of coral are projected to suffer, the beautiful ones that provide the best living conditions for thousands of breathtaking organisms—many that humans rely directly or indirectly on for food—are at greatest risk. Like the rainforests, disease-combating drugs are being developed from coral reef plants and animals, and many benefits awaiting discovery will never be realized. Can we live without the reefs? Yes, but the quality of life would take a profoundly disastrous hit.

Thankfully, there are members of the scientific community who are sensitive to the plight of the deteriorating oceans. The Mote Marine laboratory is a nonprofit, independent marine research entity composed of two hundred employees, more than thirty of whom are scientists. Their mission is to heal the troubled oceans by seeking ways to counter the negative effects of pollution, overfishing, acidification, and increasing warmth. To this end, they are engaged in projects to support the part their waters play in maintaining the planet's viability.

The Coral Health and Disease Program explores the causes and repercussions of disease within coral reef systems. DNA sequencing and molecular procedures are being used to identify bacteria that influence the corals' susceptibility or resistance to environmental stresses. The goal is to counteract the spread of disease and strengthen coral immunity.

A collaborative effort of the Florida Keys National Marine Sanctuary and the Nature Conservancy has planted more than twenty thousand corals onto weakened reefs in the Florida Keys. One program involved in the effort uses a process that accelerates the growth of critical slow-maturing, reef-building corals, and another maintains a nursery that nurtures the threatened staghorn coral. A portion of the endeavor focuses on cultivating over twenty kinds of hard corals, originally collected as fragments that were severed from the reef due to disturbances like boat groundings. The purpose of the combined strategies is to restore the reef numbers by genetically identifying and selecting coral strains that display resilience to threats that will be abounding in tomorrow's altered seas.

Mote Marine laboratory and the Nature Conservancy plan to establish a system of coral gene banks by 2020 to preserve vital tissue diversity, and five years after that, it projects to have a working relationship with the United States and international groups, the objective being the replenishment of the Keys and Caribbean reefs. These initiatives and others are exemplary and deserve praise, but in the final analysis, they rely on fundraising and philanthropic investment for implementation. Think of how much more could be accomplished if a microscopic amount of the US federal budget was dedicated to efforts to preserve our biological diversity.

The oceans collect the greatest amount of the planet's solar energy. According to a study just issued by scientists in the United States, China, Germany, and France using sophisticated new instrumentation, the world's oceans absorb around 90 percent of the excess heat generated as the planet warms, a figure 60 percent higher than that in a report presented by the UN Intergovernmental Panel on Climate Change. Although it has been highlighted that the margin of error in the findings is much larger than initially thought, the central conclusion that the oceans are harbor-

Lawrence K. Zeisler

ing increasing concentrations of heat is beyond dispute.

Atmospheric CO_2 dissolves in ocean surface waters, but the increased heat is infringing upon the efficacy of the process. Warmer water cannot hold as much of the gas, so as temperatures rise, carbon capacity decreases. The CO_2 absorption is helping to slow atmospheric warming, but for how long? At what point will the seas' chemistry be altered to such an extent that an unacceptable threshold is met?

The atmospheric buildup of CO_2 has led to excessive amounts of acid in the oceans. In the past two hundred years, seawater has become 30 percent more acidic, faster than any known change in its chemistry in the last fifty million years. The acidification portends alteration of sea life of apocalyptic proportions. When CO_2 dissolves in the water, it changes its composition by forming carbonic acid, which lowers the ph level. Carbonic acid binds carbonate ions (a critical building block for many marine organisms) and depletes their number. The ions are instrumental in the production of the calcium carbonate-rich shells and skeletons of creatures including coral, clams, mussels, urchins, and oysters. In extreme cases, the chemical reactions can lead to the degeneration of their skeletons and shells.

In the Southern Ocean near South Georgia in the Antarctic, where waters rising from the deep are more acidic, the shells of tiny sea snails called pteropods, a type of zooplankton that drift through the water, are dissolving. This would normally not be a problem, but when combined with human-induced acidification, the waters become much more inhospitable. The shells of the creatures are composed of aragonite, a form of calcium carbonate that is vulnerable to high acidity. Though regions of distress like this are currently rare, the fear is they will be extensive by midcentury, seriously threatening pteropod populations. How would this affect us? Their calcium carbonate-rich shells store carbon that is safely deposited on the seafloor as sediment when they die. If their numbers plummet, another means of carbon storage will be jeopardized, which would add to the growing list of ways anthropogenic activity dangerously interferes with natural fluxes in the carbon cycle. Zooplankton are critical components in the oceanic food web, the maintenance of which is vital to the well-being of the ocean. If you need a specific sample of how pteropods interrelate with us, how's this: they comprise about half of the diet of baby pink salmon. Need I say more?

A minor change in the ph level of seawater impairs marine life, in certain species affecting reproduction, growth, and immune responses. In some fish, it alters how the brain processes information. High levels of CO_2 can scramble a fish's senses, making it less able to avoid predation. Krill (another kind of zooplankton), the shrimp-like creatures that serve a major role in the Antarctic food chain, are under duress in parts of their range. While studies are inconclusive, evidence points to warming waters and acidification as serious threats to their fragile life cycle. Species such as penguins, seals, and whales depend on them as a food source.

The byssal fibers that enable mussels to hold onto solid objects like rocks and piers must constantly be replaced. It was discovered that ocean temperatures play a key role in determining their effectiveness. Tests show that mussels inhabiting cooler waters produce elastic and sturdy fibers, but when temperatures rise an appreciable degree as in summer, new fibers are considerably less stretchy and far weaker. Lab experiments that varied the ph in water samples revealed an inverse relationship between acid increase and a mussel's clinging ability. The upshot is that as waters continue to warm and acidify, mussels will find it harder to maintain anchorage. If large colonies wash away, it could initiate unwanted changes to coastal ecosystems (not to mention the impact on mussel harvesters who would have to probe deeper, cooler depths in search of their quarry).

Geologists study the possible future effects of acidification by inspecting soil and rock samples ("cores") taken from various depths in the earth's crust. Chemical analysis of fossils from deep ocean cores show that the earth hasn't endured the current levels of CO_2 in the past thirty-five million years. To predict what the oceans might be like by 2100 when carbon amounts will be much greater, geologists must go back another twenty million years to the Paleocene-Eocene Thermal Maximum, when a "dissolution event" occurred. Cores reveal that shelled sea life disappeared dramatically, and sediment changed from a white, chalky calcium carbonate to red-brown mud.

The oceans absorb CO_2 by means of biological and physical processes. There are disturbing signs that both are breaking down and that the oceans are becoming less efficient carbon sinks.

The earth's climate and weather patterns are regulated in part by physical forces that constitute oceanic circulation. Wind-driven ocean currents, which are strongest on the surface, exist above a slower-moving circulation spurred by differences in water density and controlled by temperature and salinity called thermohaline circulation. Also referred to as the "global conveyor belt," it is a series of interconnected deepwater currents that circumnavigate the globe, moving millions of cubic meters of water. This combination of upper-level and submarine currents is responsible for carrying warm surface water from the equator toward the poles and cold, deep water from those regions back to the tropics.

The Atlantic Ocean component of oceanic circulation designated the Atlantic Meridional Overturning Circulation (AMOC) conveys heat from the southern hemisphere and tropics to the North Atlantic region. The warm, salty, equatorial surface waters are driven primarily by the wind and move northward, discharging climate-moderating heat. As they near the pole, they are chilled by frigid atmospheric temperatures and encounter more winds that increase evaporation rates, adding to their salt content. Eventually they contact the salt rejected during the freezing of sea ice known as "brine exclusion." Combined with the high salt volume, this cooling increases density. The salty, colder, denser waters sink to the depths in an action called downwelling. The sinking, located at two spots in the North Atlantic Greenland and Labrador seas, has been labeled the North Atlantic Deep Water (NADW).

The force of the constantly sinking dense water moves it along, flows south as underwater currents through the Atlantic basin, and enters the Southern Ocean where some rises to the surface via upwelling. Upwelling occurs along coastlines and in the open ocean when winds push water away from an area and the displaced waters are replenished with cooler ones from below. Downwelling develops beside coasts when winds force surface water toward land, where it piles up and sinks, and in deeper seas where spiraling winds compress surface water and push it downward. The mixing of deep and upper waters occurs intermittently at points around the planet and are the driving forces of thermohaline circulation.

The NADW ultimately converges with the current that encircles Antarctica, the Antarctic Circumpolar Current.

Unimpeded by any land mass, it connects the three great ocean basins, redistributing their heat and other properties, which has a major effect on global climate.

Although the salt content is less (though still a factor contributing to water density) in Antarctic waters than in the NADW region, the cold surface winds blowing off the continent combined with the frigid waters underlying the ice shelves are primarily responsible for the formation of the downward vertical flow that spurs the renewal of oceanic deep water in the Southern Hemisphere: the Antarctic Bottom Water (AABW). It is the coldest and densest bottom water with the highest oxygen content and has been referred to as the deep ocean cooling and ventilation system.

The deepwater circulation produced by the AABW spreads out from Antarctica into the oceans, playing a decisive role in the movement of water. AABW forms at different spots, the most prominent being the Weddell Sea in the south Atlantic that refreshes the AMOC with enriched waters and plays a prominent role in the Atlantic climate. Some circulation heads into the Indian Ocean where after passing through it, a portion heads westward around the tip of Africa and links with the north-flowing currents of the AMOC breaking away from the Antarctic Circumpolar Current. The remainder continues eastward along the south coast of Australia and eventually into the Pacific basin, where it makes a loop and finds its way back to the South Atlantic. Another location of the AABW in the Ross Sea flows toward the Pacific Ocean. The thermohaline circulation mixes water from all the oceans, reducing their differences and making them a global system.

Without the cold, density-driven portions of the conveyor belt, there would be no deepwater currents. Any change in the temperature or salinity in these relatively small pockets at the poles could have severe consequences by interfering with water mixing and circulation, limiting, among other things, a supply of dissolved oxygen to the deep ocean the creatures there require. Global warming is precipitating the melting of the Greenland ice sheet; one recent sweltering day 11 billion tons of ice were lost. Coupled with increasing precipitation in the high northern latitudes, this is slowing circulation in the northern portion of the AMOC by diluting the polar seas with lighter, less salty fresh water. It is imperative for the AMOC to operate efficiently because of its contribution in transporting water, carbon, heat, and nutrients around the planet.

Reports have indicated that the influx of fresh water just described is weakening the flow of the strong Atlantic current known as the Gulf Stream, which is a vital segment of the worldwide circulation system. It seeds the North Atlantic Deep Water with the saltier, denser water it requires. The ability of its waters to "prime" the deepwater pump is contingent upon their volume and density when reaching their destination, both of which are being compromised. Climate models forecast about a 25 percent diminishment of the Atlantic turnover process by the end of this century.

Studies reveal a decrease in bottom-water density in parts of the AABW as well, resulting from increased warming and water freshening. If not for the moderating influence of the worldwide oceanic circulation, temperatures would be much more extreme at both the poles and equator, causing much of the earth's land surface to be less habitable.

Properly functioning polar deepwater "pumps" are critical because of their role as carbon sinks. CO_2 is more

Lawrence K. Zeisler

soluble in colder water and is extracted from the atmosphere in the polar regions more efficiently than elsewhere. The dissolved inorganic carbon sinks to the depths and becomes part of the underwater circulation. Because the rate of flow is so sluggish in the deep ocean, the NADW and AABW safely sequester the carbon-enriched waters for several hundred or perhaps a thousand years before they mix with the warmer surface water that cannot contain the carbon as well. It is then dealt with biologically.

Since warmer waters are less able to dissolve airborne CO_2 and more buoyant, any increase in water temperature at the poles would reduce their carbon intake and the tendency to sink as deep. If this were to transpire, the upshot would be additional atmospheric CO_2 and more radical changes in weather patterns. Oxygen is more soluble in colder water, which means that warming waters contain less dissolved oxygen, a staple for life that has been declining in the overall ocean system as the temperature has increased. It is impossible to predict the full effect these changes will have on ocean life, but there is no denying it will be dramatic.

As alluded to, the global conveyor belt is vital to the proper functioning of the global CO_2 cycle. It is also a major player in nutrient interchange. Its cooler, deep-flowing polar waters contain important nutrients that are dispersed on the ocean surface by upwelling, enriching the warmer, nutrient-depleted waters where they are consumed by phytoplankton. Phytoplankton are microscopic marine algae that form the bottom of the oceanic food chain and thus are critical components in the marine ecosystem. They inhabit the ocean's surface known as the mixed layer (about the first one hundred meters of ocean depth on average). Its proximity to the atmosphere ensures that dissolved oxygen levels in the topmost waters, despite their warmth, are at or near full saturation. It is labeled thus because of the churning action caused by winds.

By biologically converting inorganic carbon in the atmosphere and seawater into organic compounds through photosynthesis, phytoplankton provide sustenance for complex marine food webs, playing an indispensable role in the planet's carbon cycle. The CO_2 reduction in the surface waters for which they are responsible allows for continuous assimilation of the gas from the atmosphere, though some is returned when they respire. They comprise about half of the plant matter on the planet and therefore generate about half of the world's oxygen, which is released into the atmosphere or the surrounding surface waters where marine life use it for survival. When those that escape predation die, they sink to the depths and decompose. Most of the carbon fixed in their tissues dissolves and is released into the water as nutrients, adding to the storehouse provided by the decomposed remains of other plants and animals. Wherever upwelling brings the nutrients to the surface, often along the western continental margins, one will find the richest fishing grounds. A small but important percentage of the stored carbon becomes buried under sediment with their remains, contributing to its sequestration.

Phytoplankton are most productive where the nutrient transfer from the depths to the surface proceeds unhindered. In areas of the ocean prone to stratification or layering, there is little vertical mixing of nutrients. Stratification occurs because of differences in water density of which temperature is the main determinant. Because surface waters become more buoyant as their temperature increases, a disparity is created with the colder, denser

Lawrence K. Zeisler

waters beneath. The greater the disparity, the more pronounced the stratification. In areas of extreme stratification, the transport of oxygen-rich surface waters via downwelling, vital to deep water creatures, is restricted. It also means a decline in cooler water and nutrients upwelling from below, which has an adverse effect on phytoplankton productivity, sometimes forcing surface marine life to migrate elsewhere to feed. Less productive phytoplankton means less CO_2 consumed (and less O_2 produced), leading to more atmospheric warming. Research performed by a group at Canada's Dalhousie University reveals an alarming decline in the number of phytoplankton worldwide. They attribute this primarily to stratification.

Without the ocean ventilation provided by dissolved oxygen distribution during downwelling, the existing supply would be strained by the aerobic (oxygen-dependent) organisms living throughout the water column. The resulting increase in death due to O_2 depletion and ensuing decay would create an environment conducive to anaerobic bacteria, which thrive in oxygen-depleted conditions. While decomposing, they produce hydrogen sulfide, which is toxic to most marine species. Under excessive circumstances, reduced downwelling could lead to mass extinctions.

Paleontologists posit that some 250 million years ago in what is considered the most pronounced extinction episode in geologic history, deep ocean ventilation became so sluggish that the ocean turned stagnant. The oxygen starved, and methane (another byproduct of anaerobic decomposition) and sulfide-fouled waters created an atmosphere where over 90 percent of marine species disappeared.

Coastal ecosystems are another effective source of carbon sequestration. Occupying only 0.2 percent of ocean surface water, they perform a disproportionately key role in carbon management. The carbon stored in these vegetated areas is referred to as "coastal wetland blue carbon." Reports indicate that on a per-acre basis, they have a considerably greater capacity to trap atmospheric carbon than terrestrial forests. Included in this group are mangroves, seagrass meadows, and tidal salt marshes. Carbon is stored temporarily in the foliage of the marine plants through the photosynthetic uptake of CO_2. It is also housed in their intricate, deep-root systems that have extracted it from the surrounding debris and sediment.

On land, when leaves or a tree falls, microbial breakdown gradually releases carbon back into the atmosphere. Saltwater saturation veritably blocks the decomposition of marine plant matter, trapping their carbon-rich remains in the sediment, potentially for millennia. Between 50–90 percent of coastal wetland carbon is locked in the underwater soil. In seagrass meadows, the number can be as high as 95 percent. Add to this their contribution to biodiversity, fisheries, and storm protection. To date, 50 percent of the world's mangroves and 29 percent of its seagrasses have vanished, with more being lost yearly. Curtailing coastal development and pollution runoff and endeavors like trawling and dredging of the seafloor, as well as ill-located aquaculture ventures, would help to ensure their vitality and prevent the disturbance and release of huge carbon banks that have accumulated under the ecosystems for centuries.

Rising temperatures are affecting the distribution of large numbers of marine life, causing them to venture to areas they never occupied before. Cold-water species are seeking deeper or higher latitude waters, while warm-water species are moving to areas previously too cold, forcing them to change their feeding and breeding patterns. When a non-native organism enters an ecosystem, it is often termed invasive, and it can cause harmful interruption to the established order. The severity of change is different in each circumstance and difficult to predict, but new interactions become the norm, many with unforeseen detrimental effects.

The disruption of life patterns can change predator-prey relationships, leading to starvation. In some cases, reproductive rates are adversely impacted. A distinct species of zooplankton that Atlantic cod feed on along the US northeast continental shelf are moving to cooler waters, and scientists have discovered that the populations of cod are declining. Black sea bass are shifting their habitat, and projections put it three hundred miles northward of present by 2100. During two recent record-hot summers when a type of seagrass known as eelgrass almost disappeared in the Chesapeake Bay, economically valuable fish and crustacean populations declined due to loss of nursery habitat.

Some mid-Atlantic fisheries have been driven from their traditional fishing grounds, encountering and competing with New England vessels. Higher fuel costs and protracted time at sea put a strain on fishermen. Additionally, quotas on the particular species a fishing enterprise can keep are based on harvests common to a state or region. Summer flounder and black sea bass, once relatively infrequent in New England waters, are becoming abundant. Massachusetts congressional representatives are pressing to alter the quotas for those species. Otherwise the local operations may have to release those caught in excess of what is permitted.

Warmer temperatures can bring bacteria to waters where they were once excluded, exposing the inhabitants to new diseases. Just as on land, the overwinter survival potential of pathogens is enhanced when temperatures increase. Growing outbreaks of maladies plaguing ecologically important species such as marine mammals, sea turtles, corals, and mollusks have been associated with this phenomenon. Bacterial disease resulting from warming waters, as well as overharvesting, is responsible for the near extinction of the California black abalone, a type of mollusk important to the health of coastal food webs off the California coast. By feeding on algae, they lessen the chance of algal blooms, which can have detrimental consequences on the local ecology. Abalone predators like sea otters and sea lions must forage for less attractive prey, putting stress on predator and prey.

A phenomenon known as "dead zones" jeopardizes the rich diversity of oceans and large lakes. These areas of low oxygen caused by algal blooms get their nourishment from an excessive diet of nutrients such as nitrogen and phosphorus. Under normal circumstances, the nutrients feed the naturally occurring blue-green algae. When inordinate amounts enter the underwater system, algae overproduce, and after dying, they provide a rich source of food for bacteria. In severe instances, bacteria radically multiply and rob the water of dissolved oxygen. Fish are forced to leave the oxygen-deprived area. Bottom dwellers like oysters, clams, snails, and lobsters are less able to escape and often die.

There are over four hundred dead zones in coastal waters the world over, and they usually occur near areas where industrial and agricultural enterprises load waterways with nutrients. The primary sources of nutrient pollution are fertilizers, wastewater, and fossil fuel burning. The largest dead zone is choking the bottom of the Baltic Sea. A

Lawrence K. Zeisler

huge one extends for hundreds of miles along the Louisiana and Texas coasts, stripping portions of the Gulf of Mexico of so much oxygen that virtually no life exists there.

To make matters worse, this spring's extreme rainfall in the Midwest has flooded the Mississippi River, and a toxic mix of chemicals, human waste, farmland fertilizers, and pesticides from multiple states and two Canadian provinces contained in its water are pushing into Gulf estuaries, marshes and bayous, wreaking havoc in some of the country's most bountiful fisheries. The contaminated torrent is not only devastating shrimp, oyster and crab populations but numerous dead dolphins have been found covered in skin lesions that experts associate with fresh-water exposure. Bottlenose dolphins are highly territorial and are unwilling to vacate their spawning grounds even under adverse conditions. A fisherman recounted seeing a mother dolphin nudging her dead baby through the water. Scientists predict the nutrient overload will cause the Gulf's dead zone to expand in area, rivaling the size of Massachusetts by summer's end.

Global warming may act as a catalyst in the formation of dead zones even where there is no direct influx of nutrient loading like the one off the west coast of North America. Wind-driven upwelling brings vital nutrients from the deep, causing phytoplankton blooms and enriching the sea life. Scientists suspect that rising temperatures over land are increasing the strength and duration of winds, lengthening the periods of upwelling and "flooding" the seas with excess nutrients, causing the phytoplankton to overproduce. What cannot be consumed by the local sea life dies and decays, contributing to the formation of a dead zone. The waters along the northwestern coastal shelf off the Oregon coast, once abundant fishing and crabbing grounds, are now an oxygen-deficient graveyard littered with the carcasses of mollusks, crabs, and other organisms.

Jellyfish are an exception. They are incredible survivors, existing in various forms for half a billion years. They require less oxygen than most sea life because of their low metabolic rate and thrive in oxygen-depleted waters. Since warmer waters contain less oxygen, a climatically changed world may see jellyfish dominating the oceans. Acidification apparently poses little problem—their lack of a hard skeleton or shell makes them resistant to lower ph levels. From the poles to the equator, jellyfish blooms are already on the rise.

Complex ecosystems with their myriad jellyfish predators—some of the more noted ones are threatened species like sharks, sea turtles, tuna, and swordfish—and competitors are the primary reason the creatures have been kept under control. Thanks to overfishing, industrial waste pollution, oil spills, floating trash, and climate change, humans are destroying the complexity of the oceans, leaving the door open to organisms that tolerate harsher conditions. Sadly, many of the ones we rely on for sustenance and sport are not included on that list.

It has been proven that humans can survive diversity loss; witness life in big cities and crowded suburbs. How many more species can be obliterated worldwide before we gravely feel the consequences? One thousand, fifty thousand, one million? Many would say we've already gone too far. They can hear in their hearts the death knell of countless plants and animals that elude their ears. Less concerned individuals reply, "What we don't know won't hurt us." Or will it?

Each of life's participants is distinct yet dependent upon its surroundings. Nature is a wide spectrum of relation-

Lawrence K. Zeisler

ships interacting simultaneously. Deep within the Brazilian rainforest, one finds innumerable interrelationships. Taken separately, each drama extends little farther than its immediate sphere of influence. No one knows how many such spheres must topple before the results are severely felt, for en masse they are the rainforest. And we know how tropical rainforests critically impact regional and global weather patterns, reduce CO_2, and provide life-giving oxygen.

We all but wiped out the bison in a blood-splattered orgy of greed. Although the tragedy was pronounced, its outcome was insignificant to us. When we tore out the native grasses and plowed the topsoil in parts of the bison's former range, however, the disaster known as the Dust Bowl ensued.

As nature dwindles, so does our self-reliance. We'd best keep this in mind when determining how deep into the earth we should go when pumping aquifers for irrigation and drinking purposes. The IPBES Global Assessment Report on Biodiversity and Ecosystem Services, a comprehensive picture of the impact economic development has had upon nature over the last five decades compiled by hundreds of accomplished authors from 50 countries, concludes that almost 75 percent of freshwater resources are presently devoted to crop or livestock production. In large sections of the Midwest, we have already tapped underground prehistoric reservoirs. One of the largest aquifers in the world, the Ogallala, stocked with ice age water, is serving expanding drinking and farming needs. Situated beneath parts of eight states from Texas to South Dakota, its liquid treasure is largely responsible for the transformation of this land—some of which is semiarid—into the breadbasket that supplies the United States and world markets with billions of dollars' worth of crop production per year. In parts of the region, the groundwater is gone, giving farmers no choice but to abandon their wells. Once depleted, estimates project that it would take over six thousand years for rainfall to replenish the aquifer. Creative initiatives are being undertaken to judiciously use this precious finite resource, yet for many farmers, the drilling and pumping continue with no end in sight.

Similar actions are taking place the world over, resulting in the decline of large groundwater basins in Africa, Asia, and the Middle East. In the Far West, a battle rages over rights to a diminishing water supply. The same rule adheres on a global scale: the more harm done to the overall environment, the greater the damage to the earth's self-reliance, primarily its ability to effectively regenerate and recycle.

It must seem obvious by now that disrupting the natural system can have dire consequences. A hard-learned lesson occurred in the latter half of the last century following the radical engineering of our major waterways. Rivers swell and recede in answer to seasonal rain and snow melt. This ebb and flow is the lifeblood of a river system. During wet periods, excess water is dispersed throughout the surrounding floodplain. These low-lying areas that parallel the river are critical to the survival of a wide variety of organisms. For instance, when they flood in the spring, many species of fish enter and spawn. After the eggs hatch, the fry remain within the shelter of the gradually receding waters until they are mature enough to enter the river.

Most of the larger rivers in the Mississippi River basin have been drastically altered by the US Army Corps of Engineers. Second only to the Mississippi in size, the Missouri River was once shallow, meandering, and wide. Lewis and Clark had to pole their way along most of the river's length during their historic journey. The Corps erected dams, built levees, and performed extensive channeling projects designed to straighten the river and manage its flow for the purposes of navigation, flood control, hydropower, and irrigation. The combined factors yielded a river that was virtually deprived of a floodplain. This suited the Corps fine, and it opened the reclaimed land to farming and housing. Naturally, fish and aquatic insect populations dramatically declined.

The series of locks and dams built along many of the rivers in the Mississippi basin trap most of the sediment that was carried along with the current. The levees built beside the lower Mississippi straitjacket its flow, causing much of what sediment remains to be thrust far out into the Gulf of Mexico. This has led to the degradation of the Mississippi River's delta. The balance that existed between the natural sinking, or subsiding, of the land and the input of sediment from upstream needed for its replenishment has been disrupted. Many tidal wetlands and marshes are being converted to open water, seriously impacting the fishing and shrimp industries vital to the livelihood and culture of the local populace. The problem is compounded by rising sea levels. These and other factors such as shipping channels, canals, and oil and gas infrastructure account for a Manhattan-sized loss of Louisiana coastline every year, decimating a natural buffer and exposing New Orleans and other coastal communities to stronger storm surges.

Floodplain destruction, control of water flow, and reengineered stretches of rivers all seemed sensible last century. The flood of 1993 starkly revealed the engineering's inherent flaws and galvanized the awakening awareness that what's presumably good for humans alone is often not good for nature, and humans. The Corp's efforts came crashing down upon them when confronted with nature's raw fury. The deeper, channeled rivers could not contain the increased water volume and flow, levees were breached, and old flood-plains were inundated at the expense of whole communities.

Things are changing now. The federal government undertakes efforts to move towns that likely will be imperiled by floods. It subsidizes the relocation of key structures as well as homes to higher ground. The objectives are public safety and floodplain rehabilitation. Safeguarded inland areas that are once again marshlands resume their faculty for absorbing flooding and tidal surges and filtering and-purifying the water. The US Army Corps of Engineers now approaches matters with an eye on compromise, working on mitigation projects that will undo much of the previous environmental harm while keeping the economy's interests in view. Louisiana's Coastal Master Plan proposes science-based coastal restoration projects to be enacted over the next fifty years. Humanity is best served when a respect for nature's moods is exhibited.

The Arctic is warming at a rate two to three times faster than the global average. By the end of this century, it is predicted the annual mean temperature will rise by five to fourteen degrees Fahrenheit. The retreat of Arctic ice, with its consequent disruption of sea levels and ecosystems, has been well documented. Reporting on the melting perma-frost is now receiving significant coverage.

Permafrost is frozen ground in the far northern reaches of the world; it exists beneath an upper layer of soil that is unfrozen during warm periods and can be up to 2000 feet thick under the arctic coastal plain. Rising temperatures are precipitating a thawing of the permafrost in an ever-widening range, leading to disastrous results. Its melting causes the ground above it to sink, leading to damaged buildings and infrastructure. Environmental upheaval in the form of falling trees and shrinking or expanding (depending on soil conformation) lakes and wetlands is occurring. Instances of extreme weather and permafrost melt, along with rising sea levels, are contributing to contaminated water, flooding, and erosion along portions of Alaska's coast, forcing the relocation of villages.

To cap it off, permafrost happens to be one of the largest natural storehouses of organic carbon; a carbon sink our heating climate is slowly unlocking. Its thawing releases stored carbon in the form of CO_2 and methane. Due to the melting permafrost beneath, the upper layer of seasonally thawed soil is gradually extending deeper into the ground where revived microbes metabolize previously frozen organic matter in the soil and then expel the greenhouse gases into the atmosphere as by-products. Under normal conditions the gradual release of the carbon is thought to be mostly counterbalanced by its photosynthetic absorption from the atmosphere by newly produced plants growing in the warmer, thawed soils.

New NASA-funded research purports that a process referred to as abrupt thawing, which occurs beneath a kind of arctic lake, called a thermokarst lake, more than doubles former projections of greenhouse gas warming resulting from permafrost melt. These lakes form when erosion caused by melting ice in the deep soil creates a depression that fills with water. The water accelerates the thawing of the frozen ground around the lake perimeter, increasing its depth and size. The deeper, quickly thawing permafrost beneath the lake releases substantial amounts of ages old carbon boosting the activity of the microbes that produce methane, which then bubbles to the surface. This will accelerate the severity of a climate-related positive feedback loop, or vicious warming circle, created when atmospheric warming causes changes that result in increased warming. Though not of particular impact now, the temperature rise waiting in the wings because of the permafrost-carbon feedback loop over the course of the upcoming decades may be considerably more profound than recently thought. Estimates put the amount of organic carbon stored in permafrost at roughly twice the volume currently in the atmosphere, and the thermokarst lake phenomenon is not included in climate models predicting future effects of climate change. Anticipated increases in rainfall as permafrost regions warm may exacerbate the production of these bodies of water, which are already growing in number.

Another example of instability generated by a positive feedback loop is the accelerating temperature caused by melting polar ice. Under stable conditions, due to its light color, ice reflects sunlight with its attendant heat back to space, but as the earth warms, the ice melts, exposing the darker, more heat-absorbing land or water beneath. The ensuing temperature increase provokes more melting ice, causing the process to intensify.

All this melting and increasing warmth may be affecting our atmospheric weather makers known as the jet streams: fast-moving air currents found five to nine miles above the earth and about a few hundred kilometers wide. The earth's rotation causes them to blow west to east, traveling at speeds that can reach 250 mph but average around 110 mph. The most prominent ones are the polar jets and the subtropical jets, and each hemisphere has a pair, the polar

Lawrence K. Zeisler

ones being the strongest. The polar jet streams usually exist between the latitudes of 30–60 degrees north and south of the equator, though commonly closer to 60 degrees, and the subtropical jets form at latitudes of 20–30 degrees north and south. They meander around the planet, descending and ascending in altitude and latitude, accompanying the contours of areas of high and low pressure. Each current can be unbroken for long distances but often breaks into two or more parts, and on occasion the two jet streams merge, though they are usually some distance apart.

Jet streams follow the boundary separating polar, temperate, and tropical air. The polar jet stream has a huge influence on the weather of the Northern Hemisphere, and its positioning and formation depend upon where the convergence between polar and temperate air occurs. The greater the disparity in temperatures, the faster and straighter it flows, making for changeable weather conditions, but the temperature differences are lessening due in large part to the rapid warming of the north polar regions.

A recent study indicates a 14 percent autumn slowdown in the polar jet stream compared to the 1990s, undercutting the strength of its east-west movement and creating more pronounced north-south dips in its pattern. The slowed winds are associated with atmospheric blocking, which causes systems to stagnate for days or weeks, resulting in extended weather extremes such as above-or below-average temperatures, drought, or flooding. There are various blocking patterns, one being what is referred to as a cut-off low. This occurs when an area of low pressure disengages from the upper-level jet stream flow and stalls for prolonged periods, bringing excess rainfall to the regions beneath—events that are occurring with greater frequency. The increase in tornadoes and nor'easters is attributed to disruptions in the jet stream.

To its credit, science does not come to quick conclusions. Because the theory linking abnormal jet stream activity and rising temperatures is relatively new, there is nothing resembling scientific consensus regarding the matter, though most scientists suspect the influence of climate change. Only the most unobservant folks would deny we are experiencing conspicuous weather extremes.

Any serious discussion about climate change is predicated on the fact that CO_2 (and to a lesser extent methane) and warming are joined at the hip. Although methane's atmospheric presence is not as prevalent or nearly as long-lasting, according to the Intergovernmental Panel on Climate Change, in the first two decades after its release, as a greenhouse gas it is 84 times more potent than CO_2. After a century, its thermal energy absorption falls to about 28 times the rate.

Since the beginning of the Industrial Revolution around 1750, there has been about a 250 percent overall increase in methane in the atmosphere. It comes from numerous natural and man-made sources, a major one being the impact of growing herds of ruminant livestock (predominately cows). Microbes inside their stomachs break down regurgitated food, or cud, and emit methane gas during respiration, which enters the atmosphere. Manure decomposition and, to a lesser extent, flatulence contribute.

Emissions from gas and oil operations are a huge problem. Considering that methane is the primary component of natural gas (about 90 percent), it is imperative that leaks from well sites and discharges from compressor stations and chemical processing plants be addressed. Natural gas

Lawrence K. Zeisler

leaks from transmission stations along distribution pipelines and the pipelines themselves play a considerable role
in the global warming crisis. A 2012 study led by Boston
University professor Nathan Phillips revealed that Boston's
aging natural gas distribution infrastructure was riddled
with pipeline leaks—3,356 to be exact. That's just one city.

There is flaring, or burning off, of gas at oil and gas fields.
In many locales, especially those with inadequate infrastructure for use and transport of gas, it is a regular practice,
because facilities find it easier and cheaper to burn than to
capture it. Other, more sophisticated operations practice
greater responsibility. Satellite data revealed that in 2012,
close to 3.5 percent of the world's store of natural gas went up
in flames. While the methane is mostly burned off during the
combustion reaction, its conversion to CO_2 and water foster
environmental repercussions. More than 350 million tons
of CO_2 were emitted that year due to flaring. In 2017, using
satellite imagery, an analysis by the Environmental Defense
Fund shows pronounced discrepancies between their findings and industry figures on flaring in Texas, New Mexico,
and North Dakota, suggesting rampant under-reporting. The
analysis compares favorably with results from a S&P Global
Market Intelligence report. The waste and pollution continues. Natural gas may be the cleanest burning fossil fuel, but
there are tradeoffs that color its "green" image.

Scientists are better understanding the link between
increasing methane release from natural freshwater systems
and warming temperatures. Lakes, deltas, wetlands, and rice
paddies harbor microorganisms called archaea that live in
waterlogged, oxygen-free sediments. They perform a vital role
in the decay of organic matter, most of which derives from
vegetation that grows around or in the water. The microbes

consume and digest the buried plant material and emit methane as a by-product, which percolates to the surface.

One recent research project sponsored by the UK Natural Environment Research Council concentrated its efforts on Canada's lake-strewn ecosystem. It centered on the part that different kinds of vegetation play in atmospheric methane release from bodies of water. Experimentation revealed that the warming climate is creating advantageous conditions for the growth of aquatic plants like cattails, whose sediment the microbes favor over that left in the wake of fallen deciduous and coniferous trees that grow beside the vast network of lakes and marshes. Trees which break down into organic matter that seems to trap carbon in the sediment, preventing it from joining with hydrogen to form methane.

The scientists took samples of lake sediment that had been combined with three types of plant debris, incubated them in a lab for 150 days, and measured the amount of methane produced. The cattail sediment generated four hundred times more methane than the coniferous sediment and twenty-eight hundred times that of the deciduous samples. They concluded that there is a direct correlation between methane emissions and the kinds of plants and trees adding their organic matter to the underwater sediment.

Rising temperatures are threatening northern forests while benefiting aquatic plants that microbes prefer. Global freshwater ecosystems generate close to 16 percent of natural methane emissions. Though impossible to precisely predict, researchers estimate a 70 percent increase in gas production in these systems within the next fifty years.

Perhaps the most plentiful greenhouse gas, water vapor, gets short shrift because it is not usually associated with

Lawrence K. Zeisler

human activity. Its roughly 60 percent contribution to global warming versus CO_2's estimated 20-25 percent demands a closer look. The data are made more significant by the fact that our machinations directly impact its atmospheric concentrations. It's all about the temperature.

It has been revealed that CO_2 is the most important gas for regulating the earth's temperature. Unlike CO_2, which can persist in the atmosphere for centuries, water vapor ebbs and flows in response to temperature fluctuations. NASA studies show there is a direct correlation between temperature and humidity. Since evaporation of waters from lakes, rivers, and especially the oceans increases under warming and humid conditions and resides in the air as heat-trapping water vapor, additional atmospheric CO_2 compounds the problem. Conversely, as air losses heat, its ability to retain moisture drops, causing water vapor to condense and fall as rain, hail, sleet, or snow, decreasing the amount of the gas in that area.

This interaction between the two gases creates another positive feedback loop that works like this: increased CO_2 leads to more warming, boosting evaporation, causing water vapor buildup and greater warming, resulting in more airborne water vapor absorption which, among other things, acts as a fuel for hurricanes. It's no coincidence that wider swaths of the country are getting wetter and enduring harsher storms. Experts believe that the evaporation cycle may be the most potent positive feedback loop in the global climate environment. Hence, the way to break this cycle's severity is to decrease CO_2 production.

Scientists are serving notice that the feedback loops, in combination with human-induced greenhouse gas emissions, will likely create a domino effect that intensifies the rate of global warming, possibly making once-habitable portions of the earth uninhabitable and putting a major strain on the fabric of society. It is impossible to accurately forecast the timing and severity of this interplay of events. Even if we could wave a magic wand and automatically go "green" from an energy standpoint, the "feedbacks" would continue producing warmth; how much depends on us. The Millennium Ecosystem Assessment informs us that the earth's ability to furnish the requisite goods and services that we, and especially future generations, need for our well-being is seriously and possibly irreversibly jeopardized. This is not to be entertained as a hopeless doomsday scenario but instead a call to action requiring environmental maturity on governmental, industrial, and individual levels. As Will Steffen of the Australian National University said, "Avoiding this scenario requires a redirection of human actions from exploitation to stewardship of the Earth system."

We like quick, tangible payment for our efforts. Upgrading the environment will take patience and extended commitment. For the most part, it will be virtually imperceptible. Preserving the rainforests, suppressing global warming, and subduing acid rain does not profit us in the customary manner. The air, soil, and waters enrich us in ways money can't buy, but the state of our health and mental well-being is inextricably bound to the earth. When environmental problems are apparent and felt, the call to action is often heeded. When they are unseen, abstract notions and not overtly threatening, it's easy to take them for granted.

It often seems to be a matter of economics, but what is the economic value of a our planet? The question is absurd.

To try to state the answer in dollars and cents is impossible and an affront to life. We are using the wrong standard to measure nature's worth. Our methods are crude and unrefined, our arrogance so complete that the life-sustaining is made trivial when judged against our priorities. What standard should we use? This too is an ambiguous question. I know the answer is fundamentally linked with what makes us human and not with what makes us wealthy. The irony is that climate change hits the world economy squarely in the jaw. It is a matter of economics, and it is folly to attempt to gauge the impact of the lives lost in its wake.

More people are realizing that if we fail to fulfill our obligation to the earth, the painful aftermath will grow. A 2014 World Health Organization (WHO) report estimates that by 2030, climate change-related deaths will claim approximately 250,000 human souls. DARA International arrives at higher numbers, projecting six hundred thousand deaths annually by that year and up to four hundred thousand currently. A far greater number of unfortunates have been displaced, injured, or left destitute. Written by more than fifty scientists, policy experts, and economists, the DARA study states that global gross domestic product (GDP) has taken a 1.6 percent annual hit because of the changing climate, costing the world more than $1.2 trillion. While the numbers could be debated and arguments made about what percentage of that total betrays a human fingerprint, there is no arguing against the fact that climate change is unleashing fury.

The number of documented weather-induced natural disasters has more than tripled in the last fifty years. More than 90 percent of resulting fatalities occur in the Third World, where weak health infrastructures stifle the ability to prepare and respond to emergencies. Rising temperatures and haphazard precipitation decrease food production in poor regions already less able to cope, exacerbating the problem of malnourishment, which causes more than three million deaths a year. Children are the most susceptible.

According to the National Oceanic and Atmospheric Administration's (NOAA) National Centers for Environmental Information, in 2017 the United States endured an historic number of weather and climate-related calamities, sixteen of which are estimated to have exceeded $1 billion in losses and killing at least 362 people. The number is comprised of hurricanes, floods, uncharacteristically brutal storms (including extreme tornado outbreaks), wildfire, drought, and a crop freeze—a record $306.2 billion in damages. The aggregate cost of the 219 incidents whose damages were valued at more than $1 billion apiece since 1980 has totaled more than $1.5 trillion.

A report just released by the government warns that if significant measures are not taken to curtail global warming, the damage will shrink the nation's economy by as much as 10 percent by the end of the century. The analysis is at odds with the present administration's frenzied attack on environmental regulations; short-sighted monetary gains at the climate's expense will seem mere drops in a large bucket of future financial misery.

Our aging energy infrastructure dating back to the latter half of the twentieth century is overtaxed, and the problem is compounded by the growing incidence of major storms ravaging the nation. In a 2014 interview, Massoud Amin, a University of Minnesota professor of electrical and computer engineering, stated that in the previous five years weather had been responsible for 68–73 percent of all consequential US power grid outages, up from 17–21 percent in the years just before. Data in a 2103 Department of Energy (DOE) assessment specify that grid blackouts surged by 285 percent since 1984, largely due to its susceptibility to extreme weather episodes.

Instituting a smarter twenty-first-century national supergrid—one fortified against storms, demand surges, and man-made threats and more reliant on renewable power and storage—will require exorbitant sums. It has been projected that constructing this vast infrastructure project over a thirty-year period might run $500 billion or more, but it would present society with an extremely favorable return on investment, foremost being a handsome reduction in consumer electric bills. Other features would be consistent digital-grade power, improved and more dependable electrical services, and a healthier environment. The growing movement in the generation of power from points other than electric utilities, such as rooftop solar panels, promotes a more varied and cost-effective answer to today's monopolized approach.

Thanks to technological breakthroughs in direct-current technology, electricity can be transmitted over much greater distances with decreased power loss, allowing the convenient transfer and trade of energy from renewable and forecasted progressively decreasing nonrenewable origins. It would permit the flow of inexpensive energy from Great Plains wind farms and Southwest desert solar fields to faraway cities and towns. In a 2016 report, the NOAA Earth System Research Laboratory concluded that a move away from the regionally divided electricity network to a national integrated supergrid system could attain up to an 80 percent cutback in electricity sector carbon emissions compared with 1990 levels.

A 2017 study by the independent research organization known as the Climate Institute estimates that building and managing the new grid over three decades would launch 650,000–930,000 jobs annually throughout the energy arena. Economically impoverished rural locales would see a large boost in employment.

Increased warmth extends the length of allergy seasons and is enlarging the geographic range and prolonging the transmission seasons of serious vector-borne diseases. A vector is an organism, often an insect, that carries a disease or parasite and transfers it to another animal or plant. According to the Centers for Disease Control and Prevention, the number of mosquito and tick-related illnesses tripled from 2004-2016 throughout the United States. Mosquitoes transmit the parasite responsible for malaria and dengue virus, scourges that thrive in tropical and subtropical regions. Malaria claims almost 440,000 lives a year, many of which are African children under five years of age. Dengue is not as fatal but still kills up to twenty-five thousand people worldwide. Schistosomiasis, also referred to as snail fever, is an infection caused by parasitic flatworms commonly found in tropical regions and transmitted to humans by their release from an infected variety of freshwater snail. Children are mostly victimized, because they are more apt to play in contaminated water. Lengthy exposure can cause bladder cancer, kidney failure, and infertility. An estimated two hundred thousand deaths worldwide result from the malady each year.

Extreme precipitation events are becoming more numerous due to warming, resulting in increases in the incidence and severity of floods. Besides the obvious destruction to infrastructure and homes, floods contaminate water supplies, intensify the probability of water-borne diseases, and leave in their wake ideal breeding grounds for mosquitoes. Tainted drinking water increases the likelihood of diarrheal disease, which kills approximately 760,000 children annually.

The effects of excessive heat are felt more by the elderly by amplifying the probability of cardiovascular and respiratory failure. Increased levels of pollutants like ozone contribute to the problems. There are at least a few recorded instances of old people found deceased in their apartments or homes in our country due to heat exposure. Europe's five hottest summers in the past 500 years have occurred in the last fifteen years. During the record heatwave that ran from June through mid-August 2003 temperatures soared to 20-30 percent above average across parts of the continent and took at least fifty-two thousand lives, mostly the elderly or chronically ill. Environmental damage contributed to the disaster. Farm harvests shriveled in the heat, raising costs for livestock farmers. Fires ravaged Western Europe, rivers dried up, glaciers shrank by 10 percent, and the thawing produced rockslides and flash floods. Some nuclear power plants in France were forced to shut down because of low water levels and high water temperatures. It is predicted that heat waves like this one will occur more frequently and last longer. It is no coincidence that not only have the wildfires plaguing California grown more severe but the length of the burning "season" has expanded dramatically.

Climate change intensifies desertification: the degradation of land by deforestation, improper agriculture and drought, causing it to become more arid and thus less usable. Though humans often initiate the problem by overexploiting an area, warming temperatures and less rainfall can cause drought conditions that make regenerating the exhausted land for the sustained growth of vegetation difficult if not impossible. When it does rain upon the parched ground, it has become increasingly erratic and heavy, leading to soil erosion and flash flooding.

Because of changing weather patterns, food production zones are shifting. Sub-Saharan Africa is particularly in jeopardy. In Madagascar and some other African nations, a dust belt exists on what once was agricultural land. The future will see more environmentally displaced people, and millions may be forced to migrate to North Africa and beyond.

In the United States, air pollution is estimated to cause up to fifty thousand deaths per year and cost as much as $40 billion annually in lost productivity and healthcare. The damage to America's crop production due to noxious emissions accounts for millions of dollars in losses. Outdoor and household sources of air pollution are responsible for a litany of respiratory and cardiovascular-associated ailments and diseases and are calculated to induce about seven million premature deaths a year according to the most recent global data from the WHO. Acid rain is laying waste to streams, lakes, and estuaries, and fouled air is threatening 35 percent of Europe's forests.

The main culprits for outdoor, or ambient, air pollution are vehicle emissions, coal-fired power plants, steel mills, and crop burning. Catalytic converters and industrial scrubbers and filters have been implemented to control emissions over the years in the industrialized world but are virtually unheard of in most of the developing world, Eastern Europe, and the Soviet Union. These technologies have been of some benefit but are expensive and not foolproof solutions; increasing industrialization and the expanding use of automobiles are

Lawrence K. Zeisler

straining their capabilities. More aggressive approaches are required. Taxing emissions and factoring environmental costs of burning fossil fuels into energy planning would promote energy efficiency and advance the use of renewable sources. Drafting urban plans with the purpose of decreasing auto dependency and upgrading public transportation will further mitigate the harmful effects.

Since polluted air does not respect national borders, some countries find it advantageous to aid others located upwind. West Germany is investing $163 million in some Eastern European countries to modernize coal-burning power plants and implement other pollution-control plans. The Natural Resources Defense Council and Rocky Mountain Institute, both US entities, are offering energy efficiency assistance to the Soviet Union. The human, natural, and economic costs thrust upon us by a deteriorated environment have led to the realization that pollution prevention is a smart investment.

A Intergovernmental Science-Policy Platform on Biodiversity and Ecosystem Services (IPBES) report states that 300-400 million tons of toxic sludge, solvents, heavy metals and other wastes are released annually into the world's waters. The forfeiture of dollars incurred by ocean pollution is vast and impossible to deduce. Let's take one facet of the problem that has been estimated. The United Nations announced that the oceanic plastic epidemic alone accounts for approximately $13 billion of yearly financial damage. The costs arise from plastic's effect on marine life, fisheries, tourism, and beach cleanups.

Many national security experts and academics conclude that climate change contributes to an unsettled world. A series of UN studies found that the consequences are destabilizing various nation states. A 2014 US Department of Defense report corroborates the UN assessments, stating that changing climate poses "immediate risks" to national security and will impact the cost and nature of military responses to the problem. It spells out how natural disasters spread disease and damaged infrastructure can cause turmoil and threaten government instability, especially in countries with weak political institutions, limited resources, and degraded living standards. It expresses that climatically induced hardship aggravates poverty and creates social tensions that encourage extremist ideologies and terrorism.

A case in point are reports that climate change fanned the flames of the ISIS revolution in Syria. For the past century, parts of the Middle East have experienced warmer and drier conditions, manifesting in a crippling drought that plagued Syria in 2006–2009. Researchers posit that two circumstances contributed to the problem: increased evaporation caused by higher temperatures and less moisture-filled air drawn from the Mediterranean because of weakening winds. Both phenomena link up with computer simulations revealing how the region reacts to increased greenhouse gas emissions, suggesting the weather patterns have been too persistent and dramatic to be blamed solely on natural causes.

The intense aridity saddled Syria with a drought that stifled farming and forced many young people into cities to look for work. It's not hard to see how those unable to find employment, desperate and angry, possessed the ideal qualities desired by ISIS fighters seeking to mold militant recruits with promises of adventure and purpose.

The treasured monarch butterfly, symbol of beauty and endurance, is finding it hard to adjust to a climate-stressed world. It baffles me how such a delicate, relatively slow-flying creature can log up to three thousand miles passing over prairies, deserts, lakes, mountains, and towns during

Lawrence K. Zeisler

its fall migration, the destination being small patches of ancient evergreen forest in the Sierra Madre Mountains in Central Mexico that it has never seen before. Millions of them congregate in clusters among the tree branches, seeking security in specialized microclimates with temperatures just moderate enough to lower their metabolic rates to achieve dormancy but without letting them freeze. Sadly, monarch populations in Mexico have dropped dramatically. One study concludes that in 1997 they numbered about 682 million, compared to 42 million in 2015. The overwintering sanctuary has met head-on with changing weather patterns. Extreme climate events such as increasingly destructive storms, uncommon to that region, have become more customary. In 2002, one storm, followed by unusually cold temperatures, ravaged the mountaintops during what is normally the winter dry season, killing a good portion of roosting butterflies—a crippling event they have yet to recover from.

Recently, uncharacteristic high winds and cold rains leveled 133 acres of the area's fir and pine trees, accounting for the loss of an estimated six million of their number. Illegal logging presents a problem. Although protections have been instituted and commercial activity has slowed, small-scale logging, which is much harder to detect, continues.

Newfound obstacles plague today's migrants en route as well. Hotter and more arid conditions such as the ongoing drought in Texas, coupled with intensive farming practices in the corn belt—with their reliance on herbicide-tolerant, genetically modified (GM) crops—play havoc with the shrinking number of milkweed plants. Growing between rows of soybeans and corn, these plants are the only ones on which monarch butterflies lay eggs and the caterpillars feed. Consequently, many monarchs have to range farther in search of life cycle-sustaining plants, depleting their store of body fat in the process. If they are fortunate enough to find some before dying of exhaustion, the butterflies often lay fewer eggs. The liberal application of herbicides, with its attendant flowering plant mortality, puts stress on all pollinators with consequences throughout the food web. Warmer temperatures have been known to delay their fall migration from Canada by as much as six weeks. When the weather finally cools enough to motivate their departure, in some instances, cold temperatures in the American Midwest kill many of the southbound travelers.

The losses will not mean the end of the monarch butterfly. Some individuals in temperate locales don't migrate, and others fly to different mild climes. Populations flourish in other lands. The species is not endangered, but its annual cross-country journey is. This phenomenon is an outstanding sample of the natural world's penchant for the unique and unusual. How sad that such a distinctive piece of the mystifying puzzle may be lost, another minute portion of the divine canvas blotted out forever. This is made even sadder when you factor in the human connection. For centuries, Mexicans performed celebrations in honor of the monarch's arrival in late fall and early winter, some believing they characterize the souls of the departed.

Approximately 90 percent of all flowering plants rely on pollinators for survival. Perhaps the most obvious pollinator is the honeybee, which is credited with nearly one-third of agricultural pollination. It has been documented for some time that they are suffering dramatic increases in mortality; records disclose colonies plummeted from 6 million in number in 1947 to 2.4 million in 2008. From April 2018 to

April 2019 beekeepers across the country lost 40.7 percent of their colonies. A recent University of California-San Diego study concluded that pesticides used in intensive agriculture are 50 percent more harmful to bees than previously reported.

Honeybees are by no means the only victims. Wild pollinators including other bee species, birds, bats, wasps, butterflies, beetles, and moths have experienced declines because of pesticides, careless land management, habitat degradation, and the invasion of non-native species and pathogens. The most comprehensive global assessment of pollinators ever performed concluded that 40 percent of pollinating insects are in danger of extinction. Considering about one-third of our food derives from naturally pollinated crops and that insect pollinators improve the seed or fruit quality and quantity of thirty-nine of the fifty-seven major world crops, their plight is cause for serious alarm. A just released summary of an extensive United Nations assessment of the decline in biodiversity states that pollinator mortality may risk up to $577 billion in annual crop production worldwide.

Evidence points to a widely used class of insecticides known as neonicotinoids as being responsible for deteriorating pollinator populations. These are strong neurotoxins designed to kill invertebrate insect pests that munch on stalks, roots, and leaves, but they also harm a host of non-target pollinating visitors and acutely and chronically affect birds (which are vertebrates). An EPA analysis supports the evidence and reported that they pose substantial danger to aquatic invertebrates. Their labels should read "insecticide/ biocide." In 2015, the US Geological Survey (USGS) discovered water-soluble insecticides in over half the samples of stream water collected nationwide. Recently, a research team at the USGS and University of Iowa identified them in treated tap water, though the concentrations were minute.

Despite the findings, the EPA has taken no steps to impose mandatory restrictions on their use and announced it will consider widening the application of one of the chemicals, thiamethoxam. If approved, the highly toxic pesticide will be sprayed on 165 million acres of US cropland. Three types of neonicotinoids have been banned on flowering crops in the European Union since 2013.

In the United States, almost all corn, 40–50 percent of soybeans, a host of cereal and oil crops such as wheat, rye, barley, canola, and sunflower, and a medley of vegetables and fruits are dosed with neonicotinoid insecticides (over four million pounds annually, usually planted as chemically coated seeds). Spraying and soil injections are the other means of application. The chemicals are systemic, taken up by the plant, mostly through the roots, and transmitted to the tissues including the pollen and nectar. This means that washing before eating will not remove them. They can travel distances in runoffs and waterways, infecting plants, especially wildflowers, growing in the surrounding environment beyond crop fields. The chemicals break down slowly and contaminate the soil, threatening ground-dwelling native bees. A global review of more than one thousand independent studies linked them to declines in earthworm populations.

A field trial conducted at thirty-three farm sites in three European countries and a Canadian study indicate that neonicotinoids jeopardize honeybee survival by negatively affecting them at crucial stages in their life cycle, particularly afflicting the hive's queen, which seriously threatens the colony's reproductive capacity. Their cleaning and disease-prevention functions whereby the worker bees remove dead or sick members and gather plant resins with antimicrobial properties to maintain nest health suffer as well.

The two studies substantiated findings from other labs that revealed that when combined with a fungicide existing in some of the localities, the ensuing "cocktail" made the neonicotinoids much more toxic to bees. This begs the question of whether other combinations of pesticides are poisoning the environment in unknown ways. The US Department of Agriculture (USDA) 2014 pesticide monitoring report uncovered neonicotinoids in twelve of nineteen sample vegetables and fruits, eleven of which contained a mixture of insecticides. A study conducted by an international team of European researchers tested for remnants of five different neonicotinoids in almost two hundred honey samples from around the world; it disclosed that 45 percent of the samples were laced with two or more of the chemicals. They have even been detected in infant formula.

Professor David Goulson, a bee specialist at the University of Sussex, states:

> In the light of these new studies, continuing to claim that use of neonicotinoids in farming does not harm bees is no longer a tenable position. In my view we should also consider the bigger picture; the current model of farming based on huge monocultures treated with dozens of pesticides is causing devastating environmental harm, undermining vital ecosystem services that keep us all alive.[1]

Colony collapse disorder (CCD), wherein worker bees disappear, leaving the hive in jeopardy, is devastating honeybee populations. It is blamed on a series of combined conditions, most of which are linked to compromised and altered environmental factors including pesticides (neonicotinoids are high on the list), invasive parasitic mites, pathogens, immunodeficiencies, and nutritional shortages.

The increasingly dysfunctional EPA has dropped restrictions on the use of sulfoxaflor, another highly toxic insecticide that is manufactured by DowDupont's Corteva agricultural division. Hosts of scientists say it is a leading cause of CCD. Dow donated $1 million to Trump's inaugural committee.

Results from a joint laboratory and field analysis conducted by researchers at the University of Buenos Aires published in *Journal of Experimental Biology* suggests a direct link between Monsanto's Roundup herbicide and CDD. Using doses of the chemical comparable to what honeybees would encounter in agricultural environments doused with agrochemicals, it reported the harm occurred at a sub-lethal level from prolonged exposure, meaning the insects were not killed outright but contracted problems that negatively affected their performance over time. It was discovered they suffered a decreased sensitivity to sucrose, compromising their ability to track and find food. Their memory retention was adversely affected, reflecting a key component of CCD: an inability to retrace their way to the hive. It was speculated that the continued inflow of tainted nectar brought back to the hive (where it is stored and later distributed) by those healthy enough to make the trip would weaken the health of the colony.

The agents affecting the health of bees and other pollinators are multifaceted and complex. They are nothing to be

Lawrence K. Zeisler

trifled with. The problems indicate a sickened environment leading right up the food chain to us.

Despite the fact that neonicotinoids have been around since the 1990s, their influence on human health has not been adequately researched. It is generally held that the acute impact of neonicotinoid-laced foods on human health is negligible. The chronic effects from exposure to a mixture of the pesticides is largely unknown.

Now is not the time to relax federal oversight. Oversight probably won't lead to positive environmental action in the next couple of years, even when unbiased research is demanded and performed as in the above case with neonicotinoids. The proposed slashing of more than 23 percent of the EPA's annual budget by the Trump administration, if enacted, won't help. Its former director, Scott Pruitt, recently signed an order rescinding the agency's own edict to ban chlorpyrifos, a Dow Chemical pesticide, which studies by prestigious universities and medical institutions have shown that even in low doses retards brain development in children. If exposed to the fetus in the womb, remnants of the chemical can be found in the brain through puberty and beyond. It has been linked to neurological problems as well as persistent autoimmune and developmental disorders. Pruitt, Dow Chemical, and some farmers are at odds with EPA scientists who want it off the market.

The U.S. 9th Circuit Court of Appeals has since stepped in and instructed EPA to ban chlorpyrifos. Trump administration lawyers have appealed the ruling.

Scientists at the Fish and Wildlife Service completed an exhaustive study of the risks that three extensively used pesticides pose, concluding that they jeopardize the continued existence of over a thousand endangered plant and animal species. The chemicals under investigation were malathion, diazinon, and chlorpyrifos. The researchers found that the pesticides are both directly and indirectly toxic. The small San Joaquin kit fox no longer roams vast areas of its historic range in California's San Joaquin Valley, in large part because intensive farming utilizing liberal quantities of the pesticides has contaminated birds and grasses on which they feed. Exposure to drifting sprays of chlorpyrifos can present dire consequences to vulnerable species.

Before the study's findings could be made public in November 2017 Interior Department officials led by then deputy secretary of the interior David Bernhardt, former lobbyist and oil industry lawyer, blocked their release. Actions were set in motion to institute a new framework regarding endangered species evaluations, one with weakened standards determining the dangers presented by the pesticides. Pesticide companies and users of the chemicals had vigorously lobbied to advance the initiative.

EPA and Interior Department records disclose multiple interactions between senior agency officials and pesticide industry representatives. Mr. Bernhardt, who previously was often hired to challenge the importance of issues regarding endangered species, is currently Secretary of the Interior. Another paradoxical position choice by our backassword thinking president. The sudden change in regulatory policy since Trump's election is part of a broader trend throughout the government favoring special interests and industry profit at the expense of public health and the environment. It is emblematic of a pattern which ignores scientific evidence, a deliberate dumbing down of the government. The smell of marsh gas emanating from this administration's corridors grows

Lawrence K. Zeisler

more pronounced by the day.

Genetically modified (GM) crops fall under the larger GMO (genetically modified organism) umbrella. A GMO is any animal, plant, or microorganism whose DNA has been altered through genetic engineering in a laboratory. When the alteration is initiated by adding genetic material from a dissimilar species, it is considered transgenic. The object is the introduction of a new trait for a specific purpose. GMO crops are modified to make them more productive, drought tolerant, or resistant to pests.

Because of their advertised resistance to insect pests and weeds, GMO crops were heralded as alternatives to pesticide use. While the application of insecticides has decreased, many crops have been genetically engineered to tolerate increased doses of potentially toxic weed killers, allowing more herbicides to be freely sprayed around these plants to control weeds, exposing humans, wildlife, and non-genetically engineered (GE) crops in surrounding areas to wind-driven drifting. While not as deleterious as chlorpyrifos, studies suggest possible links with cancer, allergies, and birth defects. The herbicide glufosinate, for instance, kills plants by inhibiting the enzyme glutamine synthetase, which is found in animals, bacteria, and fungi. It's conceivable toxicity to most organisms, including mammals, cannot be ignored.

Growing evidence tells us that glyphosate, the active ingredient in Roundup, may not be as harmless as once thought. It is no coincidence that the product is designed to be liberally applied to what are referred to as Roundup Ready GE GMO crops, since Monsanto is the world's largest biotech seed company. Different studies reveal traces of glyphosate in routinely consumed foods such as corn (about 70 percent of US production), soy (about 80 percent), sugar beets, alfalfa, canola, and other vegetables. While research suggests that long-term contact (like that experienced by fieldworkers) with Roundup may cause health problems, including a greater chance of contracting non-Hodgkin lymphoma, the extent of its influence in food is still a matter of debate.

Dr. Stephanie Seneff, a researcher at MIT for over three decades, is convinced that because of the recent rapid rise in autism—recent statistics cite an incidence of one in fifty US children while thirty years ago it was more like one in ten thousand—there can be little question that it has an environmental cause and that glyphosate is a fundamental contributor. She and others contend that the chemical is harmful to animals and humans on a bacterial level, contributing to microbe imbalances in the gut and giving rise to pathogens and the toxins they generate. This leads to chronic inflammation, which is a precursor of disease and one of the problems associated with autism. Some of the gut microbes decompose glyphosate, and a by-product is ammonia. People with autism have excessive amounts of this compound in their blood.

Roundup is the most heavily used agricultural chemical in history; around 9.4 million tons have been sprayed on fields worldwide since its introduction in 1974, 1.8 million of those tons in the United States. It is a vital source of revenue, too often at the financial expense of farmers, so is it any surprise that the company assiduously espouses its lack of harm? The veracity of the medical analyses mounting against Monsanto will ultimately be displayed in the courts where lawsuits are filed on a regular basis.

Monsanto can't deny another problem. Resistant weeds have evolved in response to mass use of glyphosate. This prompts companies to develop chemicals to combat those weeds and engineer new GE seeds to withstand the chemicals, ushering in a potentially spiraling need for new generations of herbicide-resistant crops and sprays. Bill Freese, a science policy analyst for the Center for Food Safety in Washington, DC, says:

> *The biotech industry is taking us into a more pesticide-dependent agriculture when they've always promised, and we need to be going in, the opposite direction.*[2]

Allison Wilson, science director of the Bioscience Resource Project, states:

> *Industrial agriculture is a lethal combination of methods that is causing the extinction of thousands of species worldwide. It is affecting birds, amphibians, bats and other pollinators besides butterflies. Many ecosystems are staring down the barrel.*[3]

This discussion centers on the real and probable deleterious effects resulting from the excessive use of some pesticides in conjunction with GMO crops. After researching a small portion of the vast literature written about the GMO phenomenon, it is concluded here that impartiality is the best recourse relating to the crops. Many scientists claim their safety, as evidenced by a recent report issued by the prestigious National Academies of Science, Engineering, and Medicine. Others believe that commercial interests are performing inadequate risk assessments prior to employment. It has been contended that unscrupulous motives drive the GMO phenomenon, describing the effort to control seed production and plant breeding via patents and power plays and steering agriculture in ways that benefit agribusiness. Farmers have witnessed a reduction of seed choices and phasing out of non-GE varieties since the ushering in of GMOs, along with more than a threefold increase in their price.

It is difficult to deny the array of arguments defending the potential that GE crops offer to counter the adverse dynamics imposed on us by a climatically altered world. Increasing drought, heat, and loss of arable land make adaptation of crops imperative if we are to meet the nutritional needs of a rapidly growing world population. Biotechnology, if exercised judiciously—which means by reining in the need for corresponding pesticides and complementing, not greedily displacing, other farming options—could mitigate the impact of burgeoning environmental problems.

A growing number of folks assert that a thorough understanding and respect for the natural order can minimize or preclude the need for genetic manipulation of foods and chemical fertilizers and pesticides that deplete the land of nutrients and critical soil microbes, making us dependent on inorganic application. They have a holistic view of soil and appreciate the interconnected nature of its biology. This knowledge has spurred the study and implementation of ingenious practices that enhance the rate of atmospheric carbon removal by converting it to plant mass and organic matter in the soil, thus improving the composition of degraded and eroded lands crucial to planetary health. The heartland's topsoil, famed for productivity, is one of our greatest resources, yet Iowa alone has lost one-half of its rich layer of loam since coming under the plow. Any practice that slows its decline and augments its richness is worthy of implementation.

Some large industrial farms incorporate a no-till system that does not disturb the earth when preparing fields for planting, leaving the previous year's residue on the surface to absorb water and reduce evaporation. Instead of a traditional plow, a chisel plow cuts shallow furrows. Special tractor attachments inject seeds and fertilizer before covering the furrow with soil. The direct injection method saves on fertilizer, and less equipment and labor are required, reducing operational costs.

Conventional tilling turns the soil over, disturbing soil microbes and exposing organic matter to the air, which rapidly oxidizes, forming CO_2, contributing to global warming. It makes erosion more likely, which drives chemical runoff and nutrients into waterways. One of the main arguments espoused by those who use conventional tilling is that turning the soil aids in weed eradication, citing that no-till farmers must apply additional pesticides to counter weed growth; but there is a natural way to effectively reduce weeds: the use of cover crops.

Cover crops, sometimes called green manures, protect and improve soil, and they are grown between the periodic planting of regular crops. They are most often planted in the fall, blanketing the ground all winter and helping to prevent erosion by binding the soil with their roots, and are cut before going to seed in spring. The primary cash crop seeds are drilled or injected through the dead plant matter lying on the field. The mat of leaves, stalks, and stems left in the wake of the cover crops' cutting feeds the soil and the storehouse of microbes within, and their value in suppressing weeds cuts down on the application of synthetic herbicides. Before cutting, they compete with weeds for nutrients and sunlight, helping to restrict their growth.

Cover crops are best planted in combination, for as in nature, diversity makes for a more productive environment. A wider variety of cover crops guarantees a richer cocktail of organic matter with soil-feeding nutrients, helping to create a layer of carbon-rich topsoil that preserves water from runoff while providing proper hydration for plant roots. Cowpeas, hairy vetch, and crimson and sweet clover are legume cover crops that produce soil-enhancing nitrogen, saving on the purchase of nitrogen-based synthetic fertilizers that are often overused. Other important nutrients cover crops release are potassium, magnesium and phosphorus. Healthy soils nourish advantageous microbes that curb bacterial and fungal plant infections as well as other microscopic pests. This complementary mix of components results in vigorous plants and more nutritious foods for humans.

The carbon sequestration process in soils, vital for their health and productivity and a line of defense against global warming, begins when plants absorb airborne CO_2 and separate the oxygen and carbon to form sugars. The sugars are reduced to carbon compounds that are exuded into the ground through the roots. Along with surrounding decomposed plant and animal substances, they break down into nutrients that nourish the soil upon which plants depend. Soil resilience is largely determined by the condition of its organic matter.

Regular tilling prevents the final stage of the decomposition process. Soil microbes and animals such as earthworms and some arthropods need time to convert decayed plant and animal remains not used up by plants into more stable organic forms or humus.

Lawrence K. Zeisler

Humus is the thick, spongy, dark component of topsoil that stabilizes and helps protect it from the ravages of dust storms and flooding. Humus absorbs and retains water; it can hold the equivalent of almost its full weight in moisture, making it of vital importance in times of drought. As one farmer says, "It's not how much rainfall you get but rather how much moisture the soil can hold." Nutrients attach to its surface, releasing them over time for uptake through the root systems of maturing plants. Its light, downy texture promotes soil aeration and improves its structure and workability. The intricate organic molecules of humus bind toxic substances, limiting their entrance into the surrounding ecosystem. On average, it consists of about 60 percent carbon and, as noted, sequesters it underground, preventing its reoxidation to the atmosphere. It is estimated that an increase of 1.6 percent of global soil organic matter would lower the present atmospheric CO_2 level of four hundred parts per million to less than three hundred parts per million. Engaging in programs to build humus is a win-win.

No-till cover cropping makes for a diverse, organically enhanced cropping system on large-scale farms where agrichemicals, if needed, can be used to tune instead of dominate agroecosystem production. When properly applied, this practice meets or outstrips the output of less diverse and more environmentally harmful chemically reliant practices that work against the natural order by disturbing and poisoning soil, air, pollinators, and waterways. A thorough understanding of and respect for the soil beneath our feet is yielding smart farming approaches that do not merely maintain but regenerate the earth while converting CO_2 from a greenhouse gas into a soil-enriching aid.

This method of farming complements the existence and profitability of nearby small and medium organic farms whose sustainable approaches decline using synthetic fertilizers and other agricultural chemicals. Farmers should be encouraged to sequester carbon by increasing humus through the payment of carbon credits. Governments the world over need to devise incentives to encourage this first line of defense against our overheating planet.

Many of the earth-friendly farming techniques under discussion have been implemented for generations by small-scale farmers who employ an agroecological approach to crop production. Agroecology is the pursuit of sustainable agriculture, promoting inexpensive, ecology-based productive ideas designed to encourage decentralized decision making by rural communities and buttress their food economies. It blends scientific research and technological innovation with knowledge supplied by traditional farming practices and indigenous communities.

Some Kenyan farmers have tripled their yields of maize by intercropping it with plants that restrain weeds, support natural pest predators, and repulse pests. *Desmodium* is a nitrogen-fixing, perennial legume that suppresses weeds and emits substances that repel serious insect pests. An exciting strategy integrates *Desmodium* with a complementary "trap" crop grown along the field's border that releases a different chemical attracting the pests away from the staple crops to lay their eggs. Because the border crop lacks nutrition, few larvae survive, and the infestation is drastically reduced. This interaction between plants is a "push-pull technology," labeled thus because the repellent "push" plant drives the undesired invader away, and it ultimately lands on the deleterious "pull" species. *Desmodium* is used as fodder for grazing animals, and its addition to the farming complex saves on the cost of livestock feed as well as reducing or negating the need for costly, poisonous, petrochemically derived pesticides and fertilizers.

Hundreds of thousands of farmers across the globe are diversifying their operations with adaptive, locally available plant species, incorporating methods that sustain biodiversity and provide added resilience against climate change and water scarcity. This is especially compelling when compared to monocultures that are dependent on ecologically degrading chemicals and vulnerable to global commodity price swings. For example, when world sugarcane prices plummeted in the mid-1980s, farmers dependent upon the single crop and their workers suffered.

Livestock benefit when the pastures on which they feed are comprised of an assortment of vegetation. Progressively thinking ranchers are altering grazing management by using a range of crops and flowers, even preferred weeds, in conjunction with the predominant grasses to feed their stock. They have found that a variety of warm and cool season species offer the nutritional content the herds require over a longer period. Different legumes provide nitrogen, and other plants supply protein. Some thistles are higher in protein than alfalfa. Flowering plants are encouraged to attract pollinators.

By employing a simple form of mobile solar-powered fencing, the new generation of ranchers can cordon off small areas called paddocks where cattle are permitted to graze for a short while before moving to the next enclosure. This stands in stark contrast to the traditional continuous, and heavily stocked, grazing management practice commonly used, often on fields with little plant variety. Due to the time restraint, rotational grazers tend to consume just the uppermost leafy portion of grasses, which are more palatable. If too much defoliation occurs, there is less surface area to attract the sun's energy, curtailing a plant's ability to capture carbon from the air during photosynthesis, vital for maintaining carbohydrate levels to meet its growth and respiration needs. The sooner the vegetation, especially grasses and legumes, can regenerate, the sooner a given paddock can be reused for grazing.

Plants provide the best nourishment in the vegetative growth stage of development (the period between germination and flowering when they are highest in protein, fiber digestibility, starch, and sugar content). Because their forage properties decline with age, having multiple pastures allows alternating stages of plant maturity, guaranteeing that some fields will always be of higher quality. The manure trampled under hoof ensures good soil contact, initiating decomposition. With this environmentally friendly practice, the buildup of organic matter in many of the paddocks has far exceeded expectations.

In their natural state, the Great Plains of North America were one of the most fertile regions on earth. Immense herds of bison extensively grazed their expanse alongside elk, antelope, and deer. They foraged among a variety of perennial grasses, sedges, rushes, and wildflowers, leaving copious amounts of mineral-laden dung and urine behind. Each species had its unique dietary preference and grazing manner, helping to keep the plants in ecological balance, and they were always moving.

As in the wild, various domestic animals prefer different plants, and a growing number of farmers are incorporating multispecies grazing for this reason. It entails the use of two or more kinds of livestock together or separately on the same pastureland. Though there is some overlapping of plant preference, the differences in selection makes for better overall use of the pasture. For example, grazing cattle alone depletes the land of preferred grasses, leaving it exposed to less desirable grasses, brushes, and weeds. Sheep and goats willingly eat a host of the invading undesirables, preventing them from going to seed, limiting their numbers, and making room for cattle-friendly greens. This is a more ecologically balanced (and often economical) herbicide substitute that enriches the field's productivity. The compatible use of a number of animals seeking mixed forage reduces pressure and stress among individuals of the same species; less competition yields healthier, better-fed stock and increased meat production per acre.

Multispecies grazing aids in parasite control. In smaller settings like rotational paddocks, prevention works best when separating the species, allowing each one to take its turn eating alone. Since a parasite is often confined to a single host species, the life cycle of most can be disrupted when another type of animal is the first to ingest the larva or eggs when grazing. Parasites usually emerge in an animal's feces, and grazers generally decline plants growing alongside their own, lessening but not negating their chance for infection. They do not share that aversion eating beside another species' manure and while doing so perform a natural deworming function for that species.

Nature is diverse but not superfluous, bountiful but not wasteful. It's proof that quality and quantity can successfully coexist. It's testimony that variety is indeed the spice of life.

The test is before us: Can we, like nature, find balance? We cannot be called environmentally sound unless the concept of balance permeates the collective conscious. Unlocking the complexities within the ultimate system of checks and balances and conforming to or carefully amending those discoveries to our advantage will ensure a stable and profitable future.

We praise endurance and longevity. One old gentleman once remarked that if he reached the hundred-year plateau, he would gain instant recognition. From a historical standpoint, we honor those civilizations that weathered the rigors of time; much of our government is patterned after ancient Greek and Roman concepts.

Many of us don't give enough credit to a much older success story; nature's laws have been extant since time immemorial. Despite this, when entertaining discussions about American pride, I don't hear many people honoring the environment's role. Our independent spirit can be attributed in good part to nature's magnanimity. Do you think it coincidence that the freedom we cherish permeates the unique qualities inherent in our democratic ideals? Certainly those venturing to the New World had been seeking it, and geographic isolation gave it time to become firmly implanted, but without the elbow room, it would never have materialized to the extent it has. Our love of freedom mirrors America's vast landmass with its manifold rivers, forests, mountains, and prairies.

Pride in one's country is important, but unswervingly predicating one's self-respect on a complex system subject to the ebb and flow of political maneuvering makes for an unstable ride. I do salute my country, especially the superior effort put forth by the Founding Fathers. I feel admiration when the government, military, or private industry moves in a responsible fashion, but I refuse to entrust my character

Lawrence K. Zeisler

to the care of others and show special caution when analyzing the motives and actions of those in power. If I find those leaders worthy, I am careful to make sure their views are reflecting what is in my heart and not manipulating its beat.

I prefer to drop anchor in a more reliable sea. I can boast of a fellowship with an organization that has attended the rise and fall of civilizations. I claim allegiance to nothing less than the planet earth, and the thought of it makes me flush with pride.

By serving the earth, I serve America. I serve them best by nurturing a spirit independent of the out-of-sight, out-of-mind syndrome that's so easy to fall victim to. When entertaining certain actions, I seek to understand how their application will influence not only me and my immediate surroundings but also, where it applies, distant people and places. It is common knowledge that excessively running an electric light source puts a minor strain on the bank account, but it is also a minute contributor to humankind's energy demand, the sating of which fouls the planet and imperils its citizens.

The secrets compiled in evolution's tome are just beginning to be deciphered. Eons of natural research and development have laid a boundless treasure trove at our feet. It would be the height of indiscretion not to plunder the rich storehouse of wisdom contained therein by letting it dispassionately vanish forever into the ether.

The human values underlying compassion for the earth are universal and selfless in character. They are a reflection of nature herself. She plays no favorites, spreading her wealth equally while asking for nothing in return. All people share responsibility in assuring her vitality. Poverty and/or ignorance prevent the uninitiated from realizing this, and it is up to the advantaged to do all they can to elevate them to a position so they see. While so employed, it would be profitable to use the above values as a guide. Regard for the planet's health, as well as our own, resides in the unblemished human heart.

Chapter 3

"Pollution, defilement, squalor are words that never would have been created had man lived conformably to Nature. Birds, insects, bears die as cleanly and are disposed of as beautifully as flies. The woods are full of dead and dying trees, yet needed for their beauty to complete the beauty of the living ... How beautiful is all death!"

—John Muir

It's funny how something as soft and fragile as a flower can inspire confidence and strength. When I consider the myriad forms, colors, and scents flourishing amid the flowery realm, a sense of calm washes over me.

The flower's beauty challenges me to confront life with an open mind and begs me to be patient with and accepting of its harsh realities. It gives assurance that all things have a purpose, none of which proceeds from evil. How could malice have played an instrumental role in whatever process was responsible for the formation of a world housing a Queen Anne's lace?

These thoughts promote a more equable outlook. For example, those traumatized by a hurricane's power may assess its worth differently than a meteorologist impassively viewing it from a global perspective. We know that the devastation is the result of a great discharge of pent-up energy issuing from superheated air and water. The extremely destructive forces in nature—volcanoes, hurricanes, earthquakes—vent their violence in response to intense pressure and energy; apparently their fury contributes to the continuation of the overall system. Have you wondered about the characteristic calm of a hurricane's eye? I see it as symbolic of the harmony existing at the center of the physical world, one made possible by the conflict of forces. In this context, faith, far from being blind, is the precursor of knowledge. By helping one accept all facets of nature, her true function can be better seen, opening the eyes to a more encompassing reality.

The flower and the hurricane are components of my faith. Knowing this permits me to weather my own problems better, for I can see that pain and anger, even ticks and flies, are all part and parcel of a grand Truth. This awareness even helps one to come to grips with that wellspring of fear: death.

Below is a portion of a letter I composed.

A loved one recently passed away, and the anguish drove to my innermost depths, forcing me to confront for the first time their uncharted darkness. Like a ship tossed upon a restless sea, I was lost and alone, buffeted relentlessly by the ever-increasing swells of pain and utterly at the mercy of chance, unable to tell night from day, up from down.

A part of me had died with her, and the sadness threatened to sweep me into a martyred half-life of misery and woe, into a living death. I chided life,

Lawrence K. Zeisler

cursed it for its callousness, and found myself asking over and over, "Why her?" As time elapsed, I noticed the "why hers" were being punctuated with "why me." When selfless love becomes tainted with the stain of self-pity, the mourning process loses its purity, and achieving peace turns into an insurmountable task.

I grew to realize that to spite death is to spite the natural order: to reproach it wholesale is tantamount to denouncing nature and its source. Only despair can come of this. We fight our fate. Death is the ultimate humbler, the definitive reminder that we are not God and forever linked to other creatures in mortality's web. When this is forgotten, it is difficult to delineate the harshness in life from the harshness in our hearts.

Thankfully, I emerged stronger from the loss. I rubbed shoulders with death, had it saturate every pore, and found it was something I could live with. The suffering produced a recognition of the infinite never before felt, promoting a faith acknowledging that wherever she has gone cannot be bad.

I see life differently now. The sun shines a little brighter, and the winds blow freer. Since life is filled with such warmth, why shouldn't death be? Do they not emanate from the same source? I know I will one day be traveling the corridors my love and everyone else have, a comforting thought indeed. In essence, we all return to the unknown from whence we come. As a friend's father was slowly fading, he peacefully said, "I'm going home, son. I'm going home."

Every sentient being has one thing in common, which is awareness. Awareness is universal. Memory may vanish with each person's passing, but consciousness is eternally reawakening. Looked at from this all-embracing perspective, one's death is not an end, only a point on a perpetual, shared path.

The newfound warmth is not washed by waves of dispassion or guilt. Would my love have wanted me to wallow in a quagmire of gloom? Is that fair to her? She loved me. Should not the flower springing from her gentle soil be nurtured by light and grace and not wilting under sorrow's withering shadow?

There is sadness that lies tucked away inside, and it occasionally wells to the surface. This I cannot fight. This I should not fight, but if death overcooks in a mournful porridge, it becomes an affront to the deceased, oneself, life, and God.

A long time passed before the sorrow and anger abated and I was able to acknowledge death's place. Painful emotions are as much a part of our makeup as the desired ones and should be accorded the same respect. It has been said that art imitates life. In a work of art, the opposition of colors or forms intensifies each element's properties. If the anguish had never been experienced, death would have remained a relative unknown and a heightened awareness of life would not have materialized. The hurtful feelings acted as counterpoints to the more harmonious state that followed. Life's opposites can mistakenly be conceived as incompatible or at odds. The interplay between contrasting forces enriches existence with its unceasing movement and vitality.

Lawrence K. Zeisler

Hindus view death as the opposite of birth, whereas we see it as the opposite of life. Perhaps if we took their approach, it would be less difficult to discern the Bottom Line: nature, with its cycle of life and death, works.

I look at spring as the season representing hope and renewal, but since the Bottom Line's success tells me all is related, the light is always present, even in the blackest recesses of an austere January night.

The Bottom Line gains its strength from the ongoing sacrifice of its myriad parts. It's easy to see how one could recoil in shock when focusing on the natural world's hard efficiency. They might feel a tinge of revulsion while realizing that most wild animals never reach reproductive age. The stern, seemingly ruthless aspect of nature is an integral part of life's perpetuity. The warmth needs the cold. The lesson is clear: Equilibrium itself is beyond reproach; the end plainly justifies the means.

Equilibrium is fundamental to the phrase "life springs eternal." Decomposition plays a lead role in its execution. For proof, one need go no farther than the nearest undisturbed outdoor area and search until they find a sapling growing beside a fallen, rotting tree. Anyone with a hint of scientific training knows the young tree is benefiting from the other one's nutrients as well as those in the surrounding leaf litter. It would not be incorrect to say that because of this transfer of nutrients, the rotting tree lives within the sapling's fresh pulp. The passing of life does not constitute an end, for within all atoms lie the seeds of rebirth.

Knowing this, I don't feel as distressed about naturally occurring things that seem plagued by bad luck. When walking in the woods, I occasionally notice a tree whose chance for an extended life faces tremendous odds. Not only does it have an almost impenetrable forest canopy to puncture in its march skyward, but due to the dearth of soil at its base, its trunk appears to be growing out of sheer stone. Once I would have questioned the fairness of the circumstances, judging this tree against my image of what a perfect one should look like, an image that failed to include the surroundings. I now see that tree as part of a whole rather than a single entity struggling to exist.

I once set to transplanting a small oak that had taken up residence beneath a much larger tulip tree. After digging around the roots' perimeter, I started excavating the taproot. By the time I discovered the depth of anchorage, there was no turning back. If I had left well enough alone, that oak would most likely be standing today—not in arrow-straight majesty (the trunk had previously grown a sharp angle to avoid the larger tree's shadows) but alive. My tampering sealed its demise.

When a tree dies, its softer dead wood gives woodpeckers and insects opportunities to forage for food and excavate holes in which to live. When it falls, its ingredients will be reabsorbed into the biomass from whence it sprung. Things die so that others may live.

The Law of Conservation of Matter says that matter can neither be created nor destroyed; but it can change form. Without the recycling and restructuring of gases, solids and liquids, the planet's present state of equilibrium could not be maintained. She appears to be a system designed to run itself. Except for an occasional visit by a space-borne body like a meteorite, the earth has made do with its native material. The carbon atoms found within your body have been used in countless other molecules since the beginning of time; ones that, for example, were most likely constituents of airborne CO_2.

Lawrence K. Zeisler

To further illustrate an appreciation for the wondrous system we are honored to witness, imagine an alien viewing Earth from a cosmic vantage point and, being immortal, not plagued by thoughts of dying. After recovering from the shock of realizing life's plenitude, the thing that hits our space-borne visitor most profoundly is the way the earth is so self-sufficient. "I've never seen a world like this," our galactic observer muses. "It's so vital. If given careful consideration by its ruling masses, there is no telling how long it will flourish."

As the survey continues, the focus settles on the critical association that is key to survival. "What an ideal fellowship: when the bell tolls, life bows to death, and death in turn yields ground to the miracle of birth. I can see that this planet's life-forms are dependent upon the everlasting embrace of the two. I can't believe the feelings that overpower me like a raging asteroid storm. How proud the beings below must be of their miraculous home. How gratifying it must feel to be affiliated with something so self-regenerative and independent. I've encountered death on other worlds, but never was it so devoted to such a cooperative and enduring arrangement with life."

The elation gives way to sorrow. "I now know why my cosmic treks have been shadowed by an emptiness I've never been able to fathom. Though I've sacrificed much for my people by dedicating my life to founding new worlds, to satisfy our endless want for living space, some inner need to give lies unfulfilled. We've taken so much from life, and I grow weary. To be able to make repayment in full would be the ultimate act of charity. To enjoy a world's fruits and return to it the most precious gift of all, so that it and future generations may thrive, is love in its noblest form. I see that the passage of life is a tribute to its glory. To be a part of the most selfless union imaginable would quell the loneliness an era of questing has aroused.

"I would like to study this planet further, but I must hasten away ere one of my brethren pinpoints my location. For the first time in my millennia-long career, I judge that my people not settle an inhabitable world. I regard this unique interrelation between life and death too highly to allow its flow to be disrupted by the introduction of a race in which every individual will live forever."

A metaphor permits us to look at death as evil, to give it a conscience, to make it immoral. That metaphor is the devil. How much effect this perception of death's immorality has on the mind is difficult to fathom. Obviously, it contributes to some peoples' fear of the unknown. The dilemma is exacerbated by Satan's association with hell, the impediment par excellence to everlasting joy. For many individuals, death is a dark place that plays havoc with their subconscious doubts, for it is where the measure of their faith will be taken in stern, unadulterated frankness.

The noted explorer/scientist Jacques Cousteau stated that we should not moralize about nature because of the nonexistence of good and evil. Before something can be judged immoral, it must be able to make a conscious decision between right and wrong. Only humans have that ability.

Our perception of nature is strongly influenced by Charles Darwin, who painted it as a series of species interacting competitively to stay alive. I'm not questioning Darwin's findings, but we should never forget that the struggle occurs beyond the pale of good and evil.

I recall a nature program dealing with the rivalry between lions and hyenas. There were some graphic accounts of fierce

Lawrence K. Zeisler

clashes that ended in death. Occasionally, I was swept away by the apparent cruelty of the episodes. When I remembered the incidents occurred outside a moral matrix, the mark of cruelty faded, making them more tolerable. I knew this is the way it is intended to be. The competition is healthy for both species, because it keeps their numbers in check, thus maintaining balance on the savannah.

Predator and prey benefit from one another. If an area loses its predator base, the prey overpopulate and stress the environment and themselves. From an overall perspective, the elk needs the wolf as much as the wolf needs the elk. Symbiosis, more than competition or violence, is the principal rule governing the relationship between predator and prey.

There is a song entitled "Walk a Mile in My Shoes." Perhaps if we could look through the eyes of other creatures, we'd be better able to comprehend the value of all life. From my singular standpoint, I might drive myself batty trying to figure out why there is such a thing as a mosquito. If a bat could converse, it would most likely give a vivid rendering of mosquito succulence. If we were to ask an impartial party the wherefore and why of the common housefly, they would mention the part it plays in the breakdown of waste and its value as a food source for predators.

Once when in central Pennsylvania, packing my daughter's belongings for summer break, I came upon a bird I had never seen before (I since identified it as a loggerhead shrike). It had flown into a dorm window and lay unconscious on the ground with no visible injury. Those of you who have witnessed this drama know that sometimes when you have given up a bird for dead, renewed respiration and gradually increasing movement herald recovery. Such was the case in this instance. As we entered the building for another trip upstairs, my wife and I were encouraged by the shrike's progress. We were not prepared for what ensued. In less time than it took to climb two flights of stairs, grab a couple of boxes and return, a big old crow had landed on the courageous fellow and dispatched him. It hurriedly carried its prize away with a blue jay in hot pursuit. Our astonishment was followed by dismay. Nature's coldness sometimes seems unfair, but if one can get beyond the feelings it evokes, the cold relents, and a stark beauty emerges. It is beautiful because it is efficient, clean, and totally without guilt.

While periodically scanning the veldt for predators, a gazelle is more than likely doing so in response to an instinct for caution rather than a persistent, gnawing sense of foreboding. Any fear it feels will be of the moment. Most human fear, in contrast, is based on thoughts of what might happen. Fear is more pervasive in our lives. Thank goodness animals are not privy to the idea of time with its subsequent knowledge of death.

Though a creature competes for territory and food and must face the heat and cold, a good portion of its life is spent in relaxation and play. I once saw a television commercial featuring a northern species of mountain sheep called a Dall sheep. As it lay on a rock outcrop, the wind gently parting its thick, white fur, true contentment was etched upon its face. How did I know? The eyes were relaxed and on the verge of closing. The next time your dog or cat rests quietly in the sun, you may see the same expression.

An aspect often overlooked is nature's humorous element. A touch of the comic exists in each of the following.

A woodpecker's raucous antics as it flits from tree to tree, pecking and squawking like a runaway wind-up toy.

The courtship ritual of a male Canadian goose as it honks and struts its stuff.

An ensemble of croaking pond frogs, whose highest pitched vocalist is emitting notes with a range extending octaves below that of a double bass.

The shy retreat of a surprised squirrel, playing peekaboo while carefully placing a tree's trunk between it and discovery.

A family of raccoons engaged in mischievous intrigue, or at least appearing so; being victimized by robbers' masks, they are always the leading suspects.

A paddling of sea ducks known as surf scoters deftly diving beneath the crest of a foaming breaker then popping up like so many jack-in-the-boxes once it has passed.

A group of playful otters, merrily sliding down their makeshift sliding board.

A couple of questions raised by a couple of winged sprites.

Observing a nuthatch's escapades sets the mind wondering how life is lived upside down.

Passing beneath a scolding titmouse inclines one to ask what they have done to deserve such criticism.

If one early March or April evening you hear weird noises and see strange objects falling from the sky, take heart. We are not being invaded. The UFOs are American woodcocks or timberdoodles (some choose to call them by this colorful colloquial name) performing an annual mating ritual that is particularly entertaining. It starts on the ground where the male issues a soft, two-syllable gurgling note known as a tuko, followed by a louder, nasal "peent" to attract the attention of prospective mates. Next comes a forty- to sixty-second aerial display in which he ascends to thirty to ninety meters on wings that produce a distinctive twittering sound. During the spiraling descent, he emits comedic notes that have been given various descriptions and which I refer to as a kind of liquid warble. A short time in the midst of these theatrics will convince you that the woodcock's brain is indeed positioned upside down.

On second thought, perhaps timberdoodles are not of this earth. Their noises sound almost otherworldly. Translated, toku-peent may mean "take me to your leader."

If one were to point out that the squirrel is ill at ease and the goose and woodcock are all business, they would be correct. Although all are serious, we can feel free to chuckle.

Is it our predominantly mirthless approach to nature that tints our vision with a colorless haze? Perhaps when it came time to stroke the hawk's tail red with a cosmic brush, a master artisan closed its eyes and let chance decide the color. Perhaps the festive spirits were dancing when the bluebird and its gaily plumed relations flew before the palette. Perhaps a divine joy is expressed when a bird sings and a person laughs. Perhaps this sounds like a stretch, but a little symbolic imagery goes a long way in expressing a point.

When viewing the natural world, it behooves us to bear in mind the peace, frolicking, humor, and color as well as the struggle. All are comprised in the vast repertoire of life, and all should influence our conception of it. Be aware of how nature's savagery is a necessary component of an overriding balance and harmony. While the cougar brings down the deer, the snow peacefully falls, the clean, crisp air gently blows, the owl glides silently overhead, and the newborn bear cubs, safely tucked away in a cozy nearby den, suckle their mother's milk.

There is little room to argue against the effectiveness of the overall system of life support. The fact that we are here at all is a testimonial to its unequivocal merit. The network of complex balancing acts constituting life coalesce in a symmetry so profound, "miraculous" may not be a strong enough term to describe it. Take a deep breath and slowly exhale. Then consider that, until proven otherwise, there is no other place in the cosmos (outside the atmosphere) where an oxygenated breath can be enjoyed.

Although the table of life rests on sturdy legs, the place ware can use some rearranging. Disease and intense chronic suffering, for example, are conditions we find unacceptable. Some might argue they have their place, but our ethics don't tolerate their inevitability and push us to find solutions to the heartache they cause. Perhaps the system should be termed "imperfectly perfect." This does not exclude the fact that any "tweaking" to make improvements should be performed with the utmost scrutiny and consideration for life and death and the part they play in maintaining nature's balance.

Respect for the *cycle* of life and death is paramount when addressing the issue of world population. Major illnesses will soon fall before technology's ax, effectively eliminating natural obstacles to population. We know that when any species dramatically overpopulates, disease spreads more rapidly, and starvation takes a toll. These facts may not be pleasant, but to not take heed is foolish. If numerous medical breakthroughs play out on a planet suffocating under a blanket of humanity, their elegance will be tarnished. Amending nature's laws in a deliberate and respectful fashion is one thing; carelessly stepping outside of them—without carefully measuring or compensating for our actions, whatever the intention—is a recipe for disaster. When the smoke clears, it is hoped that sensible efforts to preserve equilibrium within the greater social fabric will have been taken. Indefinite life extension sounds like a sexy proposition, but how seamlessly would a plethora of centenarians blend into society?

Please do not misread this narrative in a cold-blooded light. To the contrary, its concern for the total life-support system is flushed with warmth. It's the assertion that our machinations be viewed within the larger picture, which benefits humankind. We must make every endeavor to confront the multitude of challenges presented by the conditions that fuel unchecked procreation, mainly in the developing nations. Doing so is for the betterment of all.

Almost half of the world population lives on less than $5.50 per day. Assisting poorer nations is fundamental if poverty and population growth are to be corralled. Technology collaboration, international financial and education aid, and debt relief contribute to making this possible. Poverty prevents people from caring about the environment; forests are clear cut, land is over-cultivated, animals are indiscriminately hunted, and sewage is improperly disposed of.

Various institutions assist victims of poverty, not the least of which are nongovernmental organizations (NGOs) that perform a range of service and humanitarian functions. Among these are environmental NGOs that strive to combine natural values like conservation and biodiversity with compatible economic and human development. A few of note are the World Wildlife Fund, Conservation International, and Flora and Fauna International. Some work to help farmers adopt environmentally sensitive farming practices such as crop diversification, improving soil quality, and agroforestry (combining trees and shrubs with crops and animals to produce environmental, economic, and social enhance-

Lawrence K. Zeisler

ments). They work to educate the local populace and government as to why it is financially beneficial to preserve land in its natural state. People are encouraged to act as guides and guards and informed that the proceeds from tourism and the harvesting of medicinal and edible plants will contribute to the common good. The collective mission is to empower women and men so they can make their livelihood choices in a more environmentally and societally sustainable way.

The UN forecasts that nine to ten billion people will populate the world by the year 2050, around 90 percent located in the developing world. Illiteracy, mothers' despair over the possibility of their children not reaching adulthood, and poor birth control measures contribute to population growth, and all must be dealt with before they can be expected to moderate. It's been proven that doing so works. The fertility rate in Bangladesh is 2.4 children born per woman, a major decline from 6.3 in 1975. The phenomenal reduction has occurred largely because of a countrywide network of village clinics providing contraceptives and family planning initiatives that have contributed to smaller families.

Family planning is the best check on population. If pregnancies are spread out, women tend to be healthier and happier. The key is to promote individual independence and a sense of control; when people can make decisions about their lives, they realize that smaller families make sense. Raising the status of women by giving them property rights and better access to labor markets is vital. This helps mitigate the problem of gender discrimination, still prevalent in developing countries. Along with the obvious inequities, it encourages increasing family size by trying for more sons.

These factors are hampered without the awareness provided by a sound education, which in many less developed countries is still far from realized. One in four youths cannot read a sentence. Even when education is provided, it is often of lesser quality. About 125 million children with at least four years of schooling cannot perform basic math and reading. Sometimes just getting to school can be problematic, and even when tuition is free, extra costs are often incurred for uniforms, exams, lunches, and tutors to help alleviate comprehension and/or teacher deficiencies. Small wonder many prospective students drop out and end up laboring on a farm or working in the marketplace. It is imperative that more schools be constructed in isolated areas. Expanding government and donor education programs that lead to improvements in attendance and learning skills are essential.

Mastery of the fundamental Western-style school curriculum is a hollow accomplishment if the means to implement it are not available, as is often the case in impoverished settings. Formal employment prospects are uncommon for those who make it through grade 10. Children need the relevant perspectives and skills that can be realistically applied to the limited resources at their disposal. They should be encouraged to evaluate data and problem solve as well as manage projects, individually and through teamwork, geared toward self-empowerment and making positive contributions to their communities. Living standards are improved when the syllabus encourages children to tend to the sick and exercise disease prevention, which starts with basic health practices like hand washing, boiling drinking water, and using malaria nets. Projects such as instituting a school garden or starting a recycling program represent a level of entrepreneurship applicable to existing circumstances.

Putting the horse before the cart makes more sense. The agendas that will produce the most effective outcomes socially and economically for the poor are those that tap into the framework of their lives and are fortified by a real-life foundation. Hands-on action and personal involvement, not abstract concepts, are the obvious places from which to proceed in a world that must plant its feet firmly on the ground before it can be expected to adapt to ours. The traditional models of education composed of standard government curricula and founded on achievement of standardized testing would best be served acting in a complementary fashion.

Adult illiteracy remains high; a 2015 report estimates that the worldwide number hovers around 780 million people. Adult education is largely overlooked in many parts of the world. Sadly, slightly less than two-thirds of this number are women. It has been substantiated that where implemented, educated women contract fewer sexually transmitted infectious diseases, are less subject to human trafficking, are more likely to marry later, and have fewer children.

Fair trade is a laudable movement whose goal is to reduce poverty in developing countries by helping artisans acquire an equitable price for their products in international trade. Two key objectives are the promotion of ethical supervision of workers and sustainable environmental practices. One such entity, Mayorga Organics, interacts directly with coffee farmers in Latin America, helping to advance high-quality, organic, non-GMO blends at a fair cost, and it works to teach consumers how sound agricultural trade practices benefit their health and the livelihoods of small farmers. Fair trade cooperatives enable members to invest money in their community, making it possible to fund improvements in education and medical care.

Efforts in disease prevention, undertaken in laboratories worldwide, are praiseworthy. Progress in stem cell therapies and tissue engineering provide assurance for the future of regenerative medicine. Stem cells, found in tissues throughout the body, help to repair and replace ones that have become damaged or depleted, and they may one day be used to regenerate entire organs. All other cells with specialized functions evolve from stem cells; no other cells can reproduce new cell types. Stem cell transplants are currently being used to aid people with blood and immune system disorders and specific cancers. The transplants use hematopoietic or blood-forming stem cells because of their accessibility and extensive self-renewing capability. Most of the stem cells used in these procedures exist in bone marrow where they divide and make new stem cells or develop into mature red and white blood cells and platelets. Considerably smaller numbers of stem cells (called peripheral blood stem cells) can be found mixed with the more mature blood cells in the bloodstream.

There are two types of transplant procedures: autologous (using a patient's own stem cells) and allogeneic (those provided by a matching donor). Determining which regimen a patient should undergo is based primarily on their specific medical condition. In the allogeneic procedure, the method of securing a match is known as tissue typing or human leukocyte antigen (HLA) typing. HLA is a protein found on the surface of white blood cells and tissues. The more proteins a patient and donor share, the more likely it is that the transplant will succeed. Usually, the best chances

Lawrence K. Zeisler

occur when the donor is a family member, preferably a sibling. When the procedure is performed using a matched but unrelated donor, chances for success drop. Using mismatched related donors lessens the success rate more.

An autologous stem cell transplant uses one's own healthy stem cells to replace bone marrow that has been devastated by disease and employs subsequent chemotherapy with or without radiation exposure. Historically, before treatment, the stem cells were collected from the bone marrow, but the more recent practice is to gather them from free-flowing peripheral blood. This lowers the risk of complications and spurs faster bone marrow recovery after treatment. Although the population of stem cells located in the peripheral blood is relatively small, their number can be increased by injecting blood cell growth factors into the bone marrow to stimulate release of additional cells into the bloodstream, where they are subsequently retrieved.

The process of collecting stem cells from the blood is called apheresis. During the harvest, blood is extracted from a vein and flows through a catheter. It passes through a machine that separates the stem cells and returns the remainder of the blood to the patient. Apheresis is executed for as long as it takes to secure enough stem cells to promote treatment, usually two to four days. After that, they are frozen and stored until the patient is ready.

The next step is to administer chemotherapy and sometimes radiation therapy to kill the cancerous cells, a process that also exterminates the blood-producing cells remaining in the bone marrow. This can last several days to over a week. This same conditioning regimen is used in the allogeneic transplant.

Doctors have known for some time that stem cell collections may include cancer cells. Some establishments treat the stem cells before retransplantation, and techniques are being implemented to address the problem. Often referred to as purging, they commonly use antibodies to identify and adhere to antigens—harmful foreign substances that trigger an immune response—on cancerous cells. Once attached, the cells are eliminated in different ways. One technique fastens high-density microparticles to the antibodies. These are mixed with the stem cell collection, and they affix themselves to any diseased cells, making them heavier. This causes them to sink to the bottom of the container where they can be separated, though there is no guarantee that all will be detected. Some normal stem cells can be lost during the procedure. Another process called in vivo purging returns the untreated stem cells to the patient, who is administered anticancer drugs to combat any lingering cancer cells. No attempt at removing cancer cells from transplanted stem cells is foolproof, and the research is ongoing.

Once the proper conditions are met, the harvested stem cells are reintroduced into the bloodstream by a process not unlike a blood transfusion. The stem cells travel to the bone marrow where they start to produce new red and white blood cells and platelets. Patients may require additional transfusions and antibiotics to prevent infection. The advantage of this treatment is that the patient's own cells are returned, eliminating the chance of rejection or the possibility of the donor's implanted immune cells attacking the patient's healthy tissues. However, the immune system is the same as before, one that allowed cancer cells to avoid attack. Though the allogeneic transplant involves

Lawrence K. Zeisler

the above risks, another person's stem cells, once engrafted in the bone marrow, form a new immune system, producing white blood cells that eradicate any lingering cancer cells that may have survived the chemotherapy.

Another method of stem cell donation is the use of umbilical cord blood. It is collected from the blood vessels of the mother's placenta and umbilical cord immediately after birth. The process is harmless to both mother and baby. The blood is analyzed for contamination and quickly frozen, making it available in short notice for a worthy recipient. Since the stem cells are less mature or "purer" than bone marrow stem cells, immune system incompatibilities and the chance of transmitting viral infections are reduced. Hence, tissue compatibility, though important, is not as critical. They also have the capability to differentiate into diverse kinds of cells, making them more adaptive. Although umbilical cord blood units contain fewer stem cells than a bone marrow donation and take longer to engraft, they replicate much faster.

Umbilical cord tissue can be collected with the blood. Its stem cells share some of the cord blood's advantages such as greater freedom from negative immune responses and proliferation of stem cells. They serve other purposes as well, some of which are the secretion of growth factors that assist in tissue mending, suppressing inflammation resulting from damaged tissue, and the ability to transform into one of many cell types in the circulatory tissues, nervous system, sensory organs, skin, and more. Because of their faculty for cell replenishment and less risky nature, cord tissue and cord blood stem cells serve a crucial niche in the burgeoning field of regenerative medicine. Research is progressing down avenues including treatment of spinal cord injury, diabetes, heart disease, muscular dystrophy, cerebral palsy, autism, and liver disease.

Genetically modified stem cells play an active role in the transfer of genes during transplant procedures involving gene therapy. Gene therapy entails inserting a healthy gene into someone's cells or tissue, replacing or attacking an abnormal disease-producing one, to treat a disease. It confronts disease by healing at the gene level where most maladies originate, and it uses the patient's own cells, thereby precluding the risk of rejection. The self-renewing quality of the stem cells means that repeated applications of gene therapy are less likely to be needed.

The US Food and Drug Administration (FDA) has endorsed the world's first genetically engineered immune treatment—Novartis Pharmaceutical's CAR T-cell therapy— for a type of cancer known as acute lymphocytic leukemia (ALL). It was developed at the University of Pennsylvania by a group led by gene therapy trailblazer Carl June. On April 17, 2012, a girl named Emily Whitehead was the first pediatric patient to undergo the treatment that genetically programs the immune system to attack cancer cells.

In certain cancers, including the type of leukemia afflicting Emily, a portion of immune cells known as B cells become malignant. Another group of white blood cells called T cells, which develop from stem cells in the bone marrow, patrol the intracellular environment and hunt down foreign invaders such as bacteria and viruses. These are instrumental in eliminating cancer cells. In some cancers, ALL being one, the abnormal cancerous B cells evade the protective T cells.

During the treatment, Emily's T cells were acquired by filtering her blood. In a lab, a virus's disease-producing genes were removed and replaced with a beneficial one. Viruses were used because of their ability to "invade" a host.

Lawrence K. Zeisler

The enhanced and harmless virus (or vector) delivered the new gene into the T cells, and the new gene stimulated the growth of a receptor that targets a protein, CD19, located only on the exterior of B cells. After being given time to multiply, the restructured T cells were reintroduced into her system where they circulated, locating the CD19 marker and destroying the cancerous B cells. The altered cells were referred to as a "living drug" as they continuously multiplied in their battle against the disease. Emily experienced severe side-effects, but in following years, these declined in succeeding patients as doctors acquired more knowledge in managing CAR T-cell therapy.

Five years later, Emily is in remission and leading a normal life. Since her procedure, 83 percent of patients in a global trial are also in remission, despite having relapsed repeatedly with conventional toxic chemotherapy regimens. A major drawback is that healthy B cells are targeted as well, making patients vulnerable to infections, requiring the administration of scheduled infusions of an immune-boosting drug.

Novartis and other companies are in hot pursuit of T-cell therapies earmarked for other blood disorders. The hope is that gene therapy will eventually work in solid tumor cancers, which present more formidable obstacles. The future holds promise for the treatment of diabetes, heart disease, AIDS, blindness, Huntington's disease, and hemophilia.

A combination of stem cell use and gene therapy was used by a team of stem cell researchers headed by stem cell biologist and physician Michele De Luca of the University of Modena to repair a rare, incurable genetic skin condition afflicting a young boy. Junctional epidermolysis bullosa makes the outer layer of skin or epidermis peel away from the dermis layer beneath. Minor abrasions or even friction between skin and clothing can cause severe blistering and make one highly susceptible to infections. The disease occurs when the LAMB3 gene mutates and inhibits the growth of proteins that help fuse the skin layers.

The team removed a patch of the boy's unaffected skin and, using it as a sample, grew skin stem cells in the lab. They inserted a healthy copy of the LAMB3 gene into the DNA of the lab-cultivated skin stem cells by means of a retrovirus to assist the gene transfer. The genetically enhanced protein restored skin cells developed on a special substrate. This allowed them to expand into large sheets of epidermis, which surgeons grafted onto nearly 80 percent of the boy's body. The skin layers have successfully adhered and are functioning normally with no sign of blistering, and unlike traditional transplanted skin grafts, no daily ointments are required to retain the skin's viability.

Gene therapy is still in its infancy, and many technical hurdles need to be surmounted. The dynamics of our cells and tissues are varied and need to be better understood. More effective gene-to-cell transfer designs await discovery, and it is essential to instigate guaranteed prolonged cell survival in patients. For ALL patients like Emily, serious side effects are suffered, and long-term maladies resulting from the altered genes are possible, but efforts to address such matters are underway. The future looks encouraging.

Ethicists understand that research will encounter questions about the road that gene therapy should follow, safety being a prime consideration. It would be hard to question the necessity for carefully analyzed and administered treatments of disabling and life-threatening diseases. Changes to genes in egg or sperm cells and genetic editing of embryos present an array of ethical challenges.

Operations such as those involving joint replacements that give patients a new lease on life are worthy of note as are drugs designed to relieve arthritis. We can all agree that penicillin (produced naturally by molds), which heralded the age of antibiotics, has been a blessing to innumerable people. Efforts to relieve humanity of its array of deadly scourges are meritorious and will delay but not negate the inevitable end.

Until relatively recently, death was commonplace in the home. A failing person's needs were attended to by the family, making the experience more intimate for all involved. In 1900, most people were born at home and died at home. Today, that personal association with the Great Mystery has been greatly reduced. Now the dying process is viewed sporadically, largely within the sterile walls of a hospital or a less-than-sterile nursing home and only after the patient has been prodded, poked, and pinched by countless needles, clamps, and tubes.

My mother passed away some time ago. For years she suffered from a host of ailments, and her health steadily deteriorated. The day came when her condition necessitated a hurried trip to the hospital, one from which she would never return.

They hooked her up to the latest life-saving apparatus. In her state, she was unable to verbally communicate. She lapsed in and out of consciousness and once, while awake, gave me a look I will never forget. It was that of a caged animal, a combination of shock and fear but not at the prospect of death. In an instant I realized she felt extremely degraded and exposed. The last place she wanted to be was in a strange place surrounded by strangers. All warmth had been removed from her decline. Though I perceived this at the time, I held fast to propriety. "Come on, Mom," I whispered, "please get well again. You can beat it."

Not long thereafter, she did beat it—not death but the elaborate mechanisms she had been attached to. Her prison term was over. She was liberated. The doctor shook her head and said, "If she had put as much effort into living as she did into thwarting the machines, she'd doubtless be with us still." What the doctor didn't know was that my mom intensely hated hospitals, and her lust for life had been extinguished.

I am not opposed to the campaign against death per se. The moral imperative underlying our regard for life is commendable as is the effort to eradicate disease and protracted suffering. Medical procedures employing precision medicine, which focuses on treatments based on a genetic understanding of a patient's physiological profile, have come a long way since the early twentieth century when medication was administered to minimize discomfort while the healing process was largely left to nature.

Nor is this an argument for assisted suicide. Please view it as an attempt to take the edge off the most fundamental fear of all, one grounded in our separation from the natural order. In this context, exception is taken with the endeavors to make death so remote. By encouraging us to avoid it by any means, it's small wonder that it has assumed the role of pariah. If one could look at death with greater understanding and respect, they might accept their fate easier and make more rational decisions concerning the time to go. Frequently, a patient will beat back death for a spell only to face it shortly thereafter, sometimes repeatedly. When this is accompanied by a progressive deterioration in health, the financial and emotional tolls borne by patient and family can be brutal. The question is one of when perpetuating life becomes an injustice to the dying and to death's honor. The rising use of living wills shows that more people question the virtue of maintaining life at any cost.

The healthcare system is recognizing the benefits of palliative and hospice care. Both are holistic, or comprehensive, approaches that incorporate a range of professionals providing comfort to patients suffering chronic or life-limiting illnesses. Palliative care often begins at diagnosis, continues during treatment, and is usually administered in a hospital or extended care facility. Hospice care is reserved for the terminally ill and commences when the patient has chosen to forego elaborate life-prolonging treatments with their negative side effects. At the core of hospice care lies the belief that each person has the right to die pain free and with dignity. Specialist doctors work with nurses, a nutritionist, chaplain, and social worker for pain and symptom management, emotional, social, and spiritual support, practical assistance to the patient and family, and discussions about end-of-life supervision. Their combined effort is designed to enrich one's remaining days. The focus is on caring, not curing. The goal is to neither hasten nor delay death. If the patient exhibits signs of recovery, treatment may recommence. Most importantly, the prominent role that loved ones, and especially the patient, play in the drama is respected. Whenever possible, the care is provided at home.

Over the past decade, many doctors have become sensitive to the fact that some procedures administered to a person in a persistent vegetative state border on the grotesque. Hospitals are writing guidelines that limit the use of life-sustaining machines or surgeries for such patients unless they specifically request the measures before their decline.

It has been said that we are so uneasy with death because of our love of life and that we have so much to lose by dying. It is true that a comfortable and relatively secure lifestyle affords many of us the opportunity to appreciate the "finer things," but the pursuit of them is a double-edged sword that begs the question: Do we undermine a genuine love of life when placing excess emphasis on the material things that we believe give life meaning? If those goods that we've acquired—the spacious house, luxurious car, redesigned and expanded kitchen, state-of-the-art electronic equipment, bedroom suite, or comfortable lawn tractor—were replaced by simple yet adequate substitutes, would our happiness be compromised? God forbid, what if the television set was removed indefinitely?

Do the striving for recognition and status, the effort to push harder and climb higher, the quest for riches, the thrill of the purchase, or the pleasurable reward complement the fundamental, unshakable realities underlying existence some of which are love of family and friends, following creative and intellectual impulses, obtaining satisfaction from honest labor, and doing right by others? Are the desires that motivate those efforts and accomplishments distractions that alienate us from a deeper understanding of our common humanity and the natural world's sacrificial nature? The estrangement from the true source of comfort, which is based on a sense of connectedness, is the root cause of our fear of death.

The growing isolation in modern society contributes to peoples' insecurity. We are losing the integrated qualities that comprise small-town America as well as the neighborhood composition of big cities. In comparison, suburbs are socially sterile. Not too long ago, most people lived a short distance from work and the services they relied upon for the maintenance of their livelihood. Face-to-face communication was the norm, and associations were conducted on a first-name basis. Owners of the corner grocery could

Lawrence K. Zeisler

be like a second family. Stores are now so distant and large that one can feel like a stranger when entering.

Close familiarity with others and the support offered by quality friendships, even casual interactions, engender feelings of consolation and break down the barriers erected by notions of superiority (a form of alienation). This provides one with the groundwork to better accept that their worth as a human is the same as everyone else's. Today, we are much more mobile and technologically connected but more detached.

To Native Americans who worshiped the natural order and enjoyed the unity and reassurance inherent in communal living, death was not so grave. They believed it to be the beginning of life in the spirit world. A Sioux medicine man named Lame Deer writes:

> You are spreading death, buying and selling death. With all your deodorants, you smell of it, but you are afraid of its reality; you don't want to face up to it. You have sanitized death, put it under the rug, robbed it of its honor. But we Indians think a lot about death. I do. Today would be a perfect day to die - not too hot, not too cool. A day to leave something of yourself behind, to let it linger. A day for a lucky man to come to the end of his trail. A happy man with many friends. Other days are not so good. They are for selfish, lonesome men, having a hard time leaving this earth. But for whites every day would be considered a bad one, I guess.[1]

As a rule, tribal peoples personalize death. Some African tribes treat the passing of one of their fellows with celebration. During the ceremonies, dead ancestors and the living come together in dance. They glorify death, believing it makes life more precious. The spirit of the deceased person joins the source of all being out on the velte. This process has to be reassuring to all involved.

The Mexican holiday called "Dia de los Muertos" (The Day of the Dead) created by indigenous peoples, is celebrated the first two days of November. The first day is dedicated to remembering deceased adults; the second day, to deceased children. People visit gravesites and family altars, decorate them with flowers, and adorn them with religious amulets and offerings of food the dead person enjoyed in life. Stories about the departed are recounted during picnics and other social gatherings. At home, they erect monuments on which photographs of the dead are mounted. This interaction with the living and the dead is a way of recognizing the cycle of life and death. It is a festive time where death is embraced.

I'm not suggesting that members of these societies are completely at ease with death. It underlies many of their superstitions and beliefs; certain events and signs can portend it, but it is not the deep-rooted fear it is to us, in part because the pathway to the spirit world does not run by way of eternal judgment.

Motivating the campaign to shroud death is an amalgam of altruism, pride, fear, quest for profit, compassion, Hippocratic loyalty, and curiosity as to how death's frontier can be tamed. If my words appear harsh, it's because by estranging us from death, medical technology, commercial interests, hospitals, religion, and social norms have contributed to our fear of it. Our standards do death an injustice.

We fear death as much as we do because it has become

depersonalized and distant. We have lost track of its function and worth. By now, you may suspect that the ego is the
culprit, occupied with thoughts of how it desires things to
be. Perpetual joy and pleasure are possible only in theory
and are powerful illusions that denounce life as it is.

Chapter 4

"What a fool believes, he sees."

—From the song entitled "What a Fool Believes",
co-written by Michael McDonald and Kenny Loggins

urther light must be shed upon this interpretation
of the ego. We are aware of ourselves as distinct
human beings, personally unique *I*'s or selves, yet
we possess an array of traits that twist our personalities
to the extent that *I* becomes *I as opposed to you* instead
of *you and I*. When this opposition occurs, the ego is
behind it. As expressed in the introduction, it shares
room in the mind with the intellect, which perceives life
with a clear and steady eye buoyed by the realization of
its interdependence.

Interdependence is key to this discussion. We are all
entitled to our beliefs, and all are relevant to the person
in possession of his or her own, but there is no denying
that some are less centered around the self and represent
a wider-reaching sensitivity to things beyond personal
concerns. Basing one's outlook on a broader spectrum
of reality gives them more information to consider while
formulating ideas—information that, if processed, will
reflect a better understanding of other people and events,
which usually leads to more responsible reactions.

Lawrence K. Zeisler

The ego's health hinges on its ability to convince an individual that its ideas are essential to their well-being, so it constructs judgments and beliefs that aid it in maintaining its hold. The more deeply ingrained they are, the more secure the ego's position. The beliefs and judgments spoken of here are discordant by nature, for the ego stresses differentiating characteristics and fails to see associations. Beliefs and opinions that don't produce ignorance or discord will not be considered egocentric. (The word *prejudice* will be used frequently in this discussion. For the sake of clarity, please interpret it in the context of the above negative qualities. I am talking about thoughts and ideas adversely affecting our behavior and convictions, not those affiliated with learned technical skills, applied sciences, beneficial knowledge such as nutrition and health information, or basic concerns about a family's well-being or sustaining a decent living standard.)

We feel more at ease when our minds are clogged with judgments, preconceptions, ideologies, etc., and we assume that without them governing our thoughts and actions, we would be little more than empty-minded and uncontrollable shells. The measure of an aware mind is not taken by tallying the number of facts it holds; some are based on a sound foundation, but others are truth-diverting clutter. How many predatory animals were unnecessarily slaughtered because one chose to heed the conventional wisdom of the day? I hardly need to ask how often a person fails to see the whole picture because they dutifully toe the political party line.

I am not indicating that absorbing other folks' ideas is necessarily bad. Every child should acquire the education and values that will assist them in accomplishing a smooth integration into society, and the inspiration of family and friends is critical to stable emotional progress. One's mind should always be receptive to advice. However, since the groundwork for much of our worldview has been molded by other opinions, usually during the impressionable years (which sometimes linger into adulthood), it is not beyond reproach.

It may sound as if the memory per se is being called into question, but this is not so. In many instances, we couldn't get from point A to point B if we were unable to recollect facts and events. The mind will remember pertinent information. If someone threatened me, that thought would hold priority the next time I encountered them, but I also should remain open to the possibility of that person being able to overcome the emotions that prompted the threat. We can remember things and show caution without letting prejudice dominate memory and close our minds.

Embedded thoughts can impede personal growth. Many of our beliefs come too easily, for we tend to form them around a central theme and look no further. Upon scrutiny, we might discover that the theme is held mainly because it makes us feel secure to think we know all about a given matter. Because of the need to secure a firm conviction, we often ignore crucial features that could alter the nature of our comprehension. In this way, we grow complacent about questioning why we think and feel the way we do. This is one reason why a reputation sometimes outlives its usefulness. Please take note of the word *sometimes*.

The ego is absent if I watch a news commentary without judgment. If its contents are contrary to my way of thinking and my equilibrium is noticeably shaken, judgment will surface. If the faultfinding quickly fades, the ego's impact will be minimal. If it builds upon itself, I will likely lose focus and with it my capacity to objectively interpret the discourse.

Lawrence K. Zeisler

The point of this example is to show how judgment can produce inner discord and prohibit one from comprehending information. Just because an opinion is contradictory does not mean that it is without some merit. I know it is difficult to maintain mental tranquility when someone espouses an opposing view, especially when in discussion. Disagreement is natural, as is the tendency to argue, but argument can lead to agitation if not contained. The sooner you can corral the need to impulsively act in defense of your beliefs, the more effectively you can explain them, preferably with a calm demeanor. If during the discourse some of those beliefs are proven inaccurate, you will be better able to accept the fact and learn the reasons why if pride does not get in the way. By taking things personally, the ego will not see beyond pride.

The borough for which I work provides employees with a generous credit earmarked for purchasing work boots. Over time, the floor of my closet grew cluttered with footwear, so I decided to offer my son, who wears a similar-sized shoe, an opportunity to benefit from the program. A couple years passed with no problem, but this one didn't. The cashier noticed that my son and I each held two boxes as we approached and, after charging me for mine, started to put his on a separate tab. I asked her why, and she said she assumed that he was not employed by the borough. Instead of nipping the situation in the bud by proclaiming, albeit deceitfully, that the boxes he carried contained my shoes, my failure to think fast on my feet led to a dispute. I asked her to fetch the manager, who chose to side with her. The exchange deteriorated to a point of ugliness, thanks to my stubborn refusal to let go of my conviction that it was not their right to decide how I spent my money. Their contention was that it wasn't mine but the borough's.

The argument was predicated on the fact that they saw the picture in black and white. I discerned a gray area, but at the time, I was too agitated to give in and clung to my belief. They were fundamentally right, but I couldn't see why they cared. The next day, my boss notified me that the store manager called the borough concerning its policy—thank goodness he didn't reach human resources or the borough manager—and I held my breath, hoping I hadn't jeopardized the program.

What appeared to me a harmless act to shoe my son was not shared by others. Perhaps the instance smacked me especially hard because they made me feel bad by exposing the core dishonesty I felt comfortable with (I like to think it did). Regardless, as soon as the manager stated his conviction, I should have acknowledged it and sucked in my pride, realizing the futility of the clash. There comes a point in an escalating, emotionally charged disagreement when a responsible person realizes that to expect resolution, let alone influence another's viewpoint, is fruitless.

They who take responsibility for their actions do not squander time and effort laying blame. They can accept fault, learn from it, and move on.

I can see their point and understand its merits, but still am not in total agreement. Next year, I will go to a different store and make sure I carry the full complement of boxes to the register.

When the quest to "have things your way" confronts the reality of life, dissatisfaction can ensue, upsetting one's peace of mind and stifling the ability to react in a constructive manner. The Serenity Prayer written by the American theologian Reinhold Niebuhr comes to mind: "God grant me the serenity to accept the things I cannot change, courage to change the things I can, and wisdom to know the difference." Before the wisdom in the prayer can be properly implemented, an equable understanding of reality must be realized.

While proofreading this manuscript, my brother-in-law set to work fixing a problem with the computer beside me. I tried to coexist, but the effort was doomed to failure, because I deemed his presence an intrusion. The dilemma was compounded by the time constraint I'd imposed on myself. If I had elected to conform to the ego's self-serving, inconsiderate urges, which prevented empathy for his plight, I would have had no recourse but to ask him to leave. My rude behavior would undoubtedly have caused me distress and guilt. Instead, I opted to take the high road and politely exit the room. After a short bout of frustration, I was able to collect myself and accomplish an outdoor task that had been long overlooked.

For the mind to operate properly, it must keep pace with current developments, but if it depends too heavily on habitual tendencies for guidance, it becomes constricted and unable to exercise the freedom necessary to adapt to new insights. This propensity for constraining the mind's fluidity, or openness, is the fundamental flaw of a biased outlook. Hence, questioning and/or eliminating an egocentric bias does not impair the intellect's ability to imagine and perceive. To the contrary, a mind free of its clutter can "breathe" much better and relate directly to its situation without restriction, which means without the need to think and act in a prescribed pattern.

I recently repaired portions of a retaining wall bordering an outdoor stairway. When I was through for the day, I told the homeowner, who was a good friend, I would have to return on the morrow to apply a final coat of cement over the hole I had patched in a cinder block. That evening, my wife informed me curiosity had gotten the better of our friend, and she had reopened the hole by poking at the covered area. Being that it had been particularly frustrating getting the cement to fill the gap in the first place, I was peeved by the whole affair.

En route to her house the next day, my ego cultivated friction by intermittently reminding me of the extra work that would be required as the result of her act. When I arrived, she confronted me with a fervent apology, which I quickly accepted. We broke into laughter. I mentioned that I learned something about her character I had never before realized and asked if she had driven her parents to distraction as a child. I'm thankful that the ego's influence interrupted only my driving pleasure and not our friendship; the fact that its effect on me dissipated upon contact with her is further proof of its fundamental unimportance.

Because the world does not conform to its rigid demands, a prejudiced mind is riddled with discontent. This is due in part to the fact that it has a difficult time "lightening up" enough to accept and appreciate those surprising and often subtle personality traits that make others unique and entertaining.

A flexible, inquisitive person is less likely to be manipulated by propaganda. The airwaves are bombarded with commercials and information that companies and institutions have a vested interest in promoting. Their target is the lazy mind, because it tends to grab notions by habit and cling to them without question, which makes it difficult to ascertain one's real needs. Obstinance finds a home in social media, where groups of close-knit individuals are buffered against the shock of outside opinion.

Lawrence K. Zeisler

It's sad that many folks don't have a hint as to the extent of the ego's dominance. Some aren't aware that it exists or the part it plays in self-deception, a form of delusion, which has reached epidemic proportions nationwide. While under the spell of self-deception, all judgement will be tainted. When pride guides their performance, the weak-minded individual tends to overvalue their insights and strengths, jeopardizing the ability to assess their true standing.

I know two people who were friends until a series of unfortunate circumstances eroded the relationship and set them at odds. Before matters deteriorated altogether, the woman apologized to the man for the way she had been treating him because of her displeasure with his recent actions, but he refused to accept the apology and from that point on chose to ignore her, explaining his cold shoulder by saying, "At least I'm being honest and not faking my feelings by acknowledging her when I don't want to." The "I" in the quote is representative of the ego and his continued anger a defense erected by it, a kind of white knight (black knight would be more apropos) that charged to the rescue whenever he thought about or saw her and rationalized his disapproval and hurt.

A controlling ego does not like to shoulder the responsibility for one's pain, because it would entail an alteration of the personality, and any thought of change on the part of its host is an insult to the pride that rests upon the assumption that its beliefs are the absolute truth.

When she apologized, he took offense, having linked the apology to her original discontentment with some of his previous actions. Since he didn't want to believe there was a basis for disapproval in the first place, a nod of forgiveness would have been tantamount to admitting, however obliquely, that her anger had been warranted. Deeming her blameworthy assured that his thoughts could continue to emanate from that antiquated, contentious position.

Our prejudices abound because of the failure to hold ourselves accountable for our thoughts and actions. The tendency to attribute one's unappealing inner impulses or qualities to others is far too common. These acts, known as projection, are egocentric safeguards that prevent one from taking responsibility for what rests within. Saddling her with the reason for his pain permitted his pride to freely sustain it, precluding any chance for a clear, objective analysis.

Was he being honest with himself like he suggested? If he was able to peer beyond the ego's defenses, he would have most likely discovered an inner longing to reestablish the friendship. The silent treatment directed at her inferred his reactions to the apology were emotional. Coupled with efforts to get her attention at a distance and annoy her whenever possible, indicates that conditions from his standpoint were far from settled. I'm reminded of three quotes: "All buried feelings are buried alive" and "fix the problem, not the blame." Benjamin Franklin, the master of pith, wrote: "Search others for their virtues, thyself for thy vices."

The great teacher J. Krishnamurti asks us:

Have you ever wondered why you have ideas and opinions at all- why? Why do you form an image, an image being an idea? Why does thought function through ideas, ideas of nationality, of what is right and wrong, that it is right to kill under certain circumstances, the beliefs that you have about God, the family and the non-family; you have ideas- why?

Lawrence K. Zeisler

Are ideas a means of self-protection, a resistance to any form of change, to any form of movement, to life? ... Learning implies a great sensitivity and there is no sensitivity if there is an idea, which is of the past, dominating the present. It is only a very sensitive mind that can learn and that sensitivity is denied when there is the domination of an idea.[1]

Therefore, if we are to "find ourselves"—a stale and vague but nevertheless useful phrase—we must supersede our reliance upon ironclad judgments, for a mind committed to unyielding principle is stagnant and out of synch with its environment. One is much better attuned to themselves and their surroundings to the extent that the mind is clear of mental chatter.

A movie based on the book *The Defiant Ones* is about two convicts, one white and one black, who escape from a prison truck but are chained together. From the outset of their forced exile, it is apparent there is no love lost between them, but as time passes, the initial strife wanes and is supplanted by respect and friendship. I remember a poignant line of dialogue. One of the members of the posse—after enduring a longer-than-anticipated chase (he assumed the prisoners' mutual antagonism would slow them down more than it had)—complains to the sheriff. The sheriff replies, "It's harder to hate a man at the end of a chain."

Perhaps it was harder in the long run but not in the early going. This was because despite being virtual strangers, each one painted a mental picture based on conceptions about the other man's race long before the escape and viewed its prejudiced image with fidelity.

If the unknown is the source of fear, it's not difficult

to determine that one who lives with prejudiced thoughts creates much of their own. Prejudice, suspicion, and fear are formidable allies that limit one's knowledge. When one elects to stand by past judgments, they undermine comprehension of present circumstances, and the resultant lack of intimacy can beget suspicion and fear. The dark is not really frightening, but so long as the mind concocts images of shadowy, lurking forms, it will appear to be, for its true features will remain blurred by those images. Hence, even a physical encounter with an object of fear and distrust will do little to enlighten someone if their mind is ensnared in a web of prejudice against that object.

The more familiar one becomes with something, the less likely that fear will endure, assuming the mind has been granted a measure of freedom. Digest the words of an African proverb: "No man fears what he has seen grow." I recall how I disliked a man because I chose to draw my conclusions about him around what I termed his glaring flaws, but a funny thing happened. The better I got to know him, the more I could abide those "bad" qualities. My newfound attitude was due to the goodness I began to see in him, his love of family, and his generosity. When moderated by the awareness of his redeeming traits, the questionable ones didn't carry the weight they once did. While allowing his perceived pitfalls to preside over my outlook, I prematurely closed the door on his character. Concentrating on negative images that are retrieved from memory plants a seedbed of dissatisfaction that preempts one from gaining adequate familiarity with someone. I see this lack of familiarity as largely responsible for my once being afraid to look him squarely in the eye.

It is not being suggested that all acquaintances be

Lawrence K. Zeisler

taken into our confidence, and some associates have a knack for tampering with our patience, but for the sake of mental comfort, it is wise to keep an objective outlook whenever possible.

A prejudiced mind often responds with expedience. It is automatic for one who has been raised with a fear of snakes to deem them all threatening. Rather than taking the time to assess information that would enable them to distinguish poisonous from nonpoisonous species, they prefer to kill any harmless snake that crosses their path.

You may be wondering why the concern over one snake. Does it matter in the end? Not in the end perhaps, but it matters now. The quality of our lives is inversely proportionate to the quantity of fear we fall victim to; the greater the number of objects fear can grasp, the more it will obscure the light of reason and one's peace of mind. Though the objects of fear are separate, they are related in that they all contribute to the net time it fills one with its unsettling presence. Much more comfort is derived from appreciating and observing a life form than in destroying it—even a snake.

I realize there are times we cannot help but fear. One can hardly fault a soldier for feeling a generous dose of it while girding for battle, and few people can walk a deserted subway at night without being marginally unnerved. It might accompany one who is about to make a presentation in front of a large audience. Who can blame the unemployed during the Great Depression who feared for their family's subsistence? Instinctive fear is unavoidable, and in cases of possible peril, it serves as a warning device. As a survival tool for the unenlightened, it is important. Since children cannot act in their own defense, they possess it as a safeguard against life's dangers.

The contention is that an informed mind has little use

for all save instinctive fear. An informed mind is one that, through experience, has gained the ability to intellectualize and put into play the concept of regard. In this context, regard means showing attentiveness to and consideration for someone or something. Such an approach allows one to evaluate things much more clearly. Familiarity is the enemy of fear.

A mature person can quiet fear by supplanting it with regard without losing one iota of caution. When you break it down, you see it is not fear so much as the knowledge of danger that is advantageous. If I happen upon a rattlesnake on a mountain trail, my instinctive fear will make me give pause, but it is regard for the reptile that tells me to give it a wide berth—regard founded on the knowledge of its venomous bite and its place in nature's hierarchy. When a reaction to danger is sponsored by fear and not regard, panic may set in. We all know how panic can generate more harm than the original danger.

Fear performs its function best when acting in response to an immediate or physical stimulus and not when inducing one to dwell on an idea. Most fear is spawned in time and dredged up from memories that fill the present or future with uncertainty. I understand some exclusively memory-induced fears are unavoidable, one glaring example being the dread one feels when thinking about the possibility of nuclear warfare. It's only normal that some residents of coastal Indonesia feel unease over the possible return of another tsunami and for members of Latino communities to share growing anxiety in this country's racially-charged atmosphere.

Occasionally the line delineating fear from regard can become blurred. I love the outdoors and have become distressed by the growing number of invasive tick-borne

Lawrence K. Zeisler

pathogens. The dilemma is especially perplexing because the critters are virtually invisible to the naked eye. Since they are a fact of life, I have no choice but to accept their existence. My awareness of the fact cannot dispel the fear of being infected, so I'm faced with options. I can let the fear consume me and dramatically curtail outside activity. I can rationally think the problem through and take measures like applying safe and effective spray repellents and wearing the proper clothing to lessen the chance of exposure while still enjoying the fresh air. The latter choice, though not failsafe and tinged with some fear, refuses to pander to it and allows me to continue my preferred lifestyle.

A friend was recently diagnosed with pancreatic cancer. The immediacy of the event sparked concern for my own mortality and led to cursory research of the affliction for fear that my lifestyle could possibly be contributing to my contracting it. The fear was undeniable and provided the impetus that led to slight alterations in behavior. It did perform a function but allowing it to linger will only do me harm. Concentrating on improved health practices would be the best course to follow.

Person-to-person experiences can test us as well. No one ever said a quality life comes easily; maturation involves risks and disappointments that only a strong character will endure. We are all taken advantage of, sometimes by people we thought were friends and every so often by strangers. After witnessing a couple of shady dealings, any rational soul will know to beware of hucksters bearing gifts. I remember the time a fellow sold me a ratchet set on a street corner for a bargain basement price. I did not discover until later that the sockets wouldn't lock onto the handles. At least I didn't have to worry about searching for the receipt. Disillusion is part of life. Trust in your ability to overcome it, learn, and move on.

It is not being suggested that one should let down their guard, especially in this age of computer scams and pyramid schemes. The airwaves are awash with sleazy opportunists vying for the chance to make easy money. It would be wise to be on the lookout for "get rich quick" offerings; they are almost always too good to be true.

A friend once told me his father advised him never to trust others until he got to know them. This attitude is by no means confined to my friend's dad; many people feel that if not vigilant, they will jeopardize their security.

It is important to be able to compartmentalize suspicion. This means maintaining awareness while exercising freedom from distrust's lingering shadow. Like fear, it can be excessive and clouds one's ability to make clear judgements. For instance, immigrants are not out to get you. Assuming so not only makes for an unnecessarily restive and disquieting outlook but also dishonors our humanity.

This commentary is directed primarily at the majority of folks living relatively secure lives above the poverty line, buffered from the challenges facing those inhabiting the inner city and distressed rural environs. While everyone, especially the young, should be attentive to dishonorable efforts aimed at undermining their safety, the likelihood of encountering foul play rises where the opportunity for upward mobility is virtually nonexistent.

Sometimes one's suspicion is warranted, and a probing eye is required to meet its request for an answer. The subsequent inquiry will proceed on surer footing if not straying from an objective path. My wife and her former manager were employed with a colleague who had a less than glowing work history. A few of his infractions had been brought to light and dealt with. My wife expressed how her manager had lost his trust, and carefully monitored the fellow's actions. She felt suspicion had overtaken him to the point of distress, leading to overreaction to nearly every new "transgression," some of which were reflective of the bias he had constructed. He had grounds for suspicion but had taken it to an extreme, falling prey to its distractions and often exaggerating the severity of its claims; claims that were not worth the worry, leading to needlessly reached dead ends.

Because of its undue efforts at self-protection, the bearer of a suspicious mind may live a relatively secure life, but that security carries a high price, for that person will risk missing the warmth existing outside the confines of their self-imposed exile. A Good Samaritan is empathetic to the fact that everyone wants to be acknowledged. The trust inherent in compassion gives one the impetus to tip their hat and extend their hand to others. It is a rare individual who will not pick up on such sincerity and sooner than later respond in kind.

To reference this claim, we again venture into the celluloid realm. *Places in the Heart* is a movie set in Texas during the Great Depression. It is about a farm widow trying desperately to hold onto her land. A vagrant who had been permitted entrance into her house for a warm meal steals some silver. The next day, the local constable comes to her door with the apprehended man and goods. Instead of pressing charges, she makes an excuse for him and, after the sheriff's departure, asks him to help her farm the cotton. Their friendship steadily grows, and at one point, the man saves her son's life. Perhaps her kindness is due in part to her dire straits, for she needed his expertise and labor to keep the farm solvent, but that is immaterial. If she had not taken the chance, she would have never experienced the deep friendship and would most likely have lost the farm.

Left unchecked, suspicion and fear nourish a spiral of ignorance that only a jolting dose of the truth will diffuse. Due to the unique nature of their predicament, the escaped convicts in *The Defiant Ones* received that jolt. The choice was simple: overcome their preconceptions or be caught. They were compelled to engage an object of distrust face to face. As the movie progresses, the object turns from the man standing alongside to the fear within. Being so closely bound forces them to confront their prejudices and fears on a surface level, for they are not intentionally analyzing themselves. When put to such an acid test, each man discovers that the picture that has served him faithfully for so many years proves piteously flawed at arm's length. The concept of the contribution physical interaction plays in opening the mind can be discerned in this Mark Twain quote, "Travel is fatal to prejudice, bigotry, and narrow-mindedness."

When separated from our environment by the ego's noise, a fundamental truth is overlooked: the living, feeling organism that we are and our intimate association with the changing world. Lost in egocentric thought, we become fascinated with mental concepts originating in the past that often conflict with our apprehension of current conditions. Absorbed in our personal intrigues, we jeopardize the fullness of our relation with and understanding of the moment in which we exist. Watching events unfolding while unburdened by unsettling mental distractions hones sensory and mental acuity, enabling one to react in a steadier and more

Lawrence K. Zeisler

responsible fashion, thereby enhancing their security.

There is more than a ring of truth to the existential phrase "to be is to do." In *The Defiant Ones*, both men's images are shattered by reality, for the major obstacles to surmount originate in their heads. While sheltered by stale ideas, neither man feels obliged to regard or trust the other, and their fear and suspicion are real. Once familiarity is gained, those ideas are removed along with the suspicion and fear.

If the men hadn't undergone such a severe struggle, it is doubtful they would have banished their prejudices. I believe similar forces are at work when soldiers from all walks of life attain an intense comradeship after sharing in the strains of combat. This is probably why upon returning home, they become perplexed by the trivialities of domestic life. After having performed under the specter of death, many of our suspicions, fears, and desires must seem mundane, even ridiculous.

The story in *The Defiant Ones* was a study in growth we can all benefit from. Though most of us do not display the characters' overt hostility, we hold title to prejudices that make a congenial relationship with life a tenuous commodity. Are we not distrusting and suspicious to a greater extent than need be? Do we not staunchly defend ideas that directly inhibit our capacity to tolerate the differences in people? Perhaps if we were compelled to undergo greater trials, we'd ferret out more closet-dwelling skeletons.

Whenever trust toward another surfaces, the ego is no longer present. The ego trusts nothing but itself. What it can't see is that its self-centered trust is built upon ignorance generated by isolation of its own making—ignorance based upon a fear that without its guiding light, all would be darkness. It doesn't know the truth when it's smack in front of its face.

The ego's false trust cannot be displaced and the truth realized without the courage to work through its array of artifices that beguile, confuse, and keep one from recognizing the groundless nature of most fear and suspicion. This task cannot be achieved without the clarifying aid of an open mind unafraid of unmasking inner fault. Being able to face up to it unencumbered by the fear of being wrong is key to positive growth. A candid, honest appraisal of the self is one resting on a solid foundation, and it's reassuring quality contributes to increased confidence in handling experiences whose outcomes are constructive. We all know experience is the best teacher. Trust in oneself augments one's inner strength and greatly reduces the threat of fear. As the pundit said, "If the turtle never stuck its head out of its shell, it wouldn't get anywhere." We excessively fear failure largely because of a failure to act inwardly and in the physical world.

I worked briefly on oil rigs in and around the Gulf of Mexico. While employed on a land rig in lower Mississippi, I was told to climb out on a derrick to clean up the oil emitted from an exploded hose. I had never been forced to so dramatically confront my fear of heights; I hadn't known it to be so well developed. I stepped off the platform, crawled up a ladder at a snail's pace, muttering "This wasn't in the contract," and to the problem area about seventy-five feet above the ground. No safety harness was available. Since it was night, all was darkness except for the illuminated area below containing machinery. I kept imagining my contorted form impaled upon a protruding piece of steel, but I persevered and finished my part in the restoration. The fear was real, but by making me dig deeper, events such as this introduced me to latent capabilities. It broke the ice for my future occupation as a stonemason where I would be asked to scale sections of scaffolding while working on chimneys and high walls.

Those leading more sedentary lives might wonder about the relevance of facing one's acrophobia. They may never know the feeling that materializes after completing an endeavor requiring strict coordination between mind and body. When an element of danger is overcome, that feeling is intensified.

By means of a vignette, I will portray a fearful incident and illustrate how the dissolution of a deeply held prejudice serves to enlighten one.

Light in the Early Morning Darkness (A Chance Encounter with Wolves)

Phantom figures, eclipsed by the moon's fading light, step out of snow-bound shadows and confront me at the inky edge of nowhere. Alert yellow eyes, poised at the threshold to abstract thought, stare with caution as I stop cold in my tracks, frozen in fear.

Fresh prints weave myriad patterns in the freshly fallen snow. Mild breezes blow in cadence with pounding heartbeats, gently fondling coarse gray fur, while whisking away wisps of vaporized breath. Naked tree branches span the ether and clutch pulsing stars. From beyond the canyon's rim an owl softly calls, and somewhere a piece of deadwood crashes to the earth.

Suddenly, a distant, plaintive howl cleaves the air, and the ghostly forms re-emerge with tree mass and darkness. As my trembling gives way to relief, I am overcome by a sense of shame. A great chasm spawned by centuries of fear and persecution yawns before me. I tensely look into its icy gloom, eddies of warmth engulf me, and I nod in homage at the departed pack.

I am alone with my thoughts.... time, place, observer, observed- only words, without substance, in this semi-luminous lunar cosmos where black sky and snow-clad earth blend in a soothing union of color and nothing holds sway. My isolation releases its bone-crushing bite, and I too become shadow and wind.

Fading stars, setting moon, glimpses of eastern light. I know, for the first time, I will feel the newborn sun's subdued warmth gracing the frigid air currents.

Dealing with the ego's self-styled insecurities is burdensome. Much of the mental armor we clothe our personalities in is designed to fortify us against what we perceive as an intimidating world. Though conditions in life can be harsh and people are sometimes insincere, we need not confront them with the amount of apprehension we do. We put an exaggerated premium on suspicion and fear. There are usually better ways to cope with uncertainty.

For the most part, one's distrust originates in a mind that has convinced them to adhere to ideas beyond whose boundaries the world is threatening and strange. Fear of the world much more than the world per se causes dread. Perhaps Franklin D. Roosevelt and Daniel Defoe

Lawrence K. Zeisler

realized this when each said, respectively, "Let me assert my firm belief that the only thing we have to fear is fear itself" and "Fear of danger is ten thousand times more terrifying than danger itself."

We have reached a critical turning point. By concentrating on prejudice, the mind freezes thoughts, causing them to overstay their visits, but that is not all. Those "frozen" thoughts that are forged in the ego's fires often prevent us from seeing the truth about people, things, and ourselves. In *The Defiant Ones,* it is evident that freedom is the desired end for the escapees. While their minds resonated with their egos at the expense of this awareness, their coordination suffered. When the distrust was dissolved a respect for one's fellow materialized, that resided within from the start.

Similar issues cloud the minds of those who refuse to concur with the proof of global warming presented by the near-unanimous verdict of climate specialists and prevent the revelation of a fundamental unity with the natural world. Science deniers, in general, are held hostage by mental constraint, obstructing their view of reality.

To some people, it must sound strange to hear that beneath our discordant exteriors dwells a harmonious nature. This would seem unusual to those living in a society that idolizes the ego and demonstrates that idolatry by cultivating the impression that freedom consists in letting the personality run riot with prejudice and desire.

If there is some repetition, please bear with me and try to appreciate it. These concepts are not the easiest to explain or follow.

A sound philosophy is erected upon a series of proofs that eventually converge. During the course of a proof's journey, it may intersect another proof that has already been detailed. Restating a part of a previously mentioned proof often aids in understanding the one being discussed—each proof has a unique character yet can share things with others. Because of philosophy's comprehensive quality, the intersection of facts makes for a more convincing argument provided it all makes sense. In a novel, repetition can degrade a work, but in philosophy, it often enhances it.

Lawrence K. Zeisler

Chapter 5

"If you add to the truth, you subtract from it."
—The Talmud

It would behoove anyone serious about probing their humanity to understand that they hold title to an inner "well of goodness" waiting to be tapped. In truth, many of our deeds spring freely from its depths, giving proof of its existence, while other less honorable exploits are enough to make us swear it's as legendary as the lost city of El Dorado.

Although all benevolent acts emanate from this inner well, some considerate ones require effort. One does not have to decide whether to help a crippled person up from a fall; they just do it, but we may have to remind ourselves to be patient in the presence of an unruly in-law. While these acts reflect one's inner goodness, involuntary, unsought virtue convinces me of the capacity to grow in love. The origin of vice also lies within, and before we can effectively expand in goodness, the unsavory aspects of the personality need to be brought to light.

Before proceeding, I would like to issue a warning. THIS BOOK NOW VENTURES INTO POTENTIALLY VOLATILE AREAS! I am about to graphically portray virtue and vice, those vile villains some people would rather not discuss. Wanting to avoid calling them by name,

I perused the thesaurus for substitute words, but none could do them justice. At the risk of sounding like a preacher, I have no recourse but to use them, but unlike some preachers, I will shamelessly confess to having repeatedly met vice's acquaintance, often under friendly terms.

Some people seem naturally predisposed to virtue. These fortunate souls are not bedeviled by the number of moral flaws that burden the general population, and they are blessed with the ability to let things roll off their shoulders more easily. There's little doubt that a young lady who donated bone marrow to a cancer patient falls into this category. Her selfless act was particularly beautiful since the patient was a stranger, and she gave primarily because one of her teachers lost a child to leukemia. (Harvesting marrow for transplantation required inserting a tube down the throat to assist in breathing before blood and stem cells were aspirated from the marrow cavity of each rear hip bone with a special needle.)

This book is aimed at those whose path to their "well of goodness" can be as hard to negotiate as a rock-strewn mountain trail. This book is written by one whose calloused feet bear the sting of fresh sores. I now present lists of the virtues and vices, and each definition is a simplified statement.

The Vices

Greed: "I want the whole coin collection, now!"

Selfishness: "No, you can't borrow my hammer."

Self-righteous pride: "What can you possibly tell me that I don't already know?"

Arrogance: "If you're lucky, I'll let you shine my shoes."

Lawrence K. Zeisler

Wrath: "I start to froth at the mouth every time I think of that."

Vanity: "Mirror, mirror on the wall, am I not the fairest one of all?"

Jealousy and envy: "He gets all the breaks. I wish I were so blessed instead."

Gluttony: "Why should I stop eating? It's only my third piece of cake."

Sloth: "I slept all day, the kids are hungry, but I'll stay in bed a while longer."

The Virtues

Humility: "Who am I to deem myself superior because I make a higher wage?"

Patience: "We can't wish the traffic away, so why get worked up?"

Temperance: "I'll refrain from eating sweets for the next month."

Charity: "Let's take these clothes to Goodwill."

Compassion: "Let me help you with your burden."

Simplicity: "This two-bedroom house and economy car are more than adequate."

Sacrifice: "I missed my chance to purchase the concert tickets because I helped a person change a flat tire."

Love: "The more one exhibits the virtues, the more pronounced will be their love."

There is no greater satisfaction than a heartfelt association with our inner goodness, for it enters us into communion with life's unity, but this core of goodness is surrounded by a shroud of trickery that diverts one from it by fashioning the illusion that they require far more than is physically and psychologically essential. Yes, the crafter of fabrication is the ego.

Acknowledging the ego, the Trappist Thomas Merton wrote:

> We must be saved from immersion in the sea of lies and passions which is called "the world". And we must be saved above all from that abyss of confusion and absurdity, which is our own worldly self. The person must be rescued from the individual. The free son of God must be saved from the conformist slave of fantasy, passion and convention. The creative and mysterious inner self must be delivered from the wasteful, hedonistic and destructive ego that seeks only to cover itself with disguises.[1]

I want to talk about desire. We desire a better standard of living, desire Friday, desire Sunday's big game—the list goes on and on. Even our major religion stakes its reputation on the desire that one day we will dwell forever in heaven's pastoral fields.

Desire is a natural state. It has been said that all human motivation is an expression of one or more basic desires. The needs for security, retribution, status, acceptance, independence, and curiosity owe their existence to an initial impulse to action. The action is the measure of the influence of said impulse upon the individual and can be beneficial or counterproductive.

Envy and jealousy (both founded on a desire to be like someone else) as well as greed and vanity reflect a lack of fulfillment with the present. Aren't they states that speak of deficiencies in one's makeup? All vices stem from a lack of contentment and are manifestations of the ego.

Material pursuit is built into our character. Since desire in varying degrees kick-starts that pursuit, I would like to demonstrate a material desire in action. Let's see now, what outlandish product can be chosen as the focus of that desire? Ah, an electric potato peeler.

Two quick interjections: (1) I hope any reader owning an electric potato peeler will not take exception. I would not want to offend anyone over so trivial a matter, especially a solitary one-armed person who loves homemade potato dishes that don't use potato skins. (2) I do not make the shopper a woman out of disrespect for the distaff members of society; even in today's unisex world, odds are she would do the shopping for small appliances.

A shopper is browsing a store's appliance aisle with no set purpose when her gaze fixes upon an electric potato peeler. *This gadget is amusing,* she thinks, *but is it practical? By saving my wrist the pain of peeling, it would cut down on my kitchen labor, and the whole family is fond of potatoes. Anyway, I deserve to be pampered.*

Unbeknown to her, our shopper has taken up the gauntlet issued by the ego. The more persuasive it is, the more uncomfortable she will feel with the prospect of not owning one. She muses, *Life without this product will be that much more taxing.*

It's not that one small excess is bad, but if the ego is given carte blanche, one desire leads to another, cluttering one's mind with trifles. On Saturday morning, I wrestle with the temptation to buy donuts at a store a few miles away. At times I relent and find nothing wrong with that, but I make it a point not to submit too often. I counter the desire by asking myself how much gas, calories, time, and money a moment's pleasure is worth. The quicker the desire is subdued, the sooner my cleared mind can get on with more pertinent things.

At this point, the shopper is succumbing to the ego's pressure. She hasn't considered that a little toil is good for the arm and wrist and that the willingness to sacrifice is good for the soul. Or has she? She draws her hand back. It takes only an instant's hesitation for her awareness to penetrate the ego's surrounding zone of greed. The decision is up for grabs. If said awareness can be maintained by her conscious mind, it will overcome her thoughts of discomfort, and she will reject the purchase. If it isn't, she will answer the ego's plea and buy the peeler.

Determining what is excessive can be tricky, being that one person's excess is another one's necessity. Our passions and tastes are varied and help mold our unique characters. Although everyone's tastes are equally undeniable, to say they are equally justifiable is unacceptable to those hoping for a cleaner and more efficient society. At some point, sound judgement must prevail. Unless one needs to cart a large group over exceedingly rough terrain en route to numerous drag strip competitions a 707 horsepower Jeep Grand Cherokee Trackhawk—an ego on wheels—is excessive.

Because discussions differentiating excess from waste are open to interpretation, it's difficult to form conclusions concerning the matter. A simple truism will be provided as a means of assistance. Honoring the phrase "one humanity, one world" encourages selfless acts that represent what is vital. The truth is that I don't need that second plate of grub as much as a starving soul in the Sudan does. I don't need it at all. The truth assures me that forgoing the second plate contributes to better health.

The plate analogy differentiates a need from a want. A need is more basic and essential. Every effort should be expended to meet our needs. A failure to do so jeopardizes the quality of life and can lead to distress and suffering. Needs, though essential, differ with the individual. We all need food, shelter, and clothing; some people need more food and clothing and a larger living space than others. A want exceeds the basic requirements, and the desire motivating it is often tainted by greed. The attainment of an occasional one can be fulfilling. If subsequent strivings are kept in moderation, one's compassion can be more readily manifested. If left unchecked, there is little chance. Back to the plate. Assuming my belly was empty, the first plate satisfied a need, and the second represented a want.

The enslavement to material excess is the result of ego, yet we consider this enslavement the basis of freedom. It is acceptable, nay encouraged, for someone to assuage any desire or want if the money is there and the act is legal. We are told that financial surety will buy us the freedom to purchase as we please. Some commercials tout a vehicle's ability to set the spirit soaring. Fundamentally speaking, real freedom is another word for nothing left to lose. Just ask Jesus and Janis Joplin. Money will buy me pleasure, security, comfort, and a degree of happiness, but it can't buy me love's cathartic and liberating qualities. Just ask the Beatles and Jesus.

I'm aware that in this complex society, so dependent upon money and ownership, having nothing is a handicap.

Those emulating Jesus's lifestyle would have a tough go of it today; panhandling and intermittent visits to soup kitchens hardly qualify as the actions of a liberated person. Perhaps instead of saying freedom is another word for nothing left to lose, in deference to realism, I should say that a happy person is one who is satisfied with what they have. They tend to their needs but are not oppressed by wants and material desires. Thinking less about future acquisition results in a drop in "necessities."

The truth exists in the "well of goodness." This immanent truth is the bedrock of virtue. It is the basis of equality, knowing that all humans have a minimum level of needs—a level that varies between societies—that must be met for survival. Because of this, it appreciates the virtue of simplicity. It is the undercurrent of humanness that bridges the divide between people. We are all different, but at our roots, we are one. It is the source of honesty and can never be corrupted by the ego's stratagems. It is always present and touches us throughout the day. When our thoughts and deeds are just, it is there. It has a hand in matters when one sacrifices, has everything to do with what is practical and beneficial, and has nothing to do with excess or waste. Perhaps this concept of the truth is best exemplified in the daily accounts of Jesus.

The inner truth never provokes conflict, being associated with it only because of the ego's intrigues. Any turmoil is caused by the ego's reaction to the presence of truth in its domain. Like its partner, love, it is not domineering.

Truth and love are correlatives. Have you heard the expression "having heart"? Anytime one commits an act coming from the heart, they have transcended the ego's barrier. You can rest assured that the act is virtuous. When

Lawrence K. Zeisler

the intellect conceptualizes the harmony in the truth-love core, it knows contentment. The relationship between love and truth will be explored later. For now, it is enough to know that love's selfless purity permeates the truth.

Although the truth doesn't provoke conflict, it does hurt when viewed in bold contrast to deep-rooted, egocentric images. For years I felt I needed to defend my honor against criticism, even if it was meant to be constructive. I remember when I was in a pub discussing with friends the answers to problems that were threatening a married couple's relationship. My captive audience interrupted my soliloquy and said that if I confronted the couple in the manner I was suggesting, it might cause them more harm than good. What seemed beneficial commentary to me would possibly have endangered their marriage by introducing ideas they would have been unable to tolerate. My friends rubbed salt into the wound by adding that people don't like being preached to.

I steadfastly held to my convictions in the face of the charges, but once we departed company, I lapsed into a depressed state. Whether those charges were all grounded, we'll never know, but their effect upon me was real. The questioning of my intentions made me see I wasn't as infallible (based upon prejudiced, prideful beliefs about myself) as I presumed. The self-pity didn't subside until my intellect gathered the strength to respect and embrace their words. Once it did, the conflict was put to rest and the illusion of perfection shattered, allowing me to progress.

I would like to clarify the inner truth's relation to the outside world. The conversation and the pub where it took place were real. All we see, feel, and do are real. Recorded history is a chronicle of bits of reality insofar as its accounts of events are accurate. There is no doubt that the Battle of Antietam was a horrific Civil War conflict that produced incredible pain and anguish. This we know is true. Reality is occurring everywhere simultaneously.

When one's outlook is infused with inner truth, their vision is undistorted. When the inner truth is linked with life (the outer truth), one sees reality clearly. The ego plays a big part in how we perceive things; when it does, those perceptions are clouded and limited. Egocentric images are authentic in that they determine one's beliefs and actions, but they are disruptive and clog the pathway linking the truth with the environment. This impairs intellectual and sensory awareness.

One cannot command the inner truth, but since it is associated with responsible actions, a good starting point for someone interested in cultivating its friendship would be an awareness of resource management. Whenever possible, determine how to acquire the optimum benefit from an action or task while using the minimum amount of whatever is necessary to achieve the end result. Implementing this approach requires being conscious of everyday efforts. Modest examples are gauging the most efficient expenditure of lighting when illuminating a room and the least amount of water to effectively wash anything. The more this policy underlies daily experience, the more one's deeds will reflect their true needs. In time, simplifying life becomes habitual.

The beauty is that doing so is beneficial. Many of us could cut back on energy use and consume less food. Engaging in activities like reading, walking, and biking that are healthy for the mind and body and demand relatively small outlays of money makes sense. We could forgo that new and improved model (unless it answers a timely need) and downsize our vehicles and in some instances our homes. A small pickup truck could satisfy the utilitarian needs of most truck owners except for some tradesmen, building contractors, landscapers, camper towers, and avid home remodelers. We would be better off for it. Chasing less waste enriches one's life and wallet.

Life is a give and take. Americans take more on average, having cultivated a society founded on pleasure and material acquisition. Our modus vivendi distracts us from realizing the truth. Many people will take offense, interpreting this as an affront to their inalienable right to choose and act as they please. I cherish the spirit of independence and fully concur that choice is a personal matter. I am not questioning freedom but taking issue with some of our priorities. With freedom comes obligations, many that should be considered and aren't. Because they're not, one finds it easier to indulge oneself, often frivolously.

By now you may have deduced that this "revolution" hinges on the capacity for change. In effect, altruism needs to moderate egoism; the good of the whole should be considered along with one's own fortune and pleasure. The only thing standing between this concept and reality is selfishness, for the self-absorbed person puts their desires before all else. This same person would think this sounds naïve, which is not surprising, as the selfish mind cannot see beyond its own restrictive walls.

In terms of income inequality, the United States ranks number one among the world's richest nations. Forty percent of its wealth resides in the hands of 1 percent of the population, roughly twice as much as the top 1 percent in France or the United Kingdom and more than three times the amount of Finland's financial elite. The top 20 percent of households controls an astounding 90 percent, which leaves just 10 percent of America's capital to the remaining 80 percent. Less than 40 percent of Americans say they have enough savings to cover a $1,000 emergency. Such inequality is morally wrong and economically unsound.

The Organization for Economic Cooperation and Development calculates that excessive income disparity is responsible for a 5 percent loss in economic growth in our country between 2000 and 2015. The lack of quality education is a major contributor to reduced social mobility and wasted human potential, resulting in less skilled workers engaged in the economy and propping up local businesses while spending money. The diminishment of workers' rights under the present administration—such as limiting the expansion of overtime pay and making it more difficult to join a union and collectively bargain—exacerbates the problem. The spate of deregulations perpetrated since Trump took office undermine worker protections.

Studies conclude that a company's CEO makes two to three hundred times what the average worker takes home (in 1965, it was about twenty times more) which translates to a median income of $10–15 million in total compensation in most Fortune 500 firms (a package that includes salary, stock options, long-term incentive payouts, and bonuses). While CEOs' make vital decisions designed to generate wealth, a high rate of success is never a guarantee. One must ask, even in instances where positive company advances are the norm, how much is enough.

A business's performance depends on the efforts of multiple people, and although workers today are contributing more to the company's bottom line with increased productivity, little gratitude has been displayed from those on

Lawrence K. Zeisler

top. It wasn't always so. Between 1947 and the early 2000s, in percentage terms, a worker's wages could be expected to grow at about the same rate as corporate profits. Since the Great Recession (about 2009), the American economy has been benefiting owners and shareholders much more handsomely than workers.

JPMorgan Chase and Co. estimates that the recent $1.5 trillion Republican tax cuts will contribute to S&P 500 companies repurchasing a record $800 billion of their own stock shares from the broader marketplace in 2018. This rewards executives and corporate insiders as well as the shareholders, 80 percent of whose number are the richest 10 percent of Americans. Just over half of Americans even own stock.

The prediction that the tax cuts would translate to higher wages for rank and file (production and nonsupervisory) employees has begun to bear some fruit. Wage growth for American workers is breaking free of yesterday's stagnation in real terms after adjusting for inflation, rising 0.6 percent between September 2017 and September 2018. But the cost of health care, housing, transportation, and college have markedly outpaced the inflation rate and the skimpy improvements in family income. The nation's GDP may be markedly increasing, but workers' incomes aren't. Shouldn't more of the profits trickle down to them?

Most of the wage growth is coming from service-sector jobs, not in the manufacturing and blue-collar professions (though they are experiencing job growth). Oh yeah, one demographic has done particularly well: those employed in mining and oil and gas extraction. This comes as no surprise, considering the polluted mindset of this administration. Workers' health and retirement plans, if offered by employers, have shown little or no improvement. There is no denying that the market continues to favor the wealthy. Not coincidentally, political supporters with the greatest access to politicians happen to be affluent.

Income inequality forces more people into debt. Total household debt, which includes mortgages, car loans, student loans, and credit cards, has rebounded since the Great Recession. As of December 31, 2018 public debt in America totaled close to $16 trillion. While credit can be a boon in emergencies and a needed assist in pursuing life improvements (and a stimulant to the economy), overextending oneself leads to heavy financial burdens. Unlike government debt that can be deferred indefinitely, consumer loans must be paid back. Servicing that debt will act as a deterrent to the future economy, reducing purchasing power and GDP growth, which can contribute to deeper economic downturns and extended recessions. For these reasons, wages need to convincingly surpass the true costs of inflation. Any rebuttal to this fundamental truth will be laced with greed.

Student loan debt has surpassed credit card debt in our country. Public university tuition has doubled in the past twenty years, growing by more than 60 percent in the last decade. Over one million people default on their student loans annually. The Brookings Institution projects a possible default rate of up to 40 percent by 2023 by borrowers who took out loans to attend college in 2003. Almost every year, regardless of the state of the economy, tuition climbs higher.

There is a way to mitigate the proliferating college debt dilemma that involves no congressional intervention, which is to charge students an equitable price for the increasing number of high quality online degrees presented by a growing number of prestigious centers of higher learning. Although online graduate programs have received the most

Lawrence K. Zeisler

attention, expansive undergraduate offerings would bring educational opportunity within reach of greater numbers of people. Online courses are less expensive to run, requiring fewer operating costs than those demanded by a traditional on-campus experience, especially once a newly designed course's up-front development costs are paid off. Savings that could and should be, but are rarely passed on to students.

As a point of reference, the Georgia Institute of Technology's computer science department, ranked eighth best in the country by *U.S. News and World Report*, devised an online master's program that the institution charges $7,000 to take, a price that allows it to break even. Public service, more than profit, is the motive. The University of Southern California, ranked twentieth, charges $60,150 for a comparable degree.

Democratization of businesses by giving the employee a voice could help alleviate the injustices permeating the status quo. Transitioning from the conventional, top-down business structure that focuses on maximizing shareholder value to a more equitable co-op system (where a company is owned and governed by its members who share in the profits and can participate in its management) would confront the society-rending problems inherent in modern capitalism: income inequality, stagnating wages, and severe instability.

Research has revealed that "labor-managed firms" on balance result in more effective business ventures that tend to put sound values at the forefront of their operations. They have been known to usher whole industries toward more humane practices. Consumer food co-ops led the unprocessed food campaign, fair trade initiatives, and the purchase of local foods, which often find their way onto nearby store shelves. They are honor-bound to function with the community's best interests in mind, and because most members of co-ops live in the immediate area, the profits circulate therein. Some rural utility cooperatives finance local infrastructure projects, make equity investments in businesses, and promote community-focused affairs. The results are stronger, more vibrant, and closer-knit localities.

Since profit is not the be-all and end-all of their existence, co-ops can flex with economic turbulence, a leading reason why they tend to be more resilient than traditional enterprises. Where conventional corporations may forgo strategic planning and eliminate employees to tighten budgets during downturns, co-ops are better skilled at making longer-term adjustments like curtailing expansion to conserve assets. Their commitment to cooperative interaction and democratic participation makes their members more willing to sacrifice. Some examples are agreeing to wage cuts and forsaking dividends, which help to protect jobs during lean periods. As a rule, co-ops enjoy higher productivity levels.

Cooperatives employ roughly 280 million people worldwide, about 10 percent of the working population. Cooperatives mostly operate in the agriculture, banking/credit union, electric utility, and wholesale and retail trade sectors. The United States has far fewer co-ops than the EU's number (comprised of 163,000 million citizens or one-third of its population), which includes full-scale factories.

Mondragon, a town in the northern Basque region of Spain, harbors the world's largest and most progressive cooperative economy. It consists of over one hundred cooperatives united in a federation and employing more than seventy thousand. Benefits include healthcare, unemployment payments, and pensions. Most of the worker-owners are assigned to industrial and distribution branches, effectively competing in global markets. Unlike traditional companies where executives often enjoy soaring wages during economic declines, in response to a shrinking economy in 2013, managers at Mondragon's large supermarket-based co-op, Eroski, took larger percentage pay cuts than the workers.

The cooperative approach does not lend itself to every business model. Conflicts of interest in decision making due to the greater number of people involved and slower response times to sudden changes in the market can be drawbacks. Perhaps foremost, commercial businesses can offer qualified individuals higher salaries. Regardless, it cannot be argued that many of the egalitarian qualities inherent in cooperative business models help to spread the wealth more fairly. Fundamental human yearnings like compassion for one another and the call for greater meaning in one's work are better manifested in such a business setting; conditions that the truth finds favorable.

The hurdles in the way of creating a more equitable and sustainable economy in our country are manifold and are suffused with an undercurrent of selfishness. In a world facing environmental upheaval and financial disparity, where homelessness and starvation are on the rise and technical advances are streamlining the workplace, the inherent fairness and unselfishness infused in the cooperative approach could go far in addressing the existential and spiritual challenges of a complex and uncertain future.

The ego cannot blacken the truth, but it does prevent its emergence. While it maintains a stranglehold on the intellect (as it did on mine before my friends' criticism in the pub) or if one's attempts at virtue are tainted by motives, such as assisting a fellow worker solely because the boss is in the room, the truth will remain unmoved.

The truth is ready to assist one at any time and willing to plant the seed for its conscious appearance if sensing an opportunity. This phenomenon awakened the doubt the shopper felt about the electric potato peeler's value. The truth's reaction to her hesitation was instantaneous; its light touched her conscience in a millisecond. In my case, I strongly feel that it heard my intellect calling out amid the confusion. Throughout the personal battle, the ego's control over me ebbed and flowed, and during the periods in which its power subsided, the truth gave me the strength to carry on. With it by my side, I saw the struggle through and found the equilibrium that allowed me to accept the fact that I shouldn't expect everyone to think like me. Personal growth depends upon the ability to face egocentric perceptions, recognize the strain they impose, and endure and recover from the disquieting aftermath.

The intent here is not to give the truth an official definition; such an attempt would be an exercise in futility. Its gift is its positive affect, no matter how seemingly minor, on the soul. It provides inspiration to the formulation of self-awareness, which puts one in better contact with oneself and leads to a more harmonious relation with events in the immediate vicinity.

Temptation and prejudice incessantly beset us in our country of near-limitless excess. The ego and its army of vices has stacked the deck. It's comforting to know we have a champion capable of toppling that deck in the blink of an eye. The truth can set one free if only given the chance.

Lawrence K. Zeisler

Chapter 6

*"Under capitalism, man exploits man. Under
communism, it's just the opposite."*
—John Kenneth Galbraith

E xcess was not so pronounced in earlier workaday
America when citizens were generally content fulfilling their basic needs. Back then, most manufacturing
was done in homes and small workshops, using time-
honored hand techniques. Tradesmen enjoyed a decent
degree of independence, and their creativity could proceed
relatively free of time's restrictive hand. On average, the
workday lasted five or six hours (except during the rush
season), earnings were sufficient to lead a respectable life,
and relations between competitors were generally pleasant.
A visit to the tavern where one could chat with friends usually rounded out the day's activities. Life was more leisurely.

Today, being given little time to rest on one's laurels is not
conducive to knowing leisure. Even while reveling in success,
the mind is looking to improve, to venture into new realms,
but we are not always judicious about the realms we choose.

Before proceeding with this commentary a shout-out is
in order. Like most institutions, our capitalist free market
system works fine in theory, and its practice has played
an immeasurable role in society's advancement. When

businesses are pressured to remain afloat in competitive seas entrepreneurs strive to improve their products and services. Competition induces innovations that continually transform our lives, with mixed results.

Once companies grew in response to demand; now they are dead set on creating it even when it's unnecessary. Anything goes. Force-feed the public with the newest craze, open the floodgates of the imagination, and see what spews out. The bile that litters the store shelves is incredible in scope and reads like a Who's Who of dispensable rubbish. The rubbish pile is where most of it ends up. I remember being jaded by the endless aisles of plastic merchandise in the local Toys "R" Us. Back in the "old days," a toy or hobby enjoyed a long shelf life. Today, a good portion of stock rotation is responsive to the whims of Hollywood. I can't begin to imagine the quantity of material squandered fulfilling the exhortation "produce or fall behind or out."

We have been referred to as a throwaway society for good reason. Yes, much of what we toss has little intrinsic value, but many useful items contribute to the heap prematurely. I've repeatedly heard the phrase "they don't make them like they used to" and spoken to enough disenchanted folks to confirm the belief that items such as toasters, refrigerators, printers, water heaters, and even pantyhose are designed not to last too long. As a rule, modern products are lighter in weight and more efficient, but must those qualities come at the expense of durability as often as they do? In the past, when an appliance broke, a handy homeowner could purchase the necessary material at a modest price, or a repairman was called to fix it. Today, the affected parts are usually inaccessible, obscure, and often expensive. If the circuit board containing the fundamental components

Lawrence K. Zeisler

of a computer (motherboard) malfunctions, the cost of replacement is significant. In some instances, people end up purchasing a new machine.

Another phrase, "pride in one's work," doesn't seem to resound as loudly throughout today's workforce when compared to times past. A thorough inspection of a recently constructed house and its appointments would be a good place to start when searching for proof of the previous statement. A third phrase, "I want it done yesterday" (which resounds loudly these days), does little to encourage a young apprentice's eye for detail.

Speaking of junk, let's talk food. Studies show that young children are being bombarded with snack advertisements on television and the internet. Although healthy foods like yogurt, fruit, and nuts are displayed, the majority of promotions are for sweet and savory items with little nutritional value. Researchers are particularly concerned about preschoolers' vulnerability to commercial persuasion and their malleable minds associating with the ads on an emotional level. As a point of reference, in the effort to reduce childhood obesity, strict regulations in the United Kingdom ban the advertising of unhealthy foods and beverages aimed at children under sixteen years old. This applies to television, print, cinema, and social media.

While on the subject of food, let's talk waste. America leads the world in the amount of food wasted. According to both the Natural Resources Defense Council and Harvard Law School's Food Law and Policy Clinic, up to 40 percent of our food goes uneaten, an amount worth $165 billion being disposed of annually. Those on the food distribution chain, including farmers, grumble that nutritious, high-value food is being scrapped or abandoned in fields because retailers require produce free of the slightest blemish. Supermarkets prefer not to sell imperfect food. The relentless cosmetic demands stem from shoppers' obsession with the aesthetic appearance of fruits and vegetables they purchase. It's unfortunate more folks don't think like Joni Mitchell. In her 1970 song "Big Yellow Taxi," she croons, "Hey farmer farmer, put away that DDT now. Give me spots on my apples, but leave me the birds and the bees."

Researchers at Johns Hopkins University determined that if we were able to use our mountains of rejected food, it would deliver a two thousand-calorie diet to 84 percent of adult Americans—sad yet hopeful news to the forty-one million people who face hunger. Globally, one-third of the world's food—in the neighborhood of 1.3 billion tons—is wasted or lost each year. The UN Food and Agriculture Organization estimates that about 815 million of earth's citizens were afflicted with chronic undernourishment in 2016. It expresses that the food waste could feed up to 2 billion people.

There are environmental repercussions as well. A staggering 21 percent of landfill space is comprised of food waste. When organic foodstuffs break down in the disposal sites, they rot and emit methane. The resources involved in food production also contribute to greenhouse gases. Worldwide, about 3.3 billion tons of CO_2 are released during the processing (soil and livestock emissions are included in this figure) of all the uneaten food. The carbon footprint generated on a global level by lost food is about 7 percent of humanity's total outlay. It is conjectured that if food waste were a country, its contribution to climate change would put it in third place behind China and the United States. Thankfully, the problem is receiving overdue attention. The United States recently declared a goal of lowering food waste by 50 percent by the year 2030, and efforts are underway to recoup some of the lost greenhouse gas pollutants and deliver uneaten food to relieve those in need, though the challenges are daunting.

Despite the World Health Assembly (WHA) resolution, based on decades of research, concluding that mother's milk is best for the health of both mother and baby, the Trump administration has made concessions to the powerful infant formula industry by taking actions to undermine breast-feeding and weaken rulings that safeguard parents from the spread of misinformation and the unethical maneuvers perpetrated by the industry.

In the early twentieth century, the American Medical Association's Committee on Foods suppressed marketing efforts by the formula companies that were largely respon-sible for the public opinion shift away from breastfeeding. The manufacturers decided to branch out into other regions with a concerted plunge in the developing world and the naïve and vulnerable inhabitants therein.

It is correct to state that there are babies who benefit from infant formula, but it is erroneous to assume it is the solution to malnutrition and poverty. Breast milk contains antibodies that defend the baby against bacteria and viruses. Bottle-fed babies die at alarming rates and are more subject to common diseases like pneumonia and diarrhea and face increased likelihood of ear infections, childhood obesity and diabetes. It has been shown that breastfed babies enjoy a boost in brain development and cognitive aptitude, and it's been proven that even in areas with scarce food and water, breastfeeding regularly provides adequate nutrition.

Breastfeeding plays a natural and important role in a woman's reproductive cycle and benefits her health. Studies reveal that it is linked to a lower likelihood of breast and ovarian cancers as well as heart disease later in life. By contributing to the postponement of menstruation, the space between births is usually lengthened, which is good for mother and child.

The World Bank's new Investment Framework for Nutrition recognizes that if the WHA's target of exclusively breastfeeding 50 percent of the world's children for the first six months of their lives by 2025 was met, almost $300 billion in economic advantages throughout lower- and middle-income countries could be accrued because of enhanced cognitive development and child survival rates. Healthy, capable children grow into productive, economy-stimulating adults. Savings in healthcare costs due to reduced insurance claims and hospitalizations and decreased prescriptions would lessen expenditures. Countries lose billions of dollars every year in preventable costs attributable to low breastfeeding numbers. It has been estimated that if 90 percent of nursing mothers exclusively breastfed for the first six months of a child's life in the United States alone, the country could save $13 billion per year. Once again, capitulation to big industry undermines the good of the whole.

Commenting on the litany of attributes breastfeeding provides, Keith Hansen of The World Bank states:

> *If breastfeeding did not already exist, someone who invented it today would deserve a dual Nobel Prize in medicine and economics.*[1]

What has the quest for cleanliness yielded? In many homes, especially with children, kitchen and bathroom cabinets should have caution tape encircling them; there is enough poison inside some to fell a rampaging buffalo. Household cleaners (primarily those for the drain, oven, and toilet bowl), carpet and upholstery particulates, air fresheners, insect repellents, and oven sprays taint the air and can make a home's interior pollution level greater than that outside. A government analysis has revealed that our nation's waterways are littered with traces of chemicals used in medications, cleaners, beauty aids, and foods that are rinsed or flushed down the drain every day. Many cleaning products are stronger than necessary for the jobs they are designed for. In fact, vinegar, borax, and baking soda alone or in combination, supplemented with some good old elbow grease, provide adequate germ removal most of the time.

Not surprisingly, the EU takes a much more guarded approach to questionably harmful products. It applies what is referred to as the precautionary principle: When there is credible evidence of a new article or process posing potential danger to human or environmental health, protective action should be employed despite inconclusive scientific findings. The US federal government, with its deference to industry, demands more proof of harm before regulatory action is implemented. Consequently, many items such as food additives and cosmetics permitted in this country are either banned or require warning labels in the EU and other nations.

In some cases, even when the chemical's harm is established, a warning label is sufficient. For example, some hair-styling products contain formaldehyde or formaldehyde-releasing agents that were found to cause health issues with salon employees. The FDA instructed the items' potential health hazards be labeled. Although scientific evidence demonstrated the adverse respiratory effects and possible work-related carcinogen danger, the substances are still available on the US market. The god of capitalism, the profit motive, which it could be argued is more influential than the first god and just as demanding of reverence, can be cold-hearted at times.

Theoretically, the market will bear what products and services it can accommodate and uproot the undesirable ones, but should it have to bear this onslaught? You might ask if consumers know what's best for them; are they pawns or perpetrators?

Take Americans' fascination with large motor vehicles. Like most discussions, there is ample room for debate. A lot depends on the parameters under which the discussion is subject. If it revolves solely around individual preference while disregarding the larger picture, its scope becomes limited. Favoring the self above all else reduces the complexities required for an open-ended and thorough analysis.

Gas prices plummeted in late 2014, and consumers are again clamoring for spacious vehicles, giving vent to their thirst for living large. Sixty-nine percent of new autos sold in the United States in 2018 were SUVs or light trucks; Detroit automakers are dropping small and midsize cars like hot potatoes. Admittedly, not all of the public's rationale is unfounded. Safety is an important consideration. Many SUV owners cite greater protection—along with seat height, power, and space— as foremost in governing their selection. The need for armor is so pronounced that it diminishes SUV drawbacks such as a higher center of gravity that heightens the tendency of the vehicle to roll under extreme conditions (electronic stability control has lessened but not eliminated the problem) and lack of agility, making it harder to avoid accidents.

The "me and mine first" attitude that can be attributed to some of these folks trumps the guilt that could be felt

Lawrence K. Zeisler

because their oversized machines endanger drivers of smaller cars in the event of a crash and block their view of the road ahead. It's indifferent about overused resources and fouled air. Such passionate concern for the family's welfare and comfort has little eye to the future and its generations. For the record, our 2004 Prius capably served our family of four with nary a hint of discomfort.

Automakers are quick to point out that SUV crossovers (which are based on a car chassis and not a truck's, like their larger SUV cousins, and get better mileage) are currently the rave. Their effect on fuel and emissions, though not as acute, is felt. Market research reveals that many crossover buyers previously drove cleaner, smaller sedans.

If more people thought the details out thoroughly before purchasing a vehicle and showed more consideration for others and the planet, life would be the beneficiary. Auto-makers would be forced to respond in kind. Regrettably, they are in no rush to do so. This suits them nicely, because they would not stand to benefit as handsomely. High-end SUVs and trucks, as well as the less expensive cross-overs, generate higher premiums than more basic vehicles. According to *The Detroit News*, for every $73,000 Cadillac Escalade sold, GM earns $35,000 in profit—another example of the earth taking a back seat to profit and short-sighted consumer demand.

It's worse when you consider the contagion is spreading with SUVs representing over one-third of cars sold globally, further slowing progress in curtailing greenhouse gas emissions on this front.

Big oil has a huge stake in this. According to a report issued by Aurora Energy Research, the leading energy market analytics firm located in Oxford England, if the world is home to 540 million electric vehicles in 2040, oil demand will most likely have peaked around 2025, causing up to $19 trillion in lost revenue for oil producers by 2040. Delaying the inevitable is in their best interests. One of the authors of a recent study, Dr. Rob Jackson, a professor of earth system science at Stanford, reveals that is precisely what is happening. Oil use has risen each of the last five years, contrary to expectations. He cites cheap gasoline prices and larger automobiles being driven more miles as key reasons.

The all-electric auto world is on the horizon thanks to a blend of good intentions, pressure from states and intense global competition; dozens are planned for introduction in the next five years. In the meantime, the EPA estimate of the yearly release of 4.6 metric tons of CO_2 by a gasoline vehicle driven around 11,555 miles and achieving 22 miles per gallon in fuel economy continues. The distance to the corner around which relief waits is longer than need be.

The opioid crisis ravaging the country is a stark reminder of the detrimental consequences that can stem from the feedback between consumer desire and compliant manufacturers. The United States ingests about 80 percent of the global opioid pill production. Federal health officials confirm that in 2015, around ninety-two million adult Americans used prescription opioids to manage pain, enough to keep every citizen medicated around the clock for three weeks. Over eleven million confessed to misuse. More people died from opioid-related overdoses, an estimated forty-two thousand in 2016, than auto crashes in the same year. In 2015, the number of deaths due to opioid overdose was more than thirty-three thousand. In 2014, it was twenty-nine thousand. Preliminary federal data suggests a welcoming break in the pattern; the estimated number for

2018 is 47,600, down from 49,000 deaths in 2017. Between 2000 and 2016, the prescription opioid epidemic killed nearly two hundred thousand people. Most of those victims began by taking powerful, legally prescribed pain pills—sometimes someone else's—produced and aggressively marketed by American pharmaceutical companies.

A history of deceit and profiteering has spawned today's tragic reality. In contrast to most other countries, the US health system is a commercial enterprise and not a service, giving drug companies strong influence over medical policy. By padding the pockets of enough members of Congress, regulations were revised to allow for the liberal disbursement of their products.

Prescription painkiller abuse has been problematic for some time. In 1963, the drug Percodan was blamed for an addiction outbreak in California (Elvis Presley was a reported abuser). Through intensive lobbying efforts over the years, Big Pharma pushed its agenda, encouraging doctors to overprescribe and often advertising their drugs as appropriate for moderate soreness more suited to over-the-counter pain medication. It conducted misleading marketing campaigns downplaying their addictiveness and stoked the fabrication that America was suffering from an outbreak of untreated pain, touting the idea that being pain free is a right.

People took the bait and largely fell in line. Doctors are not surprised when patients expect prescriptions for painkillers to eradicate the least vestiges of discomfort. Generally speaking, physicians have cut back on excessive prescribing. It doesn't help that opioids are the cheapest and easiest way to confront pain and that insurance providers support the less costly options, often limiting access to or excluding more expensive, safer alternatives or non-drug treatments like physical therapy, acupuncture, yoga, and cognitive behavior therapy.

Between 1996 and 2002, Purdue Pharma embarked on a campaign promoting its powerful opioid pain medication, Oxycontin. It misled the public by providing false claims as to each pill's guaranteed period of pain relief in the attempt to widen its audience and gain advantage over competitors. It funded thousands of educational programs in support of its effort and contributed financial assistance to key pain-related organizations like the American Pain Society, the Federation of State Medical Boards, and the American Academy of Pain Medicine to promote on its behalf.

Obviously, profit was the motive. *The New York Times* discovered a company sales memo littered with dollar signs touting huge bonuses to incentivize its sales reps. In 2007, Purdue Pharma and its top executives pleaded guilty to charges of misbranding the drug's risk of addiction, and the company was fined over $600 million. It is estimated that Purdue has generated about $40 billion (mostly from Oxycontin) in sales since 1995.

US drug investigators have been taking the opioid crisis seriously with multiple cases piling up against the manufacturers. However, if the 2017 settlement that fined McKesson Corp. (the largest distributor of drugs in the United States with an annual revenue approaching $200 billion) $150 million for failure to reveal suspect orders by pharmacies of millions of addictive painkillers is any indication, penalties befitting the severity of the offenses are reserved for future trials. Many of the orders were unusually large and frequent, some of which supplied drug rings. Despite what Drug Enforcement Administration (DEA) agents described as more than credible evidence unearthed over a two-year period against the company (a second-time offender), the Department of Justice and DEA attorneys struck a deal with its powerful lawyers bereft of criminal charges.

It will take a concerted effort like that launched against Big Tobacco in 1998, which led to the Master Settlement Agreement. The attorneys general of forty-six states, five US territories, and the District of Columbia were involved, contending that the companies should be liable for the costs inflicted by smoking-related diseases. When the smoke cleared (pun intended), the tobacco industry agreed to a $206 billion settlement broken into annual payments to the states over twenty-five years to fund aggressive anti-smoking campaigns. Like Big Pharma, the primary concerns were the questionable promotion, marketing, and advertising methods employed.

Perhaps exposure, the FDA and Centers for Disease Control, members of Congress not under Big Pharma's sway, and lawsuits can undo what decency and humanity couldn't prevent, assuming government lawyers comply. It's obvious the National Rifle Association and the toady Republican politicians it controls will require more than a healthy injection of decency and humanity.

The assault inflicted upon the public by the energy drink industry is relentless and shows no sign of letting up. Looking for a quick boost? Inhale one of the puppies with colorful names like Red Bull, Monster Energy, and Rockstar, and your wish will be answered in dramatic fashion. Never mind the questionable impact of these unregulated beverages on your health or that the FDA has not deemed it mandatory that nutrition labels include information on caffeine content (even though each container may contain

300 mg or more along with sugar and/or artificial sweeteners and other stimulants). Exceed 500 mg of caffeine a day (the FDA recommends no more than 400), and the health risks increase. Ingest 1,000 mg, and you venture into the realm of caffeine toxicity, symptoms of which can be hallucinations, seizure, and stroke.

Unlike coffee, energy drinks are extensively marketed to adolescents (almost one-third of youth aged twelve through seventeen regularly drink them) who are the most vulnerable to caffeine's potentially harmful effects, leading to increased emergency room visits. When mixed with alcohol, as is sometimes the case with young adults, the drinks mask the alcohol's depressant effects and can lead to binge drinking.

Lest you have any doubts about the bandwagon's passage through these streets, the fact that more than five hundred types of the beverages exist may be enough to jolt you. There are big dollars to be made in the quest for the immaculate pick-me-up.

Another product relished by today's youth are electronic cigarettes (e-cigarettes or vapes). Introduced to the US market in 2006, their sales have mushroomed since 2014 when smaller, cooler-appearing designs with candy and fruity flavors—"rocket popsicle" and "chicken and waffles" are but two—contributed to the increase in teen use. Currently, more than three million middle and high school students regularly partake. One vastly popular brand, JUUL, resembles a USB flash drive and can be charged on a laptop computer. The marketing plays on its high-tech feel. While not considered as harmful as cigarettes (research is inconclusive, and the long-term health effects are not known), they contain other additives and nicotine, an addictive drug that can adversely affect brain development. Studies disclose that most youths are not aware of the potential risks involved.

The FDA is pursuing ways to deter young people from using e-cigarettes. It has disclosed that it will ban retailers such as gas stations and convenience stores from selling cartridge-based products with flavors other than tobacco, menthol, and mint accept for areas in the shops closed off to teenagers. Vape and tobacco shops, which are used more by adults who partake with the intention of quitting cigarette smoking and are more diligent in confirming the age of customers, will not be limited by the restrictions. Age-verification requirements will be leveled on online sales, and JUUL has committed to dropping its promotions on social media. Critics complain that it's too little too late and that kids will do their advertising for them. Plans to outlaw flavored cigars and menthol cigarettes have been announced.

Despite the efforts, health advocates believe the FDA could be doing more. They are challenging in federal court its August 2017 decision to grant e-cigarette and cigar companies an added five years before undergoing an official review of their products' public health impacts. From the other end, convenience store representatives are questioning the legality and fairness of the sales restrictions, and the major tobacco companies vowed they would fight the proposed ban on menthol cigarettes.

Most of the media attention has dealt with the health and safety issues surrounding the use of e-cigarettes and little on end-of-life oversight. The conventional tobacco cigarette is comprised of tobacco, paper, and a filter made of cellulose acetate, a form of plastic that can take up to twelve years to decompose, leaving behind trace amounts of toxins and contaminants that reputable studies have proven can degrade surrounding ecosystems. Worldwide, it has been estimated that 4.5 trillion butts are littered each year, give or take a billion. E-cigarettes are more complex, being composed of nicotine, aluminum, a heating element/atomizer, a microprocessor, plastic, and a lithium ion battery, and spent ones are becoming more prevalent on shorelines and streets. To make matters worse, the lithium battery, which operates the components that stimulate the vapor discharge from the flavored liquids housing nicotine, is classified as hazardous waste as is the nicotine itself. The ideal would be for the exhausted "vapes" to be recalled and recycled. Disassembly entails separating the battery and battery charger, nicotine cartridges, electronic circuit boards, plastic housings, and cord. Each item must then be recycled separately, a difficult undertaking in its own right and made less likely by the ease of disposal. When littered, broken devices can leach battery acid, metals, and nicotine.

Some manufacturers recommend that users fling the empty items while others offer incentives of discounted or free products for so many empty cartridges returned for reclamation. Some retail stores such as Best Buy provide battery recycling programs. The EPA does not require consumers to properly dispose of batteries, though local jurisdictions might. They realize the danger the lithium ion batteries pose when placed in a trash or recycling bin. When surrounded by paper and cardboard in a recycling or refuse truck, pressure and heat can make the battery spark and set the load on fire.

If one received a nickel for every "new and improved" product label, they'd make Midas look like a pauper. How far can you take something? How far has it been taken? Is industry laden with innovators feverishly perusing their brains for watershed ideas, or is one incidental additive enough to warrant a new label? Does the end justify the means? In other words, are too many professionals over-paid architects of materials that are not worthy of the time, effort, and expense dedicated to their production and marketing? Does that self-cleaning razor with the linear, rapid-fire Panasonic motor delivering fourteen thousand cycles per minute really make for a significantly closer shave? Should razors that have served us faithfully for years be unceremoniously pitched into the nearest wastebasket? It makes you wonder how all those sensitive faces withstood centuries of abuse.

At what stage of the teeth whitener evolution are we in? How much whiter can you make white? Americans spent more than $16 billion on cosmetic plastic surgery and minimally invasive procedures in 2016, $1.1 billion of which was doled out on rhinoplasty. It's a good bet that mirror sales climbed in response.

This is not meant to imply that breakthroughs in product improvements are without merit, but our leg-endary ingenuity is best served when applied to useful endeavors. The question revolves around determining what constitutes useful. Let's look at e-cigarettes again. There will always be a need for a number of people to find gratification through some kind of hand-held oral stimulant. Endeavors to develop a harmless, satisfying, biodegradable end product would be well spent. This will be possible only on the heels of generations of research and development. Sound innovation and responsible technology policies are more important than ever in a rapidly transforming world.

The redundancy, oh, the redundancy. There are so many products out there doing the same thing. I counted over fifty different shampoos at a drug store—what they'll do to gain an edge over the competition. Finding the perfect one must be a Herculean task for the serious buyer. Crest has done an onerous job of blurring the line between redundancy and repetition with its vast army of "toothpaste systems." I was privileged to have viewed sixty-two items on the company's website. Three of my favorites are the "Crest Pro-Health Advanced Whitening Power Toothpaste," the "Kid's Crest Cavity Protection Sparkle Fun Toothpaste," and the can't-do-without "Crest 3D Luxe Diamond Strong Toothpaste." It's nice to be offered a selection; selection ad infinitum is another matter.

Conversely, there are times when some repetition would be welcomed but doesn't materialize fast enough. Take for instance the life-changing prescription drug Humira, a treatment for inflammatory diseases such as psoriasis, rheumatoid arthritis, and Crohn's disease. The list price in the United States hovers around $2,400 per dose. To ward off competition from cheaper biosimilar (alternative) European versions, the drug's creator, AbbVie, slashed the price overseas by as much as 80 percent. Germany offers a dose for about $850 while the UK charges $410.

In a deliberate attempt to stifle alternatives in our country, AbbVie repeatedly tweaks the formula to justify new patents: 247 times to be exact. The practice is not unusual. The top twelve grossing US drugs each average 125 patent applications. Humira's original patent protection expired in 2016. Even if filing efforts are rejected by the patent office, a war of attrition prevents closure. Although the FDA approved three biosimilar products in the United States, none will reach the market until 2023 because of deals AbbVie struck with the companies. AbbVie claims that patents encourage and reward the substantial investment it made in developing the drug, but how much is enough? According to a report issued by a pharmaceutical analyst at the stock research firm Bernstein, the company is not losing money in Europe.

Do you get the sense that there is a subliminal message, common to product advertising, seeking to stimulate feelings of inadequacy? They want us to think of ourselves as needy or, to put it simply, that we need their product. Far too much money is made and spent because of discontentment. An ill-at-ease mind is prone to irrational decisions. The tools Facebook and other companies employ have given advertisers the ability to distinguish people they deem most responsive to their messaging and regularly deliver targeted ads to them as they scan the internet.

Retail sales and consumer spending play a major part in powering our free market economy, but society's well-being depends upon sensible commercial activity. Shouldn't the company's good be commensurate with the peoples'?

If the buyer took more time to verify an item's function and true benefit instead of taking it at face value, companies would be forced to determine a proposed product's worth more on utilitarian and ethical grounds. It's time to weigh the unbridled push to tickle our fancies against the need to invent more useful goods. Comfort, convenience, and novelty should share more space with common sense and concern about wasteful management of resources when selecting an item to purchase.

If concepts like better health, clean energy, and sustainability were firmly embedded in the national ethos, there would be less room for pursuits ranging from trivial to life threatening. Although a change in priorities would require shifting resources, financial strain, and some job loss, a move toward emphasizing practical and salubrious endeavors need not signal the downfall of the free enterprise system. Sensibleness would not translate into vacant store aisles and homes resembling echo chambers. Weeding out the waste while developing and implementing alternative products free of questionable additives, addictive substances, carcinogens, mutagens, and endocrine-disrupting chemicals would occur over a considerable amount of time, ultimately benefiting producer and consumer. Purchasing more economical and cleaner vehicles would cut down on the sale of gas-guzzlers but wouldn't thwart the production process itself. There is no reason our economy can't make the transition to, and thrive in, a cleaner and healthier world.

What are felt to be questionable applications have been highlighted. Overall, our understanding of what is important is gaining momentum. Energy-friendly technologies in products from light bulbs to airplanes have increased dramatically, though there is always room for improvement. Take air conditioners, which account for roughly 10 percent of global electricity consumption. While 90 percent of American households use air-conditioning, only about 8 percent of the people living in the world's hottest regions own them. Like many other goods, rising incomes in countries like China, India, and Indonesia will make possible their purchase; it is predicted that by 2050, the global energy demand earmarked for air-conditioning systems will triple, which is good. Air-conditioning can be a life saver, especially during extreme heat waves. The answer lies not in asking others to renounce their safety and comfort but in making the cooling systems, as well as electrical sources, greener and more energy efficient. To meet this end, it would be wise to start by taking a page from the EU and Japanese playbooks, whose units use 25 percent less energy than ours.

A good example of positive movement is aseptic packaging, which is replacing glass, aluminum, and Polyethylene terephthalate (PET) plastics as a means of housing pharmaceuticals, juices, and some foods. Kids find the boxes convenient because they are easier to carry and weigh less than bottles or cans. They are filled in a sterile environment through a process that preserves many nutrients and requires little energy or preservatives. Their tight seal repels contaminants, microorganisms, and deterioration, increasing shelf life and excluding the need for refrigeration, which particularly helps when shipping overseas. The cartons are layered with paper fibers (averaging 74 percent of the total), polymers and aluminum, all of which can be recycled.

Until recently, the term "smart" was reserved for describing sentient creatures displaying an above-average ability to problem solve. Whether it was Albert Einstein pondering the universe's relativity or a crow bending a wire to reach otherwise inaccessible food, the adjective referred to a living, breathing being. Not anymore. Thanks to the internet, the smart revolution is upon us, linking the word to a near-limitless array of connected devices that are breathing intelligence into everyday objects and transforming our lives.

Many smart technologies have proved beneficial in the business sector, enabling the collection of more rapid and accurate data, changing production processes, smoothing operations, and reducing what were once oppressive barriers to startup businesses. Cities are implementing new sensors to detect traffic congestion and synchronize traffic lights for better precision; New York is using them to gauge the condition of older bridges by recording data on the effects of the fatigue impacting cables and weak points. Intelligent streetlight systems are being designed that deploy sensors throughout a city's lighting network, allowing for the brightening of energy-efficient LED lighting when needed. Sensors can be installed on the lights to detect foot and vehicle traffic, measure air pollution, and use acoustic technology to monitor street disturbances and gunfire. A study sponsored by the German Association of the Automotive Industry states that German motorists spend 560 million hours searching for parking spaces each year, wasting millions of gallons of fuel and spewing excess exhaust in the process. The Spanish city of Santander has found a way to alleviate the problem by installing four hundred sensors in its town center. The devices catalogue the available parking spots and transmit the information to the cloud via wireless networks, and by using connected lighting systems, they direct drivers to open parking spaces. Smart meters used worldwide that continuously track and detect power outages permit utility companies to quickly respond.

Wearable devices monitoring fitness data and one's state of health are gaining in popularity. Autonomous (hopefully smart) vehicles employing a plethora of technical innovations geared toward safety and convenience are making headway and will one day hit the road in force.

If there's an appliance for the home, chances are there is a connected version. Some are smart purchases. Take the smart thermostat that permits you to monitor your home's temperature and humidity from a smartphone, tablet, or PC. Sensors in each room let you tailor heating and cooling as needed, preparing them for optimal comfort and energy bill reduction. Smart lighting systems geared toward energy efficiency and visual relief, security systems, low-flow showerheads that track water savings, and moisture sensors are smart ideas.

I'm not so sure about the intelligence of people needing app-guided toothbrushes that watch their brushing technique and provide personalized coaching and feedback for the perfect cleaning or those who rely on discs mounted to the bathroom mirror that remind them to floss and automatically dispense an ADA-approved eighteen inches of the product. Ditto for folks requiring smart forks and plates that shadow their eating habits and help manage portion control or smart jump ropes that count the number of reps. Don't forget Nike's self-lacing app-controlled smart shoe, the Adapt BB, that automatically senses a foot's volume and closes around it and comes with Bluetooth connectivity so owners can choose to loosen or tighten the footwear by smartphone. The "brains" of the device is called the "lace engine" which houses all the vital components: a microcontroller, 505mAh battery, Bluetooth module, pressure sensor, accelerometer, gyroscope, motor, capacitive touch sensor, lights, temperature sensor, and wireless charging coil. Oh, it also emits musical chords, a distinct sound when the battery is above twenty percent charged and another an octave lower when it is below that threshold. With all that tech. underfoot, for the asking price of $350, one might be tempted to tread softly. P.T. Barnum, what hast thou wrought?

The Internet of Things (IoT) has a bright and enduring future. Not surprisingly, the endless array of offerings run the gamut from the ridiculous to the sublime.

In what ranks as supreme irony, the plethora of environmental applications attributed to the IoT are not without serious environmental repercussions. Because microprocessors require multiple metals in their construction, great expanses of the earth are being blasted during mining. In less regulated countries, mining can lead to disastrous alterations to the terrain while polluting drinking water.

The resources are finite. Take the smartphone, for example.

> *Of the 83 stable and non-radioactive elements in the periodic table, at least 70 can be found in smartphones. According to the best available figures, a total of 62 different types of metals go into the average mobile handset, with what are known as the rare Earth metals playing a particularly important role. Of the 17 rare Earth metals, 16 are included in phones.*[2]

No one knows how long supplies will last, but it is obvious some of the rarer metals and minerals will become increasingly hard to find. Unless we can come up with effective alternatives, take greater advantage of refurbishing and recycling phones, produce longer-lasting devices, and improve mining technologies that uncover new reserves, we may have to revert to low-tech substitutes.

Whether because of internal and/or external pressure, phone-making firms have become increasingly conscious of the ethical and environmental costs of their actions. Assuming greater accountability for their supply chains—which results in fairer wages and safer workplaces for miners—and regulating harmful environmental actions costs money. They are making efforts to steer clear of material sources that stem from mining operations in violent locales engaged

Lawrence K. Zeisler

in human rights abuses and illegal profiteering. In some cases, doing right comes with financial burdens.

Regarding energy production, we are realizing the benefits of the clean and limitless bounty inherent in the natural forces all around; sources that don't require the mutilation of the earth's deep-seated strata or the defilement of azure oceans. The primary renewable ones are solar, wind, hydroelectric, and geothermal. Lesser ones are biomass, tidal, wave energy, and micro hydro power. All these technologies will someday be implemented jointly on a grand scale, contributing to a diverse energy picture.

Although natural gas is America's leading source of electric power generation renewables are the new driving force in America's electric energy economy, attracting large outlays of capital and investment. Pennsylvania sustains more than eighty-six thousand clean energy jobs across all its 67 counties. Worldwide, nearly a quarter of electricity generation is produced by renewable energy technologies. Nationally, renewable energy sources easily surpass coal in electrical production.

Despite the fallout from President Trump's tariffs on solar panels and market unsurety because of his proposed rollbacks of clean vehicle and energy efficiency policies, according to the 2019 Clean Jobs America analysis about 110,000 clean energy jobs were added to the workforce in 2018, The more than 3.26 million jobs in the total clean energy industry which includes solar, wind, alternative vehicle development and production, clean storage, grid modernization, and energy efficiency markets outpace those in the fossil fuel fields by almost three to one. The energy efficiency sector is the power behind America's job growth. It alone employs 2.25 million workers, accounting for more than one out of every six construction jobs (nearly 1.3 million) in the country. Clean energy jobs are growing twice as fast as the rest of the economy. Republican lawmakers, seeing their districts benefiting from a renewable energy job boom, are jumping in on the action in increasing numbers.

The President's wistful return to the twentieth century has not resonated with common sense folks. States, cities, businesses, and communities across the nation are formulating determined sustainability programs that will ensure continued market growth for renewables. Even utilities are stepping up and voluntarily incorporating renewable sources in their systems. In the face of federal tampering solar saw a slight job loss in 2018, although the U.S. renewable energy sector as a whole was able to break about even. But there is no stopping the inevitable . The U.S. Department of Energy's Energy Information Administration (EIA) forecasts that solar generation will steadily increase through 2019, and the Solar Energy Industries Association predicts that total installed photovoltaic (PV) capacity in the U.S. will more than double over the upcoming five years.

Due to technological progress, the costs of solar and wind energy have dropped precipitously over the years, making them cheaper than dirty fuels in some locales. Within the next twenty years the electrical costs of solar are projected to be half that of natural gas, and worldwide estimates by Bloomberg New Energy Finance place investments in renewables at $7.2 trillion versus $1.5 trillion for fossil fuels over the same period. It predicts that by 2050 half of the planet's electricity will derive from renewables. Commodity prices for gas, coal, and oil fluctuate, but technology costs for renewables trend unalterably downward, and its generation is not subject to electricity price spikes. Just eighteen days of sunshine contain energy equal to that stored in the earth's estimated fossil fuel reserves. Whether the inducement is a cleaner environment, lower bills, or more jobs, the future is undeniably in clean energy. The president claims to corner the market on business acumen?

In a bow to objectivity, although no pollution is generated when solar panels are producing energy, the photovoltaic (PV) solar cell manufacturing method involves use of hazardous materials (predominately acids), most of which are used in cleaning the surface of semiconductors. Heavy metals needed for panel assemblage pose a danger while being mined. Let's not forget the greenhouse gases emitted during their creation as well as potential pollution problems resulting from improper waste disposal.

Efforts to correct the ills are underway such as those being pursued by researchers at the University of California-Berkeley and other academic laboratories working on the advancement of thin-film PVs that do not rely on toxic metals or rare elements in their production. The quest for safer alternatives is ongoing, and design improvements to the solar cells themselves are increasing their efficiency. Refinements to the process are continuously evolving. With a concerted effort by scientists, manufacturers, and concerned consumers, solar power production will continue "greening," widening the scope of the impressive edge it currently holds over dirty fossil fuel alternatives.

Then there is recycling. Because solar panels have a life expectancy of at least twenty-five years and installation didn't gear up in the United States until 2010, a systematic national recycling infrastructure has not been established, though a couple of farsighted states have implemented requirements. Individual companies see the importance of devising plans of their own, some patterned after Europe's proven model; most of the panels there end up at glass recyclers where they are crushed or shredded, separating the glass from the metals and other material. As far back as 2005, the US company First Solar realized that in order to justify a green label, it was necessary to factor in an end-of-panel-life recycling strategy. It was looking out for the company's welfare, comprehending that retrieving the stuff composed therein would contribute to its sustainability. It presently recycles two million thin-filmed cadmium-telluride panels globally every year. Its desire is to include crystalline silicon ones in the recycling inventory as well.

The time is now for our country to follow Europe's position and start recycling plants nationwide willing to invest in solar processing. Its solar panel disposal guidelines fall under the jurisdiction of the Waste Electrical and Electronic Equipment Directive (WEEE Directive), a major waste stream in the EU that deals with gathering, treatment, and reclaiming diverse types of electronic equipment. Taking a page from their book would assist us in formulating our own overdue policy, incentivizing innovation and leading to global environmental and economic advantages.

The world's foremost waste management program focused on the range of PV technologies, PV Cycle, has devised a treatment methodology that attains a 96 percent recovery rate for silicon-based PV panels. The remaining 4 percent of material is employed in an energy recovery process. The recovery rate of non-silicon-based panels can be as high as 98 percent. This reuse of raw materials helps to conserve natural resources, which is important because some are finite. A 2016 study by the International Renewable Energy Agency (IRENA) estimates that by 2050, the recyclable substances in used solar modules will be worth $15 billion in recoverable value. It forecasts solar panel recycling will give rise to new industries and green jobs.

Another source of renewable energy is biogas, a type of biofuel. It captures gases, especially methane, and uses them as fuel. It is produced by the decomposition of organic material by microbes in anaerobic environments in digestion plants, wastewater facilities, and landfills. The United States manages over five hundred landfill-to-energy operations.

Sewage and manure, grease from restaurants and food processors, organic municipal, agricultural, and food wastes, and plant materials including scrap lumber and yard clippings provide the necessary biomass for its production—problematic waste materials that would otherwise be burned or left to rot. They would alternately be disposed of in the majority of landfills not designed to anaerobically ferment biomass where greenhouse gas escape is considerable and toxic liquids can contaminate underground water sources.

The conversion of organic waste into biogas curbs the atmospheric release of methane. Though the primary by-product is CO_2, the reduction in greenhouse gas discharge is significant given methane's potency. If it were used in conjunction with carbon capture and storage (CCS), an emerging technology that separates the CO_2 and injects it underground, the harmful emissions released during the process would be corralled.

Besides the obvious benefits of treating and reducing landfill and industrial waste as well as harnessing escaping gas for energy, anaerobic digestion has been used to develop a variety of useful soil products similar to finished compost and peat moss. Included in this list are organic fertilizers that can displace synthetic ones that emit high outputs of carbon and often contain chemicals that have toxic effects.

This technology that closer mimics nature's sustainability has been around a long time and is becoming more relevant in today's world. Digestion on a small scale, or microscale digestion, to produce the gas and fertilizer is used by farms, individual family settings, and "eco-neighborhoods," often in rural areas, in underdeveloped and industrialized countries. In Sweden, refined biogas has been utilized as a fuel for autos and buses—it has been calculated that one day it may replace about 17 percent of vehicle fuel in the United Kingdom. Germany, in the forefront of renewable technology research, has processed enough electricity from biogas to serve over 8 million homes. Another plus is that biogas can be stored and tapped during times of high electrical demand.

The United States has more than twenty-two hundred sites refining biogas in all fifty states. The potential is limitless when one factors in the nearly four thousand water resource recovery facilities, dairy and swine farms, landfills, and over nine hundred food scrap-only systems. An industry assessment performed by the USDA, EPA, and DOE ascertained that a serious commitment to biogas production could generate $40 billion in capital investment that would promote approximately 335,000 short-term construction jobs, 23,000 permanent jobs earmarked to run the digesters, and a multitude of opportunities in the organic waste collection stream.

Yes, we have the wherewithal to curtail climate change at a profit. Since the current administration has largely forsaken renewable energy, localities, states, and the private sector must exercise greater self-determination while forging individual clean-energy policies. Many are embracing the positive market trends favoring pollution-free energy with traditional businesses and institutions working to reduce their environmental footprint.

Seventeen states have committed to adhering to the goals laid out in the Paris Agreement. California, which produces roughly 14 percent of the nation's GDP and is the fifth largest economy in the world, has taken steps to implement the bold initiative of transitioning its powerful economy to 100 percent carbon-free sources by 2045. Massachusetts is projecting a 100 percent renewable future by 2050, and by 2030, New York aims to have 50 percent of the state's energy coming from renewables. New Jersey's new governor, Phil Murphy, signed the Clean Renewable Energy Bill that requires that over 50 percent of the state's energy come from renewable sources, principally offshore wind, by 2030. The goal is to achieve 100 percent clean energy production by 2050. Seventy US cities have pledged to go 100 percent renewable. Talking about the decarbonization of our electricity system, renewable energy expert Christian Beyer stated, "Energy transition is no longer a question of technical feasibility or economic viability, but of political will." A Stanford University study reached similar findings.

Advances in green technology, along with decreasing costs, have enabled Germany to derive 40 percent of its electricity from renewable sources in just fifteen years. Norway and Iceland run almost exclusively on renewables—Norway primarily on hydroelectric power and Iceland on geothermal. Denmark plans to wean itself off fossil fuels by 2050. Helped by concerted reductions in energy consumption, the country expects a full one-third of its energy output to be produced by wind power and biomass by 2020. A report compiled by a group whose board is headed by former New York City mayor and philanthropist Michael Bloomberg, and issued by California governor Jerry Brown at the Global Climate Action Summit in San Francisco, disclosed that twenty-seven major cities have decreased greenhouse gas emissions over the last five years and are currently 10 percent below their peak output (the list includes New York, Los Angeles, San Francisco, London, Berlin, and Paris).

A landmark international agreement to which more than 170 countries have consented has exceeded the twenty-nation ratification threshold for enforcement. Some of those that have ratified are Germany, the UK, France, Canada, Australia, Sweden, Ireland, Belgium, Hungary, and Finland. Called the Kigali Amendment, it is appended to the 1987 Montreal Protocol that was highly effective in protecting the ozone layer. It addresses the impact of a class of extensively used chemical coolants known as hydrofluorocarbons (HFCs). While HFCs are weak ozone-depleting substances, unlike their ozone-draining predecessors, chlorofluorocarbons (CFCs, out of production since 2010), they are strong greenhouse gases. The amendment calls for an 80 percent reduction in the use of HFCs by 2047, transitioning to climate-friendly alternatives, and promoting new energy-efficient technologies. It is estimated that doing so will prevent up to 0.5 degrees Celsius (0.9 degrees Fahrenheit) of warming by the end of the century. The United States has not yet signed on. If President Trump does not send it to the Senate for approval and ratification, failure to meet the treaty standards could hamper the entry of American chemical companies into global markets for substitute, innovative refrigeration and coolant equipment, leading to a decline in exports and an increase in the trade deficit. It

Lawrence K. Zeisler

is not surprising that most of the principal US companies working in related sectors have endorsed the amendment.

Energy self-sufficient houses that produce as much energy as they consume (known as zero-energy homes) are of environmental and financial value, and they are beginning to make their presence felt in the home building industry. Incorporating a unique blend of architectural designs with high-efficiency features—superbly insulated windows, airtight construction, integrated heating/cooling/ventilation systems, Energy Star-certified appliances, and clean onsite energy generation—they are gaining in popularity but remain on the fringes of new home construction. Slightly more than eight thousand single-family and multifamily units were built in the United States and Canada in 2016; their savings to the earth equates to almost seventy-eight thousand fewer tons of CO_2 emissions compared with the pollution outlay of similar-sized standard units built to code. Though the initial investment may be 5–10 percent over the price of a comparable conventional home, after the energy proceeds are factored in, the total cost of ownership is far less; the breakeven point will vary, but ten years is a good estimate. After that, it's all profit. Considering that homes and commercial buildings are responsible for nearly 40 percent of the total US energy use, zero-energy structures are a vital part of a reduced carbon future. The challenge is getting them established in the production world. Predictions are encouraging with the market research firm Lux Research forecasting a $1.3 trillion global market by 2025.

Inner-city residents benefit when measures dedicated to improving and greening their environs are implemented. The primary objectives of a recent Philadelphia program financed by the National Institutes of Health were urban revitalization and job creation, most of the work going to local contractors and neighborhood residents. The efforts ranged from full-blown grading and horticultural improvements to basic clearing and mowing of lots. An added perk was noted: It was found that clearing debris and trash from vacant parcels cut down on overall crime including gun activity and burglaries. Gun dealers and gang members could no longer stash their weapons among the clutter, forcing them to hide them in cars parked in front of the newly cleared lots. Residents began to take pride in and use the lots, driving the criminals and their vehicles away. Gun assaults in the renovated areas dropped by as much as 29 percent compared to locales surrounding unmanicured properties. The authors speculated there were almost thirty thousand decaying lots in Philadelphia alone. Think of how much valuable work could be done addressing abandoned tracts nationwide.

Companies participating in the Plastics Industry Association Zero Net Waste (ZNW) program exhibit leadership in plastics recycling and related environmental efforts. Their goal is maximum waste reduction and resource recovery of plastic materials and other manufacturing by-products, compatible with the sustainable materials management model being implemented by regulatory agencies and governments worldwide. To this end, they offer education, guidance, and resources that aid member companies to recycle or reuse waste material and avoid disposing of it in a landfill or being incinerated without energy production. Though it is realized that "absolute zero" net waste is difficult if not impossible, "near zero" net waste is not. Eighty to ninety percent recovery of substances is obtainable for companies committed to the endeavor.

Besides the obvious environmental benefits including landfill life extension, the economic advantages of striving for zero net waste are many. Along with reduced landfill costs, revenue is generated from the sale of scrap materials in some instances. Green marketing often enhances customer relationships and engenders new business. Companies prioritizing sustainability usually disclose higher employee contentment and retention. Workers appreciate representing companies that are reputable stewards of the community and environment, and growing numbers of consumers recognize their value.

Automobile recycling is a leading US industry, employing over 140,000 people and accounting for more than $32 billion in annual sales. At least 95 percent of vehicles are recycled to some extent. On average, around 80 percent (by weight) of each is recovered. Wheels, tires, batteries, glass, engines, suspensions, drivelines, and interior pieces are recycled or used as replacement parts. The remaining scrap metal is sent to steel mills where it is converted into new steel. Quality recycled auto parts can cost 20–80 percent less than a corresponding new part.

The recycling of plastic parts is another matter. Plastic is becoming more common on automobiles, helping to reduce costs, weight, and fuel consumption. Plastics make up about 50 percent of a modern auto's volume and only 10 percent of its weight. A single vehicle contains various plastics that in turn can be composed of different resins. Technological hurdles must be met and overcome before recycling some plastic and polymer composite car parts becomes feasible. Efforts to identify the challenges and find solutions to improving recycling practices by working with the complete supply chain, from resin suppliers to recyclers, are progressing. The industry has enlisted the aid of the ZNW program to assist in the endeavor.

Employment of naturally occurring, waste-eating microorganisms in unique treatment regimens is gaining momentum. It's common knowledge that bacteria are used in wastewater plants to consume and treat incoming waste. Researchers at Southern Illinois University have worked with plentiful, natural bacteria that can be used as toxin eaters in anaerobic, dark environments. In one application, the bugs target a toxic chemical used in munitions manufacturing called perchlorate that has seeped into groundwater. The by-products of the process are harmless table salt and oxygen.

Another exciting possibility is the use of microbes in containing radioactive materials stored underground. Scientists have discovered specialist bacteria that flourish in a highly alkaline environment like that in which it is anticipated nuclear waste encased in cement and buried deep in vaults will reside. It is forecast that subterranean waters will eventually reach the vaults, and the resulting saturation and ensuing spike in alkalinity (cement has a ph of about 11) will incite chemical reactions leading to the breakdown of cellulose-based ingredients in the waste's complex of materials. An alkaline-friendly acid known as ISA would be a product of the reactions. It is potentially problematic because it can bind to the hazardous and unstable components of the waste, primarily uranium, causing the toxic material to become soluble and more apt to leach out of the vaults into the surrounding environs where it could contaminate drinking water.

The microbes under observation at a badly contaminated, extremely alkaline, nonradioactive industrial site in

Lawrence K. Zeisler

England consume and break down ISA and thrive in conditions that resemble those predicted to exist in and around toxic underground sites. Researchers are amazed at how quickly the microorganisms can evolve to survive changes in their environment. When oxygen is not available, they can alter their metabolism to use other chemicals in the liquid, such as iron and nitrate, to breathe. The investigators feel it is likely that similar bacteria will be able to adapt to radioactive waste habitats. Preliminary studies show that radiation levels commonly existing at nuclear waste dumps do them no harm. It is hoped that by degrading the ISA, the bugs will neutralize the effects of any chemical reactions and stabilize the radioactive materials, keeping them fixed underground.

Naturally existing bacteria living hundreds of meters below the surface in the rock formations chosen to house Swiss nuclear waste could consume hydrogen gas that it is supposed will be emitted when the steel canisters containing the material corrode. Before the discovery, it had been feared that hydrogen gas pressure accumulations would undermine the soundness of the surrounding rock and result in escaping radioactive gas.

An exhaustive study was conducted at the proposed site in which the bacteria were given excessive levels of hydrogen gas. Once the available oxygen and iron had been used up, their metabolisms switched so they could benefit from the increased hydrogen. The ensuing reduction in gas was considerable. The knowledge gained might lead planners to modify the design of the underground storage area by introducing a biological barrier of porous material between the physical vault and rock, the intent being to boost the effectiveness of the bacteria by enlarging their zone of operation.

The ability to manipulate microbial genomes is expanding and has revolutionized biotechnology to the extent that the bio-based economy will one day become an integral part of our lives. As previously noted, innovations in the health and agricultural spheres are leading to major breakthroughs. Industrial biotech can be considered biotechnology's third wave. Microbes, microorganisms, enzymes, and their genetic engineering provide the underpinnings for a range of technologies and processes that companies, researchers, and scientists are seeking to create for commercial use. Advances in genomic studies have enabled participants to unveil and tap into the richness of genetic diversity in these minute organisms by probing their DNA at the molecular level.

Different methods of genetic editing have recently been devised to facilitate research in the biotech phenomenon. Like humans and other forms of life, bacteria can be infected by viruses. A group of scientists discovered that some bacteria acquire snippets of the DNA of attacking viruses and use them to develop DNA segments referred to as CRISPR arrays—a kind of "memory bank" or genetic "archive" serving as an immune defense. If infected again, the bacteria can equip a specialized Cas9 attack enzyme with a "guide" RNA, or messenger, packed with the stored information. Once the RNA locates the invader, it compares the genetic code with the sequences in its files. If it detects a match, the Cas9 enzyme severs the virus DNA, incapacitating it.

An effective technology known as CRISPR-Cas9 can trace its genesis to this naturally occurring bacterial genome editing system. It is the most precise, versatile, and simple method of gene manipulation to date, and it provides

Lawrence K. Zeisler

geneticists and medical researchers the means to edit sections of the genome to acquire a specified result.

The CRISPR-Cas9 system produces a predesigned, synthetic RNA with a guide sequence, the purpose of which is to locate a corresponding distinctive sequence in a target DNA where a desired alteration will take place. The RNA is considered a guide because it binds to and then delivers the DNA snipping Cas9 enzyme (or one like it) to the spot in the genome where its target sequence match resides. The Cas9 protein cuts the section so that bits of genetic material can be removed or added. The cell's natural DNA repair mechanisms repair the gap with a sequence of nucleotides—the building blocks of DNA. To accomplish this, it utilizes a short strand of DNA as a template. By furnishing a template of their choice, scientists can introduce a reengineered DNA sequence to effect a desired change. The idea is that gene modification systems like this will one day be able to treat and possibly prevent genetic causes of disease and disabilities by correcting mutations at specific locations in the human genome.

It is worth noting that the procedure relies less on transgenic practices, as is often the case with GMOs, while enhancing crops for agricultural purposes. Although CRISPR can involve the addition of genes from other species, much effort is being dedicated to harness an individual plant's own immense gene diversity (twenty to thirty thousand in number). Genetic engineering is considerably less able to analyze a plant's vast gene network, making it likely to look elsewhere to achieve a desired trait. The more efficient CRISPR gene-editing technique might be able to unearth a gene within a species to deliver the same result, precluding the need for the risky, less appealing transgenic alternative.

Industrial biotechnology sets out to isolate natural enzymes, which are specialized proteins that evolved to be efficient biocatalysts that aid and accelerate complex biochemical reactions. Once isolated, the enzymes can be used to function in precise industrial applications. In some instances, companies are experimenting to improve their performance using technologies like CRISPR-Cas9.

In the 1970s, industrial biotechnology resolved the water pollution crisis resulting from the presence of phosphates in laundry detergents. Biotech companies developed enzymes that were superior to phosphates in eliminating clothing stains. The bio-based alternative not only yielded cleaner clothes at reduced water temperatures but lessened the severity of phosphate-associated algal blooms in estuaries and coastlines worldwide.

Industrial biotechnology presents businesses with the opportunity to promote new markets in an environmentally sustainable way. Nature's living, enzyme-based processes function at lower temperatures and yield less toxicity and fewer emissions than man-made chemical processes. Most of the waste produced by bio-based, or renewable, chemicals are biodegradable or recyclable. Engineering nature in a contained environment uses less energy at reduced capital costs with potentially higher returns.

Integrated bio-refineries producing diverse environmentally compatible products and incorporating lean enterprise techniques will likely transform the economics of industrial production in the near future. While hurdles need to be overcome before large-scale implementation, the production of select chemicals from biomass energy, which includes renewable raw materials such as crop or forestry residues or organic waste, could be used to fashion sub-

Lawrence K. Zeisler

stitutes for many of the industrial materials and products presently derived from natural gas and petroleum. A few of the possibilities are bio-based plastics, lubricants, foams, and industrial chemicals. The Australian company Plantic develops biopolymers and plastics obtained from corn. An enzyme-based substance called Landguard, derived from naturally occurring soil bacteria that feed on chemicals, can quickly degrade some pesticide residues in soil and water, inducing by-products of considerably diminished toxicity and superior biodegradability than the original pesticide. The enzymes were isolated from the bacteria and their effectiveness improved through molecular biology procedures. It is being sold commercially. The potential exists to exploit enzymes to lessen the amount of harsh chemicals used by the textile and pulp and paper industries.

Finding biobased alternatives for today's plastics would confront an urgent problem plaguing the planet, namely the growing mounds of the ubiquitous material never finding its way to a recycling facility. While "clean" plastic recyclables like industrial plastic waste are mostly recycled, contrary to what most people believe the majority of the stuff tossed into the recycle bin never gets processed and increasingly ends up in landfills. Two-thirds of the states in the U.S. are now facing a recycling crisis; some municipalities are dramatically restricting or even canceling their programs. Because sorting is so labor intensive and many of the plastics are contaminated with food residue and other materials, dealing with the substance is not cost effective. Add to this the prohibitive transportation costs. Using EPA and industry data, Chemical engineer Jan Dell estimates the U.S. recycling rate of mixed plastic waste to be less than five percent in 2018.

For decades China received huge shipments of plastics, mixed paper, cardboard, and metals from numerous nations, including the United States, to satisfy its burgeoning manufacturing sector. It was more economical to recycle the material than to make it from scratch, and the available plentiful and cheap labor made sorting and separating feasible. Labor costs have increased and the momentum of manufacturing has eased. Last year, citing public health and environmental reasons, coupled with the decision to end its world trash dump status and the desire to become more self-reliant, the country imposed serious restrictions on what it would accept. The reverberations were felt worldwide, leaving former clients to deal with their growing mountains of garbage. Some of which, plastics in particular, is arriving in poorer Southeast Asian countries with inadequate and less well-regulated recycling programs, where it is often burned or left to rot, polluting surrounding ecosystems and endangering the lives of local residents; a scenario which can't and shouldn't be sustained.

The silver lining in this scenario is that countries will be forced to confront the broken global recycling system and develop their individual domestic industries. Sending at least eighty percent of our mixed plastics abroad is unacceptable, and subject to variability: look at China's announcement. The market advantages will not be accrued overnight; it takes time to construct and test equipment. But in the long run a self-sufficient domestic market makes logistical, environmental, and security sense.

Federal, state, and local governments must all support and invest in viable waste management and recycling infrastructures, and corporations have to step up and change their packaging. Citizens need to be more responsible about

Lawrence K. Zeisler

sorting and careful about what they deposit in recycling bins. All of us have to come together and request a shift away from single-use plastics. Faced with mounting pressure, petrochemical companies are finally responding to the crisis.

Improvements to recycling technologies are paramount. Though expensive, employing robots using artificial intelligence and cameras would help remedy the labor intensive process of separating recyclables from trash. Every effort should be made to find more sustainable nontoxic alternatives to the pesky petroleum-based substance.

Efforts that employ scientists to search for sound solutions to environmental problems cannot be overvalued. To this end, training specialists whose primary function is to analyze and develop benign chemical compounds that constitute a material's structure is of the essence. Research dedicated to refining state-of-the-art equipment that causes as few pollutants as possible to be emitted during a product's manufacture and eventual reuse or recycling will be to the advantage of all. The intention should be to restructure production and distribution systems to reduce waste. Hiring technicians and workers to implement the projects will expand employment opportunities. Promoting energy efficiency and low (or no) carbon-emitting technologies will ensure a better future.

Commitment to the zero waste philosophy would provide meaningful focus. It encourages product designs geared toward conserving and recovering resources and endeavors to pattern its efforts after nature where one process's exploited materials are used by others (such as during photosynthesis and decomposition).

There is no stopping the biotech revolution. The upside is too great. The potential to alter the status quo for the better holds unlimited promise. The challenges are manifold and complement the ever-increasing need to summon our unquenchable intellectual thirst. The floodgates are open, but to prevent the waters from breaching the dam, the utmost caution is required. Debating the ethical merits and the possible consequences resulting from introducing the gene tampered with are exercises in common sense. Each considered application should be met with multiple investigations and rigorous laboratory testing, even contingency planning if necessary, especially if the development is slated for environmental release.

Such is the case with proposed gene drives. These genetic modifications can be inserted into DNA to alter the rules of inheritance in sexual reproduction, providing a means to remodel specific populations or an entire species. Some ideas are inhibiting or eliminating the spread of pathogens by reprograming the genomes of their insect carriers and controlling invasive species.

While both sound good in theory, actual discharge into natural settings is not without possible complications. One is the concern that gene drives might become invasive themselves, dispersing deep into nature with unwanted effects. If a non-native species transformed by a gene drive designed to interfere with its capacity to reproduce were to return to its natural ecosystem by unintended human transport or natural migration, it could lead to the extinction of that species.

At this point, the risks outweigh the benefits. Thankfully, ethical, technical, and safety hurdles must be surmounted before technologies like CRISPR can be widely applied in germline (cells containing genetic material that could be passed to offspring) therapy trials. Perhaps technological advances will convincingly check all potential drawbacks off the list, though some specialists say the most difficult part

Lawrence K. Zeisler

of the development phase is over. It would be nice if endangered species could be engineered for improved fertility or if the three species of mosquitoes most accountable for the transmission of malaria were made resistant to the parasite. The fungus responsible for white nose syndrome, which is decimating bat populations in North America, most likely spread from Europe where bats appear to have evolved resistance to the infection. Researchers have sequenced the genomes of the fungus and hope to parlay that knowledge into developing a means to counteract the malady. A naturally occurring bacteria has been discovered that may limit the growth of the fungus but further tests are required before wholesale release to ensure it presents no threat to both bats and the ecosystem. Scientists are exploring ways to edit tick genes, hoping to counter the spread of diseases, although such strategies are far from implementation.

Scientists have already deciphered the genetic codes of many killer pathogens. The knowledge gained will enable them to develop ways to target vulnerable areas in the microbes' systems. One such microbe is *Plasmodium falciparum*, the most virulent of the malaria parasites. Within its genes are the instructions for making protease, an enzyme that aids in the digestion of its food source: hemoglobin found in the red blood cells of its host. Scientists speculate that if they can incapacitate the protease, the parasite will starve. Gene experimentation is important because some parasites have evolved measures to resist administered drugs.

In extreme cases like the screwworm fly, whose larvae eat the healthy, living tissue of warm-blooded animals (unlike the maggots of other species that may infest an old or putrid wound), elimination of the species by the release of sterile individuals might not be so bad. If the non-native

Burmese python's rampage through the Everglades could one day be halted, without consequences to indigenous Asian populations, go for it. Researchers at the University of Kentucky are experimenting with a new technology called RNA interference to fashion a revolutionary insecticide that obstructs the expression of genes crucial to an insect's vital bodily functions. If applications of biopesticides (pesticides sourced from natural materials) prove ineffective, it might one day be used as a means to precisely target the invasive spotted lanternfly.

Supported by thorough research and probing inquiry, smart science and sound technology will play key roles in delivering us from certain conditions deemed damaging to our way of life, some compounded by anthropogenic interference. Careless science and indiscriminate technology will herald chaos. It would be wise to remember that the phrase "the road to hell is paved with good intentions" applies here as well as anywhere.

Chapter 7

"The most beautiful thing we can experience is the mysterious. It is the source of all true art and science. He to whom this emotion is a stranger, who can no longer pause to wonder and stand rapt in awe, is as good as dead: his eyes are closed."

—Albert Einstein

What is fundamentally necessary? Taken to the raw bone, it is anything that is vital to survival: the elements such as air, water, and soil that have served to perpetuate human existence. In this context, are high-priced luxury cars and state-of-the-art computers indispensable? Are office copiers and fax machines crucial?

Note the emphasis upon high-priced cars and state-of-the-art computers. In present day America, both a car and computer are essentials for many people. As a society's living standard rises, the basics increase. Some of the manufactured ones rank alongside clean air and water in importance. Ask a Los Angeles native if they would forgo their refrigerator in exchange for smog-free air, and the answer might not be quickly forthcoming. A suburbanite or city dweller unhappy with their tap water would likely find it less inconvenient to buy bottled spring water than doing without a television or dare I say, a cell phone.

Humans have adjusted to life within a jeopardized environment; we are a resilient species. It comes down to a matter of degree. To what extent must the air and water be sullied before they reassume their rightful place in the hierarchy of values? There is no arguing that breathing is more fundamental to life than driving.

We are programmed to believe that the level of an object's worth increases in direct proportion to its monetary value. Perhaps if money did grow on trees we would be better able to comprehend their contributions. I know that more people would be planting them.

One can learn much by walking among and watching trees. Enfolding oneself within a sylvan shroud lends inspiration to a dispirited soul. Limbs that provide sustenance and shelter, leaves that give nutrition in death, cleanse the air, provide oxygen and change the weather's face in life, roots that loosen the soil, making possible the absorption of surplus rainwater, and loveliness that excites the eye are proof of a boundless generosity we could all learn from. Trees can tell us a thing or two about the virtue of patience. Whether reeling under a gale's savage onslaught or reaching for the sun, one is mindful of a total lack of resistance, a profound harmony.

Patience is another quality sadly wanting in these times. Sometimes waiting is the only sensible thing to do. Studies have determined that intensive overfishing of the oceans over the last fifty years has caused the disappearance of up to 90 percent of some large predatory fish populations (fishermen dispute the data). Included in this group are tuna, swordfish, marlin, and various species of sharks. The only recourse is to sit back and let them repopulate. Living creatures can't increase reproduction to meet demand. The

Lawrence K. Zeisler

second god needs to be reminded of what the first one said long ago: "You reap what you sow." You take, take, take, and sooner or later, you must bite the bullet.

Impatience is not a virtue and is partially accountable for rash, even dangerous, episodes on individual and corporate levels. Its role as a contributor to stress cannot be overlooked. Not so apparent is the hand it plays in stifling the capacity for wonder. Wonder is best experienced when the mind is relaxed and unburdened.

Those who associate wonder only with naivety may care to look no further. I've often heard it expressed that children are so blessed, but once we reach a threshold—key elements of which are responsibility and expanded knowledge—the age of wonder fades into the past.

Adult responsibilities exact a toll; bringing home the bacon occupies a good portion of one's attention. It's hard enough to sustain the status quo let alone strive for greater wealth. Societal demands suppress our youthful, unrestrained immersion in the immediate world and supplant it with a developing personality that manages and shapes perception. The field of awareness becomes narrowed and selective, diverting our attention from much of what is occurring around us.

One theory suggests that science has unlocked the secrets of nature, answering her riddles and removing life's intrigue. The moon, once a nighttime mystery, has been measured and analyzed, even walked on, for God sake. How can one be blamed for stifling a yawn whenever they look at it? It's as if we think we've seen it all and there are no more surprises.

Balderdash! Many new scientific discoveries are enthralling. The potential for experiencing wonder increases with knowledge. Granted, wonder based in knowledge is different than a child's—dependent on innocence, openness, and spontaneity—but its power to fascinate can fill one with childlike awe. What ancient scholar could have guessed that each human cell contains the seeds of life? How could they have known that if the DNA from all cells in the body were lined up end to end, it would create a strand around 10 billion miles long?

The system of checks and balances responsible for the maintenance of life is nothing short of spectacular. The atmosphere supports and protects us. Its sheltering blanket wards off the frigid vacuum of outer space as well as high-energy radiation. The story of its evolution from an originally inhospitable mix of gases to the present reservoir of life-sustaining chemical compounds would make for a compelling chapter in a book mingling science with faith. The earth is truly a blessed planet.

Two bands of radiation known as the Van Allen Belts surround the earth. Most of the charged particles comprising their makeup originate from solar winds and are held in place by the magnetic field produced by Earth's revolving, liquid-iron core. This causes the particles to spin around our planet and not penetrate the atmosphere and bombard its surface. Even when solar winds are especially strong or a massive solar eruption occurs, the cloud of chilled, charged gas known as the plasmasphere, filling the upper regions of the atmosphere, acts as a boundary and scatters residual fast, highly charged electrons, preventing harm to the life below.

The interplay between plants and animals in what is called the "energy cycle" is another riveting component of the earth's strategic balancing system. The energy cycle is dependent upon photosynthesis, a process whereby green plants, algae, and certain bacteria use the sun's energy to transform CO2, water, and minerals into organic compounds and oxygen. In land plants, photosynthesis requires the green chemical chlorophyll, which absorbs light energy from the sun. Chlorophyll molecules are embedded in the membranes of chloroplasts, structures housed within a leaf's cells that store the energy and are the site of the photosynthetic reaction. Roots soak up most of the water necessary for photosynthesis from the soil. Along with some nutrients, it is transported up the trunk and through the stems by the xylem tissue. When the water reaches the leaves, the energy in the chloroplasts splits its molecules, taking in hydrogen, and it releases the oxygen into the air as a waste product through pores called stomata.

During photosynthesis, carbohydrate molecules are produced, mostly in the form of the sugar glucose that the plant uses for energy and growth. Some of the glucose is put in reserve as starch for use at night and during the cold winter months. Starchy foods, often termed complex carbohydrates, provide essential nutrients in the human diet.

When an animal consumes vegetation, the sugars within are transferred to its own energy storehouses called mitochondria, the source from which the animal draws for its survival. Carnivorous animals that don't consume plants indirectly ingest the sugars when eating their herbivorous prey. During respiration, some of the sugars are converted by the animal into CO2 and water, which are reused by plants with the aid of the sun's energy. Thus, photosynthesis provides the oxygen we breathe and is the source of our food supply.

If deciduous trees and perennial shrubs did not shed their leaves, winter's ice and snow would cause them serious harm. A distinct tier of cells known as the abscission layer is located at the base of each leaf. During the summer, the tubes transporting the nutrients and water to and from the leaves pass through this layer. In the autumn, the cells of the abscission layer swell and create a cork-like substance, eventually shutting off the flow between tree and leaf. The process is thought to occur primarily because of the diminishment of chlorophyll due to decreasing sunlight. Each leaf dies, becomes brittle at the stem, and falls off.

A legume is a plant that acquires atmospheric nitrogen through "nitrogen fixation." Nitrogen that has collected in pockets of air in the soil is converted for use by the plant by virtue of a symbiotic relationship with the soil bacteria known as rhizobia. The bacteria enter the plant roots and multiply, causing a swelling that produces a rounded knot or lump called a nodule. The nitrogen is "fixed" there by the bacteria and made usable by the plant. This relationship provides the plant with valuable nitrogenous compounds that enrich its photosynthetic capacity and growth. When the plant dies, the fixed nitrogen is released, fertilizing the soil and aiding other plants. The bacteria are provided shelter inside the nodules and benefit from micronutrients and carbon found within.

There are four stages in the life cycle of a butterfly. The third, the chrysalis stage, is miraculous and equals anything produced by science fiction. The chrysalis is a protective case of tough skin where the metamorphosis from caterpillar to butterfly occurs. Inside it, the caterpillar's body, eyes, and legs are dissolved into a thick liquid. Over about ten days, an adult butterfly is formed.

While on the subject of butterflies, let's return to the monarch. Scientists have determined that four generations of monarchs, the first three of which have about a month-long lifespan, rise and fall over the course of spring and

Lawrence K. Zeisler

summer. In the late summer or early autumn, the fourth generation that can live up to nine months emerges. They make the historic trek to Mexico. Unlike the earlier generations that reproduce in a couple of days, this last one won't begin mating until the following spring. In late summer, they emerge from the chrysalis in a condition known as diapause—a period of delayed maturity in which their reproductive organs remain in an immature state, probably in response to environmental indicators such as decreasing day length, fluctuating temperatures, and the poorer nutritional quality of deteriorating host milkweed plants.

Temperature increases and the availability of milkweed seem to be the main triggers signaling the end of diapause and the onset of sexual maturity the following spring. On the return trip north, most of the monarchs die (a small number probably make it all the way). Before perishing, they lay eggs on milkweed plants across the southern United States and northern Mexico, and the hatchlings complete the journey.

Scientists believe they have cracked the secrets of the monarch migration code: Studies reveal they possess an internal compass integrating the time of day with the sun's position that keeps them on a southern or southwest path, depending on the point of origin. The scientists assert that the light information is transmitted to the brain from the large compound eyes, and the "clock" located in the antennae reports its findings to the brain by way of a series of neurons. Another feature, referred to as the separation point, is thought to be a continually changing "line" in the monarch's visual field that it will not cross if an event causes it to veer off course. In this manner, the butterfly constantly corrects itself to maintain its direction.

A more abrupt turn might mean crossing the separation point. In the spring, the mechanics reverse the process so the compass points in a north or northeasterly direction. How can these and countless other natural revelations be described as anything but wondrous?

The writer Aldous Huxley stated something to the effect that each day is as the first and as full of untold wonder for anyone having the eyes to see it, but the eyes see best when the mind is not burdened with worry and anticipation that distracts one from present conditions. Wonder exists only in the here and now. One would find life much more novel and exciting if they could unchain themselves from time's constraints and face each moment with abandon. Is this feasible? For the most part, no, but just because one can never be a child again does not mean they must condemn their inner child to lifelong imprisonment. Wonder is all around us; it's all in the way you look and feel.

Two intimate communions with life:

"Ageless as the Wind"

As cold air on soft skin sends frigid shivers throughout me, I draw tight my scarf on this cold winter's night.

Skeletal branches, revealing jagged silhouettes, sway on swirling air tides.

A shooting star traces a fiery arc across the sky.

Shimmering ponds, rippling silvery oases brought to life by the moonbeams' touch, sparkle more precious than a freight load of gems.

Lawrence K. Zeisler

Austere hills, haunted by restless gusts, sing a lullaby as pure as a mother's song.

With the night's lusty scent hot on my heels, I run with the pack.

Warm vapors flow from laboring lungs as pumping legs race along timeworn trails.

Keeping pace with the wind, sudden heat, as flesh, blood and air embrace in joyful dance.

Spurred by firm lunar urgings and howling songs of footloose praise, my primitive core shakes free of rusted moorings.

Ecstatic shudders of passion surge like spring meltwater and I feel whole again and very clean.

I am one with the ages; I am one with myself.

The smell of wood burning in the air.

A roaring fire and cozy bed.

I will sleep well.

"Unwinding"

I slowly unwind to the rhythm of the spring frogs' tunes, soaked in the night's soothing caress.

Blanketed by joyous hymns of wordless praise, varied cares vanish, and a smile greets my face.

Succumbing to the mist's gentle enchantments, shamelessly exposing myself to soft wind-blown caresses, the evening's bounty lavishly presents itself, for God's dripping manna is everywhere, and I feast in blissful gluttony.

Touching, constant touching, nothing shy about this night.

Steeped in the air's fresh innocence, the spirited chorus sings in accompaniment to the throbbing of a reborn child's heart, and I squirm in a field of open love.

I cry to the stars, "Not tonight my fiery brethren, rest your eternal vigil, for the damp shrinks and engulfs my world."

No postures, no shields, no thought … just a feeling, and a gradual unwinding.

I stand at the crossroads; enfolded within the essence of the night,

I stand at the threshold of peace.

One fine May morning, my daughter asked if I believed in magic. I told her to step outside and peer around. The newborn sun boldly highlighted a rich mosaic of bark patterns on the tree trunks scattered throughout the woodland, in stark contrast to the shadows cast randomly about. The emerging leaves were on full display, dressed in a medley of fresh-faced pastel greens. Spring songbirds, in full-throated glory, proclaimed their resolute ardor. Life was renewing itself everywhere; all the magic in all the fairy tales ever written could not do justice to what was transpiring in the forest that day. I told her of the most magical moment of all: the morning she emerged from her mother's womb. Life is indeed more enchanting than fiction.

Wonder lies in the enigma of creation. Take the moon once again. We can inspect and dissect its properties but cannot uncover the mystery of its origin. That mystery touches all life and constantly eludes us. It humbles me, puts me in my place, and provides comfort, not fear.

Any philosopher worth their salt will concur that the best things in life are free. Nature's offerings apply here; sunshine, rain, and wind are examples, but there are countless less conspicuous ones. She possesses a subtle side often overlooked. It is not surprising that the young are more attuned to her gifts. A friend told me how as a youth, he spent periods lying on his back, transfixed by the movements and patterns of clouds, a pastime he no longer has time for. Once while visiting, a young man spent over a half hour closely observing and feeding a praying mantis. We laughed when we saw it gobble up some cake crumbs. Another friend related how his child once analyzed a ray of sunlight shining through the living room window for at least ten minutes.

I once watched two jumping spiders battling over an insect one had killed. They are referred to thusly because they do not lead sedentary lives, preferring to travel in search of prey and leaping upon it when found. They have large front legs and heads and appear athletic. I was mesmerized by their fighting technique, grappling like sumo wrestlers pushing and vying for position. This went on until one was able to push the other over the edge of the porch. The victor claimed the prize and dragged it into a crevice.

One misty October morning, I happened to look up into a hemlock tree and see an abandoned spider web among the branches. It was anchored at three spots, and two of the supports were nothing more than a single gossamer strand. As I watched it catching the wind like a ship's sail, it snapped in the middle, and the bottom half faded away. How many of these remarkably engineered little traps are constructed every day and night and then vanish without a trace?

Dragonflies are fascinating in flight. Their herky-jerky motion, so random and capricious to the eye, is anything but when chasing their prey; each movement appears to be in response to a winged quarry's dodges. In the waning days of summer, when an almost palpable stillness falls over the land, the insects rule the meadow while celebrating their last hurrah. Butterflies and swarms of bugs and their dragonfly pursuers perform an unbridled, airborne dance amid a throng of serenading, six-legged field vocalists.

As a storm was ebbing, I recall seeing a section of rainbow spanning the distance between two billowy cumulus clouds. It appeared as if alone, for the rest of the arch was concealed. Who knows, perhaps it was a "mini bow."

I'm fascinated by the way the windblown tree canopy rolls like ocean waves when seen in panoramic view on a mountainside. On rare occasions, following a freshly fallen snowstorm, if my pupils can withstand the January sun's assault, I notice how the cold's frigid fingers have left their icy prints upon the tree limbs. Framed by a sky of the clearest shade of wintry blue, the shimmering spectacle is a testimonial to the season's majesty. The day after one such instance, I stood before a stand of white pine and watched the topmost snowbound boughs releasing their fluffy burden. During the descent, the wind scattered the flakes into a fine mist, exciting the sunbeams filtering through the branches. With every facial pore refreshed by the frosty air's cleansing touch, the sheer beauty held me captive for some time.

The degree to which nature reveals herself depends upon the amount of attention she receives. An alert eye will be rewarded more than a distant one and a gracious heart more

Lawrence K. Zeisler

than one tarnished by indifference. As Confucius succinctly said, "Everything has beauty, but not everyone sees it."

Human interactions are rewarding too. What is more basic and free than the feeling you get when a good friend or acquaintance puts a warm hand upon your shoulder? What is more wondrous to behold than a child's expression of joy while engaged in play?

I see a striking similarity between a baby's purity and nature's. Each is unmarred by the ego. Neither one is judgmental; we can relax and be ourselves around them, unhampered by the inhibitions so often displayed in public. The gaiety of a tree's leaves set aflutter by a touch of wind reminds me of a child's gleeful laughter. Have you noticed how few harsh thoughts are entertained when in an innocent's presence or while sitting by a stream?

Prescription for Peace

I have discovered a tonic that can work wonders for a distressed soul. What I prescribe is not chemical or a psychological inquisition. Just give me a day or even half of one. It's best you come alone and try to leave responsibilities behind.

When was the last time you felt peace? Was it while lying in your mate's arms? If so, I can appreciate that. Perhaps it was when you were absorbed in activity with loved ones or earnestly thinking about God. I would like to show you a different type of serenity, a profound tranquility. We will journey to your core and, if all goes well, liberate fragrant, little-known sensations.

You think I speak in riddles and sense a flimflam in progress. I assure you that no wagonload of elixirs, containing cures for whatever ails you, waits around the bend. Leave your wallet and watch here. Hop in the car, and let's go.

I realize we have been driving awhile, but we are searching for a special setting free of outside interference. Stop here—this is perfect. Let's walk a short distance. Sit by this stream. Lean back and unwind. Don't tense. Relax. There is no reason to fear. Drown your thoughts in the soothing rhythm and chitchat of the frolicking waters. Allow their buoyancy to bathe your every pore. Forget everything; nothing else exists. Let the outside world become a forgotten memory. It takes time to let go, for pressures engulf you and are reluctant to release their vise-like grip. Dispense with concerns about washing the car or mowing the lawn. This is your personal pleasure excursion.

There—are you starting to notice? The spirited water nymphs begin to chip away at the tension. Can you feel the curative process taking hold? Be brave, and let the mind roam. Do you recall the man on the phone the other day? I know the questions in his survey were boring, but you were a mite harsh. After all, he was only doing his job.

You exploded at little Tommy. When you chased him up the stairs to spank him, it was hilarious when you removed the belt and your pants dropped. He can't be blamed for laughing. Instead of increasing your fury, wouldn't it have been better to share the humor?

Last week, when the quarterback threw that interception, you were ready to kill. I know he is paid handsomely not to err, but he is only human.

Look at the tiny chickadee. You like its bravery, its nearness. Its call is interesting; it sounds like its name. Watch how it performs acrobatics as it flits about. You think it strange to enjoy a bird's company, but there's no need to be self-conscious.

I see you are watching the swarm of insects hovering low above the water. Wow! Did you see that swallow strafe the surface? Look, there's another. It nabbed a drink without missing a wing beat. They and their nighttime counterparts, the bats, perform an immense service by consuming countless insects each day and evening, many of them pests. A nursing mother bat can eat as many as forty-five hundred a night.

Observe the strength and quiet calm of the trees. Silence is golden, is it not? You've never seen moss so closely, have you? Isn't it lovely how it carpets the stones and roots? Doesn't it complement the delicate ferns growing all about? Go ahead—touch its velvety softness. Do you smell the clean dampness of the forest floor? Breathe deep; let it clear your nasal passages. Yes, I agree the rising mist conjures images of medieval enchantment. There was a slight chill in that breeze. By your smile, I can tell it was bracing and invigorating.

Your pulse rate now flows with the stream. I have never seen such an easy look on your face and detect nary a trace of stress. You are beyond the confines of thought. Ah, you feel the tingle deep inside, immersing you in shivers of warmth that signify a strange familiarity. Does it promote a sense of belonging as if you rock once again in your mother's womb, in harmony with the world in which you dwell? Funny how it binds yet liberates, holding you in chains of intoxicating servitude.

Do you feel sinful somehow as if you seduce yourself and cheerfully remain unrepentant? For the first time, do you sense a fellowship with life and your true place within? Clutch this sensation to your bosom. You are grasping your birthright, your roots. Dance with it; sway in its essence.

Don't hold back. It's harmless. This experience is new only because you have never found the time or felt the freedom to release your resistance to it.

You twitch and sit up with a start. You've never felt so alert yet soothed, have you? The insights you have uncovered will make it easier to tolerate yourself and others. The relaxing backdrop required for the discovery of inner peace is one of nature's greatest gifts.

I can feel the intimacy you've gained for this stream and woods. Maybe you won't feel quite like the stranger that you once were. Next time we will bring little Tommy.

When there is no division between the mind and its experience, when one's intellect is firmly in the present, free of judgment and seeking no conclusion, one's regard for life is enhanced. Notice how once our woodland friend was no longer bothered by concerns, natural things were seen that had never been witnessed. Wasn't it obvious that everything was interconnected and harmonious? Thoughts were perceived more clearly and in a more compassionate light. When acting alone, with no interruption from the ego, the truth is a source of instant awareness, clarifying one's vision and unveiling each moment's hidden reality.

A profound feeling—not to be confused with individual emotions—links one directly to the spiritual more so than a response to a contrived thought or desire. Such thoughts demand that you restrict your attention, which causes distraction, whereas a feeling abandons itself to the moment's spectrum, simultaneously indulging one in all its sensations without reservation. It brings the outside in, linking it with one's heart and soul. This state is personal, being both immediate and tactile. A heartfelt feeling receives God's warmest touch.

Lawrence K. Zeisler

Although thoughts, even those of a reverential or compassionate nature, cannot match the depth of feeling described, they can help set the table, like the empathetic ones that were awakened while lying beside the stream. But the moment's full dimensions were not felt until the mind was hushed. Perhaps this is because all thought takes place in time, while a feeling is pervasive or timeless. There is always a distance between the thinker (subject) and the thought (object). Something that defies description is lost in that infinitesimal distance or span, something wondrous, nonjudgmental, and ever present that touches us all. Eastern thought calls this indescribable presence the Tao. It has been referred to in this book as the Truth.

Appreciation of fundamental, life-sustaining things tends to instill in one a more sensible approach to worth. When it is thoroughly understood that a drop of water is beyond value, it is easier to determine true importance. Using what is precious as a yardstick, one realizes they can do with less, for they see they have so much already. This puts things in clearer focus, enabling them to differentiate the necessary from the unnecessary. With the truth in evidence, the vast carnival act of products loses much of its luster.

Traditional peoples are immersed in nature's freely given gifts. Anthropologists have noted childlike qualities in tribal cultures that still live in their natural states. This is due in part to the fact that they, like young children, are absorbed in the present. They are aware of the need to provide for the future, but do not dwell on it. Their living standard requires little more than the basics—food, shelter and clothing—and is not responsive to the whims of a profit-hungry economy. They don't have to consume themselves with concerns about employment, the political climate, crime, insurance premiums, tax payments, bills or lawsuits. Stress, which is epidemic in our culture and not theirs, is added proof of our overburdened lifestyle. Eight in ten US adults confess to feeling stress on a daily basis, and 44 percent declare that their levels have risen over the past five years. There is something to be said for simplicity.

Those espousing that a less complicated, simpler existence shares space with discomfort and monotony have no conception of what life beneath the open sky offers. When we want to know the weather, we flick on the iPhone or television and are given the temperature, wind direction, and a detailed analysis of what to expect from the upcoming week. When conditions outside are uninviting, we are happy to be inside, and when they are pleasant, it is often not possible to enjoy them. Contrast this with North America's free-roaming Native Americans who studied shifts in the wind and observed animal behavior to aid them in determining the impending weather. They were much better acclimated to temperature changes and appreciated climatic nuances: the sun's warmth on a cold, biting day, a pocket of cool air on a hot summer night, the bracing encounter between skin and moist air following a rain shower, and the option to savor the perfect quiet of almost any given moment.

Affinity with the natural world enabled the Native Americans to endure times of privation; sacrifice and physical hardship weren't as distasteful to them as they are to us. They believed some of both made one stronger and wiser.

To further my point, I will retell an experience that the Sioux medicine man Lame Deer underwent in his youth. At sixteen, he was left alone in a hole dug into the side of a hill, called a vision pit, for four days and nights without food or water. The trial was his initiation into manhood, and though it may seem offensive to you, he emerged with a new, more stable identity. While in the pit, he gained strength from gifts presented to him by loved ones and friends. Foremost among them was a gourd containing forty pieces of flesh his grandmother had cut from her arm, her purpose being to give part of herself to him in his time of need.

This portrayal squares with accounts by early explorers writing of Northwest Coast Native Americans walking barefoot in the snow without discomfort. Tribal peoples participated in early-morning swims in icy waters to toughen themselves. The Native Americans' hardiness served them well during the long trading expeditions some of the tribes endured. The Hopewell peoples, who lived in parts of present-day Illinois, Indiana, and Ohio, procured obsidian for their artisans from the Yellowstone Park region of Wyoming. Copper for embossed breastplates, ritual weapons, and ornaments was obtained from the northern Great Lakes area.

Long before the time of Christ, the peoples of eastern North America constructed mounds of various sizes and shapes. Some contained tombs, and others served as foundations for temples. The oldest, located in the Southeast, are around four thousand years old. Made of saltwater shells, the largest measure hundreds of feet across. Archeologists have found the first evidence of pottery on the continent inside them; it is composed of clay and plant fibers, and some pieces exhibit unusual geometric patterns.

The only other place similar shell mounds and pots have been found together is the Caribbean coast of Columbia. There is a distinct possibility the more advanced populations of Columbia made far-flung coastal voyages to what are now Georgia and South Carolina, leaving cultural elements in their wake.

Assuming the existence of the voyages, after the ritual celebrations and sad farewells, think of the air of anticipation that must have overwhelmed the Columbian Indians as they prepared to embark on the expedition northward. We can only imagine the wonders they encountered: whale, dolphin, and manatee sightings, countless flocks of gaily plumed shore birds, awe-inspiring sunsets and sunrises, steamy days spent under the blazing sun, and only slightly less sweltering nights camped under stars so numerous they threatened to engulf the darkness, all the while fishing and hunting when necessary.

Such an excursion would not be without its share of danger, but the wanderers were set to face whatever they met. Their bodies and minds must have been honed to a sharp edge, their senses quickened by exposure. Equipped as they were, I doubt they feared danger's imminence and most likely welcoming it at times. Danger has a way of testing one's mettle, and its inherent excitement would have interrupted the tedium that accompanies a long voyage.

Officials of the government of India and anthropologists feel that groups of indigenous tribes clinging to their Paleolithic lifestyles on islands in the region escaped one of the tsunamis triggered by the 2004 Indian Ocean earthquake because of their knowledge of natural phenomena. It is believed they possess a sixth sense, lost by modern people, that allows them to smell the wind, discern its and the sea's movements, and gauge the depth of the water by the sound of their boat oars.

There is nothing like being there. Familiarity with nature's ceaseless rhythms and cycles engenders a kinship with the eternal scheme that can be comforting. Fruit growing on the vine and geese flying under a full moon's light are examples. Many generations will come and go, but the

Lawrence K. Zeisler

geese will continue to migrate, and the grapes will ripen.

The poet Robert Browning wrote, "I trust in nature for the stable laws of beauty and utility. Spring shall plant and autumn garner to the end of time."

There is another noteworthy factor in the equation. Native Americans did not distinguish the natural from the supernatural, viewing them as unified, a broad kinship network. While interwoven into the framework of the universe, the Great Spirit or Great Mystery was enmeshed in the material world or immanent. They found their spiritual nourishment on earth, recognizing a sacred element or presence in everyday phenomena.

The spiritual could reveal itself in a multitude of ways. Sometimes spirits communicated through an animal or a lifeless natural object. Many warriors of the plains tribes carried medicine bundles containing sacred objects like feathers, skin, claws, fur, or other animal material through which the divine force spoke to them during fasting and prayer. The belief was that its presence might always be near, especially during battle.

Direct contact suggests a personal and spontaneous relationship with the Creator. Their church was much larger than ours. Intertwining the divine with the physical facilitates one's reverence. Some of the more aware Christians, like Thomas Merton, felt God's universal presence.

The only true joy on earth is to escape from the prison of our own false self, and enter by love into union with the Life Who dwells and sings within the essence of every creature and in the core of our own souls. In His love we possess all things and enjoy fruition of them, finding Him in them all. And thus we go about the world, everything we meet and everything we see and hear and touch, far from defiling, purifies us and plants in us something more of contemplation and of heaven.[1]

The world is wondrous to one imbued with the possibility of encountering the sacred anywhere, anytime. The corresponding sense of gratitude, in conjunction with basic survival requirements, explains why those untouched by civilization are conservative with resources. There is little room for waste in nature, and the same holds true for those whose lives revolve around her.

It's tempting to discount the Native American spirits and rituals as hocus pocus. The primary purpose of any cosmology is to sustain cultural equilibrium, and many of their rituals and ceremonies helped to support it by providing the means to overcome the challenges of life and bring partakers into harmony with themselves, the people, and the environment. For example, the Nootka Indians of the North Pacific Coast underwent rigorous rituals before embarking on whale hunts. If the hunt ended in failure, they assumed it was because someone had not conformed to the ceremonial customs. The foundation of a strong esprit de corps rested on the cooperation of the participants. Ritualistic preparations were a way of achieving camaraderie by putting everyone "on the same page." Teamwork was a key to success. Celebrating events like marriage, puberty, and death served to further tribal bonds.

Time proved the durability of Native American beliefs. Will it be as kind to ours? Are spirits in trees any more fantastic than a bearded monarch sitting on a heavenly throne?

This is not meant to be an indictment of civilized living.

Nor is it a proposal to adopt a ritualistic lifestyle revolving around nature. In truth, a couple of qualifications need to be injected to counter the pitfalls associated with an overly romantic presentation. Life for Native Americans could be harsh and short. Although securing the larder was especially easy in regions where the climate was good and the land abundant—the Haida tribes of the Pacific Northwest would say, "When the tide is out, the table is set"—in the less fertile parts of the country, winter presented special problems. If spring arrived late, depleted stores of grains and meat signaled suffering and even death to the weak and infirmed. Mirroring the natural way meant territorial competition was always a possibility. Tribal conflicts were not uncommon, and each tribe harbored its own array of spirits, some of which would not only consent to warfare when the time arose but could assist those participating in the struggle. Torturing captives was practiced by some nations.

It is pointless to proceed with further criticism. Doing so would distract from the chapter's intent, which is the belief that our worldview needs refinement. The ability to assimilate the positive and weed out the negative is instrumental to proper growth. Being mindful of the instructional qualities in discussion assists in its effort to clarify how reverence for and appreciation of the natural world produces worthwhile effects. Today, more than ever, said mindset is vital and would be a positive complement to our living standard.

Chapter 8

*"Ye people, why do you seek without for
the blessing that is within you."*

—Boethius

I t is time to examine the meaning of humility. In the
Christian realm, true humility constitutes a total submission of the self to God, but how can worshipers fully
deny themselves while concurrently longing for heaven?
How can they abandon themselves to God if their prime
reason for doing so is to possess him? How can they find
consolation for long while simultaneously yearning for its
future blossoming? Giving oneself to God and grabbing at
him are contradictory acts.

Jesus's doctrine, preaching the virtues of compassion,
forgiveness, humility and self-denial, is inspirational. Issue is
taken, however, with the inordinate stress put upon the literal
interpretation of the miraculous events in his life, specifically
the resurrection and its associated heavenly pursuit.

The physical resurrection is not being unequivocally
ruled out, for it is felt here that anything is possible under
or above the sun, but when a heavenly goal becomes paramount, when it becomes the critical cog in one's faith, it is
difficult to differentiate between a selfless love of God and
a selfish desire for immortality.

Lawrence K. Zeisler

The medieval mystic and theologian Meister Eckhart wrote:

We ought to learn through God's gifts to get away from selfishness, to care no more for what we have a right to, to seek nothing for our own, neither instrument, pleasure, spirituality, delight, reward, the Kingdom of Heaven, nor that our wills be done. God never gave himself, nor will he ever, to one whose will is alien to his own.[1]

Please reread the last line of the quote and take note of the word *alien*. Can we agree that it connotes distance, one created by the litany of desires Meister Eckhart spoke of? Whenever one views God and heaven as "other," the ego takes the form of the subjective *I*, which means that it is the source of one's thoughts and actions. The longing for God and heaven is at heart egocentric and presupposes a lack of continuity between one's present state of consciousness and the divine.

Now you may say, "But it is the desire for God that keeps me humble. If I lost that desire and thought I was like him, my arrogance would be complete." You are not being asked to think of him as physically inhabiting a place inside or to liken yourself to him. It is the understanding that the divine is the foundation of awareness, that love and truth are at the source of all action and thought, no matter how unlikely it may seem. His universal property is also recognized, regarding him as the identity binding all natural phenomena. Such appreciation, far from condoning arrogance, is the font of humility; esteem for all creation in conjunction with a belief in one's and humanity's intrinsic goodness hinders the ego's penchant for self-importance and materialism.

To further this point, I present successive quotes. The first, substantiating the claim of the sense of God's otherness, is by Alan Watts. The second depicts the poet Walt Whitman's feeling for God's universal presence.

> *Despite the fact that the realm of spiritual experience is so often described in Christianity as the interior life, and that the unanimous testimony of mystical and metaphysical tradition in every part of the world is that "the Beyond is within", that God is to be found in the deepest and innermost reaches of consciousness, our religion is so largely "extroverted" that the way of realization as we have described it must necessarily seem strange. In general, the religious mind looks up to God and devotes itself to him as the object of human life, with the feeling that the divine being and the innermost depths of man's consciousness are discontinuous.*[2]

> *I believe a leaf of grass is no less than the*
> *journey-work of the stars,*
> *And the pismire is equally perfect, and a grain of*
> *sand, and the egg of the wren,*
> *And the tree-toad is a chef-d'oeuvre for the highest,*
> *And the running blackberry would adorn the*
> *parlors of heaven,*
> *And the narrowest hinge in my hand puts to scorn*
> *all machinery,*

Lawrence K. Zeisler

And the cow crunching with depress'd head
surpasses any statue,
And a mouse is miracle enough to stagger
sextillions of infidels.[3]

The more I read the words of the medieval masters, I am struck by the stress they put on the potential for experiencing the divine within, which the Holy Spirit represents, and the joy its realization elicits. This realization can't be deeply felt unless the proper preparations have been made, ones that revolve around the central act of turning from the ways of men and ardently devoting oneself to Christ. To achieve effective results, said devotion should be ongoing and practiced with increasing dedication. One must be willing to pattern themselves after Jesus, to endure privation and suffering in his name, and to bear insult and loss of numerous possessions. Remember, he reminded us not to lay up treasures on earth and that one cannot serve God and mammon (money or material wealth). The assortment of well-heeled televangelists bow to both, shamelessly exploiting the first to acquire the second. It was he who said, "It is easier for a camel to go through the eye of a needle than for a rich man to enter the kingdom of God."[4]

Our society is living proof of how remote we have become from authentic scriptural practices. Today's religious, who are by no means immune to the wealth of societal temptations, face a greater uphill battle than did their medieval counterparts. In fact, the medieval masters would find many of the indulgences that we take for granted to be serious roadblocks on the path to Christ. I find it difficult to conceive that the *essence* of their doctrines would be relevant to any but a handful of those enjoying the fruits of contemporary living.

As intimated, the Holy Spirit likes an environment free of clutter. Our lives are replete with mental and material excess. Jesus lived a life of sacrifice, while we scarcely comprehend what it means to be genuinely sacrificial. The immense majority of present-day converts haven't sacrificed or endured nearly enough to entertain a clue as to the true breadth of divine, inner peace.

Another fact catches my attention about the old writings. Especially when viewed in contrast to today's evangelical rhetoric, less emphasis is put on heavenly reward when contemplating the merits of the holy life. This does not strike me as strange since spiritual desire and hope, more than earnest experience and introspection, accommodate a culture like ours that is immersed in material pleasures and averse to deep thinking.

Using Jesus's final sacrifice, whereby he forgave our sins, as assurance of a believer's personal redemption makes it easier to skirt the hard issues, removing much of the burden of proof regarding the validity of one's spiritual commitment. Putting undue weight on it encourages circumvention of the dedication necessary for feeling Jesus's present comfort. The oft-recited declaration that one has found Jesus would no doubt strike the old masters as the highest form of impudence. One doesn't find Jesus; they can only condition themselves and humbly wait. Some feel that stating that they have and making token efforts at virtue guarantees them safe passage to heaven. They are representative of this age of "instant gratification," eternally speaking. Anyone can talk the talk; not many walk the walk. If I were a mite brasher, I would state that many of these folks appreciate what Jesus can do for them more than Jesus himself. Oh, I did say it, didn't I?

The ego dreams that its will be done in heaven as it is on earth. Heaven's scent is a strong lure, and the hypocrisy of these self-righteous persons rests upon the assumption that their prayers for virtue have been answered. They will abstain from overt temptations such as drinking alcohol and smoking cigarettes, protest abortion, attend church on a regular basis, pledge themselves to virtuous precepts, and claim the role of model citizen. Then they swear it is only a matter of time before Saint Peter rolls out the red carpet, all the while neglecting deeper moral weaknesses. This hypocrisy betrays an imagined faith in God and defines the difference between the truly faithful and those who believe themselves so. When entertained in this manner, Christianity can indeed be termed the "opiate of the masses." Knowing this, I was not shocked when a doctor of theology told me, barring the blatant criminal element, that he sees the Christian virtues more often displayed by the secular community than by hard-core religious conservatives. On a more light-hearted note, this idea of self-righteousness inspired a character's description of a female associate in the movie *Paint Your Wagon*: "There is nothing more ruthless than a respectable woman."

The last laugh is on those who leapfrog sincere spiritual commitment, for the fear of death, which is at the root of one's immortal quest, may go out of sight but not out of mind. Herein lies the crux of the guaranteed salvation problem as I see it. Just because one asserts they have found Jesus and, by implication, will physically meet him in the future does not mean the subconscious agrees. The ego can convince the conscious that a state of grace is inevitable or, in the more deluded that it is present, but its flatteries vaporize at the gates that open to the truth. Do these adherents know deep within that they don't pass muster? I believe so. The inability to live up to what is expected of them by their religion plays on their mortal fears.

Many of their number, having convinced themselves of absolute faith, will deny the fear exists and discount the part it plays in their search for the everlasting, but must a pious person's faith be contingent upon an immortal guarantee? More crudely put, is it contingent upon striking a deal with God? Doesn't this show a lack of trust in God's entire plan? Should they not be content to unconditionally lay their fate at the master's feet? Only a fraction of those striving for immortality realize that the grandest illusion is that anyone has the right to *expect* perfection or complete goodness in this or any other life. Such an illusion defiles the spirit of humility.

Sugarcoating the dread of death with heavenly visions does not make the fear go away. The precarious tightrope to immortality is stretched out above a bottomless abyss in which the idea of death lurks—a rope slipped off frequently but one the true believers quickly levitate themselves back onto by means of promises of divine forgiveness and false, ego-made assurances. They stake a claim in the hereafter and assure themselves of a victory over their darkest fear. Talk about the easy way out.

More Americans confess to a belief in heaven than in hell. Those who do believe in hell (roughly 58 percent) vary in their interpretations, which range from its being a metaphor connoting conscious suffering and isolation stemming from personal evil and detachment from God or an eternal separation from God because of choices

Lawrence K. Zeisler

made by unrepentant individuals during their lifetimes to its existence as a material place of everlasting torment. In recent years, numerous Christians have chosen to adopt less chilling versions of hell, expressing that a loving God would not condone an agonizing afterlife. Most evangelicals, on the other hand, hold to the heinous interpretation with all the attendant unease that goes with it.

The road to immortality is littered with potholes. For all of his kindness, Jesus was a strict disciplinarian, laying out a rigid set of rules to follow that change character when subjected to the glare of the eternal spotlight. Can those claiming rebirth honestly profess to be leading a life in accordance with those rules? Can they come close? This quote by Jesus disqualifies many aspirants.

> Not everyone who says to me, "Lord, Lord," shall enter the kingdom of heaven, but he who does the will of my father who is in heaven. On that day many will say to me, "Lord, Lord, did we not prophesy in your name, and cast out demons in your name, and do many mighty works in your name?" And then will I declare to them, "I never knew you; depart from me, you evildoers."[5]

In the parable of the rich young man, found in three of the Gospels, Jesus states that to achieve eternal life, the questioner should sell his possessions, give to the poor, and follow him. The pursuit of wealth and its dispensation are personal matters, but it is apparent that most members of the evangelical community, who claim to ride on divine coattails, do not favor the redistribution of wealth for the betterment of society in general. They choose to put their political clout behind the party that advocates that money stay sequestered in the individual's pocket, safely out of reach of income-sharing government programs.

Do you think Jesus harped on the virtues of sacrifice and self-denial just to hear himself talk? He realized that they were key to the ego's exorcism. He knew it and its fears run deep and that the false comforts (which are the source of its pride) it builds over the course of one's life had to be dismantled before God's can be freely felt. Those hypocritical false comforts are based in thought. Sacrifice and self-denial are the antithesis of the ego, because they force one to confront its thoughts and any actions they promote head-on. The pain produced is a direct consequence of exposing the selfishness and fear inherent in egocentric consolation, which finds expression in the spiritual facade evangelicals cling to. Personal growth lies in understanding and acting upon that pain.

It is not intimated that those who worship an objective God cannot grow in self-understanding, the foundation of all love. To the degree one is sincere, the search for God aids self-awareness. By using Christ as a role model and sounding board, the diligent questers of contentment will overcome many of the prejudices and deceptions that keep them in the dark about themselves. As a source of advice and direction the search is of genuine value, witness the large number of good Christians who practice virtue in varying degrees, quietly. The more committed among them most likely would not identify personal salvation as the key reason for their virtuous effort. For one experiencing true spiritual awakening immortality is not a factor, for their love, emanating from within, supersedes dogma and desire. When this union is felt, one no longer needs Christ

Lawrence K. Zeisler

as a reference, for God is not perceived as being separate.

Dignity is abundant in those who weather the rigorous challenges innate to a life of austerity and self-contemplation and who have assiduously cultivated the inner garden from which godlike beauty sprouts. The divine comfort that is the essence of this truth does not come cheaply. Hope and belief alone do not provide the nourishment required of its flowering. For the Christian, self-abasement and contrition of heart do.

The ego's self-love was more than the medieval Roman Catholic Church could contend with despite centuries of near-universal power. It was unable to convince the penitent masses that God's divine grace would cleanse their souls and grant salvation. The evil within was too much to surmount. Try as they may, individuals could not rid themselves of the guilt that inevitably resurfaced upon exhausting good-intentioned efforts. Isolation and insecurity were the results.

The Church's fall from grace at the end of the Middle Ages, a consequence of its own greed-inspired corruption, compounded the problem and paved the way for the schism known as the Protestant Reformation. Martin Luther and subsequent reformers were angered by administration and organizational abuses resulting from an overall decline in the clergy's morals. Their indulgent, luxurious lifestyles were incompatible with the principles of simplicity and piety that they preached. How could it help the populace surmount the stain imposed upon their souls by Adam's misconduct with its own "evils" bared before the day's harsh light?

Always reluctant to relinquish power, the Catholic Church engaged the upstart Protestants in the deadliest European religious war in history known as the Thirty Years'

War. This complex and multifaceted event intermingled with the rash of inquisitions the Church conducted in the medieval period and beyond to stamp out heretical movements. Many whose biblical interpretations differed from the Church's paid a steep price. Thankfully, time, scrutiny, and soul-searching have captured some of the impulses centuries of Christian belief could not, but the self-righteous element precipitating much of the violence still flourishes in the minds of numerous modern worshippers, including members of the clergy, giving rise to hypocrisy and vice.

One of the ways the Protestants, especially the Calvinists, dealt with the psychological void left in the wake of the departure from the Catholic Church—with its guarantee of salvation to those submissive to clerical authority—was to teach a doctrine of double predestination. It stressed that God had chosen in advance which believers would be saved and which were slated for damnation. The inability to exercise sway over one's salvation presented an obvious problem. It became incumbent upon individuals to convince themselves that they were worthy of being chosen. Confidence in oneself was crucial to achieving a heavenly future.

A means to that end was the official establishment of one's occupation or trade as a calling from God. Luther believed that a person could serve God through their work but that they should not pursue wealth for its own sake. The Calvinists went a step further by stating that the pursuit of profit was morally permissible and that success and worldly achievement were indicative of a saved soul. The needle's eye swelled to camel-sized proportions.

This revolutionary Protestant ethic complemented the changing economic structure of the time. Centralized governments, the growth of commerce, expanded trade, and the rise of a new middle class of businessmen and merchants all reflected a system whose lifeblood was hard work. There is disagreement over whether these societal and economic conditions strongly influenced the Protestant reformers and debate as to what extent the conditions were an outgrowth of the new theological tenets. In the end, both combined to form the supports of an emerging capitalist structure that stressed traits such as diligence, ambition, self-discipline, and thrift.

Considering today's realities, it's difficult to imagine that in its original form the Protestant ethic shunned material acquisition, dictating that men were to reinvest profits in their businesses, which gave a boost to the capitalist economy. It appears that unrepentant materialism didn't arise in our country until the Industrial Revolution made it possible to flood the market with accessible goods, and with religious disciplines giving way to a strong secular attitude that took much of the guilt out of buying; manifested in today's involuntary capitulation to mechanized industry and its plethora of products. A reality most modern Christians embrace as religiously as their secular brethren.

I'm amazed at the extent of tragedy following the bite of an apple. When the Bible affixed partial blame for humanity's fall from grace on a devious tempter, often regarded as the source of evil known as the devil, it marred the fruit of that bite with a dark brand. Suffering, sorrow, and death were born, and the earth was cursed (a curse God later renounced). In the beginning Adam and Eve lived in harmony with nature, free of temptation and torment.

It's sometimes hard to determine where God's influence ends and Satan's begins. If death and pain were ushered into our lives with the devil's coaxing, was not God the one who made them manifest? After all, he is life's prime mover. Phrases like "acts of God" and "it was God's will" hint at this, but unless Satan is shed and God made unequivocally responsible for life in its entirety, one more obstacle to improving our dubious relationship with its "dark" elements will remain intact.

You may be asking yourself what the devil Satan has to do with your distaste for discomfort and death. Isn't it natural to want to live one's life as long and comfortably as possible? Maybe so, but our obsessive aversion to pain, suffering and death if not unnatural borders on it. If the concept of absolute evil symbolized by the devil had never been spawned, Christianity would more closely resemble most of the world's other religions and traditions. Their adherents are not plagued with the idea of eternal damnation and better accept the natural cycle of life and death. When Satan subverts God's will and wrests control, he muddles reality and frightens and confuses the unaware, causing them to shade a good portion of life with an unjust quality. One must wonder if he's more trouble than he's worth.

The declaration that man is inherently evil does nothing to alleviate the problem. We put such a premium on morality because it is the first line of defense against the evil within and without, but the pursuit of rightness is a check at best, for this deep-rooted evil constantly threatens life's joy. Like an invidious pall, it hovers about, provoking errant behavior and delighting in any ensuing guilt.

Many try to run but cannot hide from their inner evil. Those fleeing themselves are in a real predicament; like a dog chasing its tail, the pursuit goes round and round. Not

Lawrence K. Zeisler

even performing good acts can halt the dizzying spiral for long. No wonder they dream of a paradise where they can rest their weary souls.

I understand why some individuals want to take their minds off the chase by leveling blame at the godless world. They don't realize that Satan is getting the last laugh, for his goal is to foment disharmony. They play right into his hands when they judge themselves better and try to force their will upon others. I find it amusing, in a cynical way, how these self-professed moralists point their fingers at the "evils" outside themselves. This often transpires while shutting the door, or at best leaving it open a crack, on their own sinful emotions.

Christ deals with the judgment of hypocrites when he states the following:

> *Judge not, that you be not judged. For with the judgment you pronounce you will be judged, and the measure you give will be the measure you get. Why do you see the speck that is in your brother's eye, but do not notice the log that is in your own eye?*[26]

Thomas à Kempis reaches across the centuries to address today's evangelical activists:

> *The spiritual man puts the care of his soul before all else; and whoever diligently attends to his own affairs is ready to keep silence about others. You will never become interior and devout unless you refrain from criticism of others, and pay attention to yourself. If you are wholly intent on God and yourself, you will be little affected by anything outside this.*

Where are you when you fail to attend to yourself?
And when you have occupied yourself in countless
affairs, what have you gained, if you have neglected
your soul? If you really desire true peace and union
with God, attend to yourself, and set aside all else.[7]

Christian extremists validate their actions because they feel society is sliding into a faithless abyss. Though I cannot totally disagree, I take issue with a number of their methods and priorities. Societal conditions cannot erase the truth inherent in the above quotations. Good intentions notwithstanding, their efforts condemn them to a shallow level of faith.

The devil must be evicted. He has been used as a scapegoat all along. I don't think he ever made me, or anyone else, "do it." He's been the ego's foil, taking the hit for the role it plays in promoting vice. Ignorance, not evil (evil is too closely allied with hate), directs our greed and envy. Ignorance keeps the religious and nonreligious isolated from and uninformed of the inner love that unites us with all life. We are all part of something bigger than ourselves—a grand, bold world full of beauty and danger, joy and sadness, light and darkness, pain and pleasure, life and death. And it works.

Removing the evil from the temptations renders them more palatable. Doing so makes it less difficult to view life and death with an open mind. Under this scenario, one is more likely to accept their faults and hold themselves accountable without fear, making it easier to note the part they play in the discord that keeps us off balance and out of sync with things. Pride, arrogance, greed, and vanity are all at work when we thumb our noses at the earth and its peoples by declining to alter our selfish, extravagant ways.

Lawrence K. Zeisler

Though issue is taken with certain aspects of the Christian religion, please don't view this as a recrimination of God. The ineffable, universal Truth is beyond reproach. Nor is this a wholesale refutation of Christianity. As illustrated, a high regard has been and will continue to be extended to those who pay homage to the esoteric doctrines at its heart. These doctrines transcend what are considered here unsettling distractions—the devil, cheap and ill-gotten spirituality, and immortality's quest—that interfere with the inner pathway to peace and love. Exception is taken with the idea of God as some master playwright, studiously scripting our individual destinies. From this point of view, such a scenario is absurd at best, horrific at worst, and extremely self-centered. Imagine the creator of reality as we know it taking the time to watch little old me. It is believed here that he, she, it, or they—or, better yet, ?—put the game in play but is not keeping score.

William Anders of the Apollo 8 mission took the famous Earthrise photograph on December 24, 1968. In an interview commemorating the fiftieth anniversary of the event, he declared how the image fractured his religious convictions: "It really undercut my religious beliefs. The idea that things rotate around the pope and up there is a big supercomputer wondering whether Billy was a good boy yesterday? It doesn't make any sense."

Conventional Christians will cite that omitting heaven from the equation is a recipe for hopelessness. Heaven is not seen here as an impossibility, just not an expectation. They will posit that its perceived existence makes the loss of a loved one more bearable, but is faith based on a presumed promise any more concrete or comforting than one that is not? One has no need of that promise if their appreciation of life is well grounded. Moreover, holding a puppet master God accountable for a loss can be disturbing and severely strain the limits of one's faith. For a couple close to my wife and I, heaven's incentive could not support the weight of their two-year-old child's death. Church no longer provides refuge.

Love connects, and fear divides. The barriers must come down and the "well of goodness" exposed as our true center and source of light and strength. Love sees the relationship between things and acknowledges this undeniable truth. Each of us has it within to grasp this. We all have the strength to deal with pain, tragedy, and suffering, but our strength cannot be felt so long as we feel wronged by hardship. One will not realize their potential until they are able to accept whatever befalls them. Even death should not get in the way. Personal loss is never easy, and the anguish it elicits is painful, but there is comfort in knowing that death has a critical place in a system whose purpose is life: diverse, plentiful, and in balance.

Meister Eckhart speaks of the good that overcomes the effects of pain and suffering:

> *The first is that there is no hardship without some comfort; there is no loss that is pure loss. Accordingly, St. Paul says that God's good faith and the essential goodness which characterizes him permit no suffering to be unbearable or any temptation to be overwhelming. He always provides some solace for man's use. Both the saints and heathen masters say that neither God nor nature permits the existence of undiluted evil or suffering.*[8]

We can only speculate what existence would be like without some of its unpleasantness. Without physical pain, we wouldn't know when to come in from the cold. Without emotional suffering as a contrast, we'd probably never experience true joy. Does not the heartbreak of a loved one's departure make the delight of reunion more pronounced? Those fighting the campaign against disease and sickness are required to call upon levels of intellect and compassion that could very well go untapped in a world free of their discomfort. How large a part does the satisfaction gained upon overcoming injustice, by seeing things set right, play in the overall quality of life? Without temptation and immorality, life would present few challenges that, if overcome, inspire one to greater goodness. If not for death, this planet would have been crushed by the sheer magnitude of the "life force" long before your or my birth. When viewed independently, life's less appealing elements appear much more unsavory than they really are. In the proper context, their contributions are easier to discern. Sans Satan, easier still.

The devout understand the parts pain, suffering, and a measure of guilt play in helping a person develop their spiritual maturity, assuming one is forthright. Combating the ego's prejudices and desires is no easy task, mentally or physically. It's no joy forgoing immoderate pleasures and material excess (at least initially), nor is it fun uncovering the false assurances and lack of mental effort that the adherence to narrow-minded viewpoints affords or owning up to obvious wrongdoing. I think it's safe to say that the struggles and sacrifices one must face to recognize and root them out produce strengths and feelings that would otherwise never be experienced. Suffering and pain are the vehicles through which egocentric waste is purged. One must go through the pain to make the gain.

Thomas à Kempis states the following:

Although temptations are so troublesome and griev- ous, yet they are often profitable to us, for by them we are humbled, cleansed, and instructed.[9]

In all these trials, our progress is tested; in them great merit may be secured, and our virtue become evident. It is no great matter if we are devout and fervent when we have no troubles; but if we show patience in adversity, we can make great progress in virtue.[10]

In his book *Ethics for the New Millennium,* the His Holi- ness the Dalai Lama writes:

It is also worth remembering that the time of great- est gain in terms of wisdom and inner strength is often that of greatest difficulty.... We also find that our confidence and self-reliance can grow and our courage become strengthened as a result of suffering. This can be inferred from what we see in the world around us. Within our own refugee community, for example, among the survivors of our early years in exile are a number who, though they suffered ter- ribly, are among the spiritually strongest and most cheerfully carefree individuals I have the privilege to know. Conversely, we find that in the face of even relatively slight adversity, some people who have ev- erything are inclined to lose hope and become de-

Lawrence K. Zeisler

spondent. There is a natural tendency for wealth to spoil us. The result is that we find it progressively more difficult to bear easily the problems everyone must encounter from time to time.[11]

Concealed among mountains of archival records at the U.S. National Library of Medicine in Maryland lies a piece of brown paper with the German inscription "Der Weg des Leidens", literally translated "the road through suffering." It is signed by Albert Einstein. He wrote the note in 1947 wherein he expressed his belief that suffering paved the way to human greatness.

I'm convinced virtue often doesn't come easily for this reason; one appreciates something better and feels more fulfilled after having worked hard for it. For instance, altering lifestyle patterns can improve body and spirit. Proper diet, exercise, and nutrition regimens are healthy alternatives to chemicals that demand the use of willpower.

There are backaches, muscle aches, toothaches, headaches, stomachaches, earaches, heartaches, and definitely pains in the neck. It's not easy coping with all this unpleasantness, and we've gone to great lengths to blunt it, dull it, and deny it. One cannot be blamed for wanting to soothe the irritation, but we should be aware that pain's purpose is to warn us that all is not right with the world. Without it, we would do much more harm to ourselves. If it didn't accompany a sprained ankle, one would dedicate less time ensuring that it healed properly. A painful sensation in the lower right side of your abdomen may be an indicator of appendicitis. Professional sports are rife with stories of athletes numbing injuries and further harming themselves. Not too long ago I contracted a harsh throat infection. I was given antibiotics and took ibuprofen to ease the distress. As the condition improved, I stopped taking the ibuprofen, but the next day, a mild pain notified me that the infection lingered. I was careful not to overtax myself.

Years of physical exertion have saddled me with a tender back. The stretching program I undergo lessens this handicap tremendously and usually preempts the need for pain-killers. There are added bonuses: stress reduction and increased limberness in muscles and joints come to mind. Stretching is more time consuming than popping pills, but it is more salutary and less expensive. I still feel discomfort at times, but I've come to accept that a little pain is part of life. No one should have to endure intractable pain.

George Bernard Shaw conveyed the concept that youth is wasted on itself, expressing that so much of its vigor is squandered on unproductive or counterproductive enterprises. Youth hardly has a chance to catch its breath; it can be compulsive, stubborn, indulgent, and explosive. I succumbed to far too many whims during mine. Like a raging cascade, I poured forth energy. It seems we must learn to slow down. To this end, there is no better teacher than experience. A painful feeling suffered can say more than a thousand parental admonitions.

This is not meant to imply that we always obey pain's lessons. Take that infamous party-pooper, the hangover. I've lost track of how many times I would awake writhing in bleary-eyed torment while throwing softly issued expletives at the morning or afternoon. How I'd curse the pain, not thinking I should be thanking it for offering warning signals.

The withdrawal symptoms displayed upon cessation of narcotic abuse are proof of how far one has deviated from normalcy. It would be wise to take heed. I recall repeatedly baking myself in the sun in hot pursuit of a tan, even though I'd endured painful sunburns numerous times. The

Lawrence K. Zeisler

cumulative effect has come home to roost, and I've had a couple of sun-induced melanomas removed from my back.

Sometimes a painful experience prompts deep introspection. My sister's house was vandalized years ago. After being swamped by anger and self-pity, she told me trivial things didn't bother her as much, and she felt more at peace. We figured her tolerance emerged because the trauma had put life in clearer perspective. Using heartache as a touchstone, most subsequent problems didn't stack up. With minor worries taking up less space, she saw more clearly the truly important things such as family, friends, and the environment.

The ability to break down barriers is another of pain's attributes. Showing compassion for another's suffering and sharing in their time of need can create a bond between individuals.

Yes, pain is a reminder that we are sensitive organisms, but the same sensitivity that incites an "ouch!" introduces one to the soothing warmth emitting from the hearth on a cold winter's night.

By engineering a chemically "improved" world that seeks to abolish the unpleasantness that impels one to seek virtue, self-understanding, and healthier physical well-being, pharmaceuticals are removing our awareness of and interaction with pain's contributions. There is the clear and present danger that psychotropic drugs and painkillers will insidiously pacify us with their comforts to the extent they fashion the fiber of our future. Pleasure and convenience have become our raison d'etre and are so ingrained in our consciousness that some people see their inordinate craving for them a right. This only impedes personal growth.

At the turn of the century the problem was escalating:

So change us they have. In the United States alone, over 50 million of us are on psychotropic medication, various mind-numbing drugs, to get through the workday. About the same number of us are on medication to try and get through the night. And 5 million of our kids are on mind-altering pharmaceuticals to get through the school day. Not to worry if the medication is required at ever higher doses or stops working altogether, or if you've chosen instead alcohol or illegal drug addiction; the genetic engineers promise us that genes for depression, anxiety, alcoholism, and even shyness will soon be found and removed.[12]

In the decade following 2001, the use of pharmaceuticals (painkillers, antidepressants, ADHD drugs, antianxiety treatments, and antipsychotics) skyrocketed. While women are still the leading users, participation among men aged twenty to sixty-four quadrupled. Use by children doubled, a cause of concern because, among other things, weight gain often results. It is commonly noted that medications are overprescribed, which contributes to abuse.

Medications administered wisely, especially when used in conjunction with psychotherapy, can be beneficial. It has been discovered that a number of psychoses are the result of chemical imbalances in the brain. In some cases, the proper medication relieves anxiety, clearing the mind for purposeful pursuits. But there is always the potential for side effects, some severe. Genetic engineering of the personality is another matter. I'm sure its proponents will tread with the utmost caution.

Yes, pharmaceuticals can be of service to humanity. Too

often, however, they serve as the perfect component of a society that likes to forgo pain in its search for gain, that has neither the time nor curiosity, and some might argue the wherewithal, to plumb the potencies within.

When one is increasingly provided for, less demand is put upon their inner strength, which impairs self-reliance and independence. An unchallenged mind becomes lazy and uninquisitive, making a person less inclined to reach decisions, let alone proper ones. They are easily led and a perfect pawn of the powers that be.

Whether by open admonitions or less direct references, the world's great faiths encourage self (ego)-denial, which entails mental and physical sacrifice. Buddhism and Taoism acknowledge the invaluable part it plays in unveiling inner peace, although they teach one shouldn't sacrifice with spiritual gain in mind. They instruct that wisdom can be achieved only by acceding to the inevitability of suffering and pain, saying that "letting go to them" neutralizes their effects, advocating that the organism must be allowed to follow its own natural patterns. A problem arises when the mind restrains mental and physical unpleasantness, which diverts one from their true purpose. Without sufficient understanding of that purpose, one will not be able to relate to them in a logical manner and properly appreciate life's positive and negative aspects.

In Native American cultures, self-denial and generosity were required of the people and the chief. He had to constantly think of the tribe's welfare and be willing to step down from his position if called upon to do so. Tribe members still perform vision quests—a purification ritual undertaken to mark meaningful life transitions. The procedure entails fasting alone for three to four nights and days. Its purpose is to face one's fears and empty the body and mind of extraneous material. The lessons learned can be profound and sublime and almost always result in positive growth that links one to nature and community.

The strict Christian ascetics such as the saints of old "renounced all riches, dignities, honours, friends and kindred" in their effort to empty themselves of distractions so they could commit themselves solely to the contemplation of God. They felt that the needs of the "body" conflicted with an intimate realization of his love. In all these traditions and disciplines simplicity, or at most moderation, and courage lead one to the Promised Land.

Christian doctrine posits that one should seek to imitate Jesus, and since his life contained considerable hardship, a faithful servant's will as well. Though the road is long and arduous, it is felt that by willingly enduring trials and tribulations in Jesus's name, the spirit can be fortified. If this takes place while holding to the sincere belief that suffering is God's will, one's troubles can be transformed into tolerable and even joyous occasions.

The ascetics subjected themselves to mortification to strengthen the will against temptation and the pursuit of personal gratification. Some of the more fervent among them administered self-inflicted pain. They must have known that except for love, nothing renders the ego inoperative like physical suffering; the self-serving schemes that so effectively close the mind are as straw before a strong wind when faced with its arrival. These sought-after, albeit painful, ego-free periods, wherein the focus is on nothing save the present discomfort, were of some worth to their spiritual quests. The account of St. Benedict is an example: In response to a violent temptation of the flesh imposed upon him by the devil, he disrobed and threw himself into a dense patch of briars to quench the fire of lustful thoughts. It was written that the wounds of his soul were cured by his bodily ones. Suffering enjoys universal religious recognition.

While their methods seem harsh and unrealistic for any but the most committed, determined Christians who "broke through" to God appear to have realized the universal principles underlying the world's major faiths. Though the Eastern traditions stress that a key to understanding these principles is acceptance and observation of whatever emotion, negative or positive, one is presently experiencing (as opposed to the ascetics, who battled what they perceived to be the evil inherent in negative feelings and worldly pleasures), the results are similar.

The common thread of this discussion is that the ego must be confronted and dealt with, not masked or blunted by fear or pacification. Neither the Eastern traditions nor the ascetics wanted anything to do with it. The ascetics practiced suffering and self-denial to purge its impact, whereas Eastern traditions undergo exercises specifically designed to counteract it, knowing that doing so clarifies perception and makes pain more bearable. A shared lack of ego explains why despite differences in their approaches, both saint and enlightened Eastern master enjoy the blessings of heightened awareness.

Though the odds are heavily against us achieving a glorified state, we can take some comfort in what the holy ones felt. The relative few who have known such honor have affirmed the existence of a universal presence in a simple and humble way. Witness once more the words of Thomas Merton:

A saint is capable of loving created things and enjoying the use of them and dealing with them in a perfectly simple, natural manner, making no formal references to God, drawing no attention to his own piety, and acting without any artificial rigidity at all. His gentleness and his sweetness are not pressed through his pores by the crushing restraint of a spiritual strait-jacket. They come from his direct docility to the light of truth and to the will of God. Hence a saint is capable of talking about the world without any explicit reference to God, in such a way that his statement gives greater glory to God and arouses a greater love of God than the observations of someone less holy, who has to strain himself to make an arbitrary connection between creatures and God through the medium of hackneyed analogies and metaphors that are so feeble that they make you think there is something the matter with religion.[13]

It might be mentioned again that the Eastern traditions express that enlightenment is possible only if one accepts life's vibrancy and unpredictability, the "bad" as well as the "good." They insist that the spirit can be felt while immersed in the natural world but only during times when the mind is empty of imagery. The Native Americans also value the role nature plays in stimulating their spiritual recognition.

Perhaps a share of the above faiths and traditions accepted suffering because the ancient world's inhabitants were more at its mercy—at least regarding physical suffering—than people today, and their authors realized it was foolish to discount the inevitable. Sheer necessity helped mold their thoughts, but what is said about necessity? Something about it being the mother of invention.

The book of Job in the Old Testament is an excellent rendering of a man forced to confront suffering head-on. Satan challenged God to a test of Job's unparalleled faith. God concurred, and Satan purged all the poor man held dear—his children, fortune, and worldly possessions—and then afflicted him with boils from head to foot. Like many trials found throughout the Old Testament, the punishments seemed severe, but there is no denying they made their point.

Job did not reject God but did question his justice. He debated with friends attempting to convince him that he, not God, must be at fault for his predicament. Job stood firm in his claim of innocence and implored God to grant him an audience. In the end, the Almighty appeared and asserted his dominance. Job repented, all was forgiven, and his losses were restored.

The story deals with the unavoidable nature of suffering, and it could be interpreted by nonbelievers as a metaphor for a person wrestling with their conscience. In such a scenario, God signifies the hand of fate that eludes our grasp and which one might question but never alter. The fundamental message is clear: Embrace reality, the good and the bad.

It is only human to protest what one perceives to be the unfairness in life. Protest Job did, which produced self-pity, nurturing his inability to accept current conditions with a clear mind. His confusion and doubt were further abetted by a wall of self-righteousness, justifying the defensive arguments that compounded his distress. Religious folks liken the emotional struggle and desire to come before God to prayer, a process that God regarded as Job's necessary and honest attempt to see through his suffering.

Ultimately, God embodies the strength to acknowledge and endure the distasteful parts of life by instilling in one the faith that all things happen for a reason, some of which defy explanation, making it easier to accept that the complex and unpredictable ways of the universe do not necessarily adhere to our definition of justice. As a direct result of his suffering, Job is humbled and better understands his place in the cosmos, having learned to trust in God's wisdom without question. The reestablishment of Job's possessions might be construed by the nonreligious as representative of his growth or newfound appreciation of life. The story has much to offer whether or not one chooses to believe the biblical interpretation.

It is not being suggested that all efforts to thwart pain and suffering be dismantled, but proceeding without recognizing their place in life is imprudent. Accepting their inevitability puts things in a more benign light, as in Job's case, allowing one to react to hardship in a better way. Suffering's existence is reason enough to give it intense scrutiny. It will never be totally eradicated. Let's hope not anyway.

It is important to make rational distinctions between the hurtful and beneficial aspects of suffering. The focus should be on remedying aspects that cripple and damage the body and spirit. The qualities that present challenges can be of service to one's maturation.

Life is what it is. We must deal with it. Genuine belief in and gratitude for an overriding good with which we are connected, providing us with the wherewith to engage life's uncertainties with a level head, allows compassion to overcome selfishness, courage to overcome fear, and security to overcome insecurity. This defines faith's true strength and expresses its undeniable practical value.

Chapter 9

"Power is of two kinds. One is obtained by the fear of punishment and the other by acts of love. Power based on love is a thousand times more effective and permanent than the one derived from fear of punishment."

—Mahatma Gandhi

This chapter is dedicated to investigating the inconsistencies found in the Jesus narrative. With minor variation, the first three Synoptic Gospels corroborate their mutual accounting of Christ's activities. Taken at face value, certain aspects of the story stretch the limits of credulity, but I suppose that's where Christian dogma earns its keep. Whether its unyielding faith is moving mountains or blurring the vision, it doesn't like to be questioned.

For the sake of clarity, let me reiterate that because of the vast universal unknown wherein we exist, it is felt here that anything is possible. Expanding on this premise, walking on water and converting it into wine, even reinstating life to a corpse, though fantastic, must be assumed possible. Nor can Jesus as the divine son of the universal creator be ruled out. On a purely fundamental level, no argument can hold the aforementioned precious liquid.

The disadvantage with discussion of Jesus's authenticity is that it is empirically impossible to prove or disprove his existence let alone his immortality. Any disagreement with aspects of the biblical rendering lie firmly in the realm of logic. One has no recourse but to base their analysis on deduction, which can be defined as inference deriving logical conclusions from premises known or assumed to be true.

Whether mortal or immortal, a good portion of Jesus's message is inspirational. The concepts of humility, forgiveness, compassion for the poor and coexistence underpin his celebration of love and light. If the exposition ended here, it would be much more difficult to justify a critical commentary, but it doesn't. Hell, the end times, and references to eternal suffering elicit disturbing images incompatible with the above principles. To those of little faith, this paradoxical quality might seem reminiscent of a split personality.

Assuming the Bible is true and Christ is the immortal son of God, nonbelievers (as well as many believers) and the earth are in for a world of hurt. Despite its uplifting qualities, the religion's monstrous undertones cannot be glossed over. Visions of planetary ruination in preparation for the Second Coming are difficult to trivialize. Some denominations interpret Jesus's words concerning the matter symbolically, but this does not erase the fact that according to the Bible, he did speak them. Symbolic portrayals are more comforting and palatable, but strict literalists argue that handpicking certain biblical passages as being metaphorical in content undermines the book's veracity. Those same folks debate that moderating the definition of hell to make it more appealing to congregations and potential converts is tantamount to taking the words from the Lord's mouth. Parsing what is considered immutable can be tricky.

Lawrence K. Zeisler

The current inquiry proceeds from the standpoint that Jesus was a mortal of extraordinary intellectual and psychic abilities, possibly blessed with an awareness of the divine nature, perhaps a master practitioner of "energy healing." His foundational message of love and forgiveness was edited with ideas of eternal consequences, superhuman miraculous elements, and a direct pipeline to God to add persuasive muscle to the missionary effort. Such modifications would have been unknown to him since the Gospels were written after his death.

Jesus as a mere mortal would help explain why he had difficulty wresting a regard for nature from the surrounding desert. If he was linked to the all-knowing God, one would think that by dint of his innate wisdom, he would have been able to surmount the period's parochial limitations and carefully craft insights relating to the preservation of his father's creation while adroitly sidestepping the trap of paganism. He doesn't. There are numerous references to God's connection with the earth in the Old Testament. Perhaps he had become bored with his handiwork.

This critique owes much of its momentum to the error of omission just described. I believe it has provided humanity with subliminal license to respond in kind, made more powerful by a sacred stamp of approval. While it is impossible to quantify the cost, it cannot be denied that the repercussions stemming from a divine disregard for the earth, however unintended, are responsible in some measure for its imperiled condition. It seems highly unlikely that the anointed son of the planet's creator would be guilty of said oversight, fraught with such dangerous implications as it is. For this reason and the others mentioned above, efforts questioning his immortality ensue.

I often marvel at the unpretentious behavior of little children. They seem to have nothing to hide, perhaps because they have no ego to protect, no pride that says, "I'd better defend my dignity and status at any cost." Having no ego enables children to relate to their feelings and environment without fear of doing the incorrect thing; they react to both without hesitation or doubt. This forthright quality, which some might term innocence, keys their capacity to sense wonder.

As we grow, we make this instinctive link between mind, feelings, and environment subservient to a discipline that teaches the right and wrong way of doing things, but when children are forced to respond to self-governing regulations that frown on what are referred to as improper emotions, an innate trust in their natural responses to life is displaced. Now they must be leery of any action that may trigger embarrassment or scorn. Don't interpret this as a repudiation of the value of morality and ethics. The point is that they conflict with a child's unabashed innocence.

Inherent in a child's unconscious trust for free-flowing, spontaneous feelings is an openness, a humility that is unimpaired by mental barriers and self-importance. In other words, the natural trust in one's feelings was real at one time before thought got in the way. Because of its instinctive, inborn quality, I can only surmise the trust was meant to be.

This instinct may be thoughtless, but it is anything but unrealistic. In fact, there is nothing more basic. Due to its openness, it is without egocentric guile or pretense. We tend to overlook that trust and openness are keys to honesty, and honesty with oneself is prerequisite to self-understanding. Preempting this instinctual open-

Lawrence K. Zeisler

ness splits us asunder and deals a damaging blow to the formation of self-awareness.

Christ's love was genuine because his knowledge of self was so advanced that his feelings contained nary a trace of mental deception. He had come full circle, possessing the intellectual compatibility with the feelings that must be achieved through rigid self-examination of their true nature, unimpeded by mental obstacles fostering misdirection or distortion, especially the fear of being wrong. Free of the truth-diverting quality fundamental to devilish self-deception, he found inner harmony and reawakened the subtle link between the head and heart, opening the door to the goodness within. His childlike trust restored, he found the kingdom of God. It was he who said the following:

> Truly I say to you, unless you turn and become like children, you will never enter the kingdom of heaven. Whoever humbles himself like this child, he is the greatest in the kingdom of heaven.[1]

A child's innocence convinces me we are born in love (not evil), but as time passes, fears, prejudices, and excess desires blunt its light, leading to self-confusion and errant behavior. True, vice is inevitable, but knowing we were once free of its restraints would have to be encouraging to anyone searching for peace of mind.

The story of Jesus is a glowing depiction of a selfless individual not plagued by egocentric desires and fears, especially the fear of death. He was able to endure ridicule, slander, and treason with grace because of his union with the truth. Since he knew his own nature through and through, he understood and was able to recognize the fears and insecurities that moved those who were antagonistic to him. This knowledge formed the basis of his doctrine of forgiveness.

One thing continues to puzzle me. Why would one so blessed buttress the essence of his teachings with such an alarming desire? Fear is inherent in the idea of a personal resurrection. The only thing more troubling than the possibility of missing out on an eternity of bliss is the likelihood of spending one's days in hell. Using the threat of damnation to keep one on the straight and narrow is inconsistent with the principles of compassion and love. One should not feel forced to do good, especially under such extreme conditions. I know I couldn't effectively comment on these matters until gaining the confidence that I wouldn't face the fury of God's wrath.

While pondering this conundrum, I would like to return to Christ's insistence that one must become like a child before entering God's kingdom. What attributes do children possess that would cause him to make that statement? It has just been noted that children are unmarred by mental deception because their egos are not yet developed, and freedom from ego means freedom from vice. Less obvious but important nonetheless is their unawareness of death. For that matter, the past and future are of no significance to them. Free of the concept of time, their lives revolve around the moment in which they exist.

The great Asian traditions do not look at the eternal in terms of past and future. In fact, they do not view it in terms of time at all. They believe it exists in the here and now, that it is ever-present or timeless. It is continuous, ceaseless. As soon as one tries to seize it, it's gone. It has been described as the eternal Now. It is where God's presence can be felt

Lawrence K. Zeisler

but only by a mind devoid of the ego's enslavement to time, like a child's. Perhaps Jesus was privy to the Eastern concept of eternity; according to scripture, he had an intuitive recognition of God. Would he not want others to feel the same comfort? Why would he jeopardize its experience by placing the opportunity beyond one's immediate grasp, beyond life itself?

When Christ spoke of death as the prelude to eternity, perhaps he meant dying to the ego. When he referred to the resurrected experiencing the kingdom of heaven, what if he was talking about the rebirth of one's psyche, free of ego, at peace with the eternal Now? Could hell be that state of confusion one suffers while prey to the ego's delusions? This may sound absurd to those grounded in conventional thought, but I know that one cannot be like a child while desiring a future beyond the confines of death.

I don't purport to put words in the Lord's mouth but don't discount that earlier writers may have. The promise of immortality is a persuasive concept to hold over a potential convert's head, a concept that once believed puts one at the mercy of that faith's leaders. Now there is much more to lose by straying from the ordained course and much more to gain by being obedient. It can be a powerful tool indeed.

While on the subject, what greater power is there than that of a force capable of overcoming death? This belief, coupled with Jesus's litany of reality-altering miracles, can have a pronounced influence on one seeking comfort in an uncertain and sometimes threatening world and who is fearful of what lies beyond. Despite that the miracles were often performed for the good of others (and to make a firm impression) and the resurrection is viewed as a divine gift bestowed upon those of firm moral fiber, the subliminal message is clear: Jesus is power incarnate. Although he didn't flagrantly wield it like his father, its allure is undeniable. For many, it is a stronger draw than his message proclaiming the principles of humility and love.

Unsolicited humility and desire are mutually exclusive. The desire for immortality gives humility a purpose, but to anticipate a result of any kind contravenes humility's basic tenet of self-denial. A humble nature does not reach for things but sheds them, meaning it should be free of expectation—a near impossibility for most people to uphold made impossible by such a powerful, unrelenting motive. Genuine humility surfaces spontaneously and unprompted from within.

Jesus realized the weaknesses of human nature and knew how repeatedly surrendering to temptations, with each one's embedded desire, arrested the development of all he stood for, yet the Bible tells us that he dangled the ultimate (eternal) carrot. Was he so naïve as to think, with so much at stake, that the ego wouldn't be waiting in the wings and licking its chops, ready to pounce on the first opportunity to entice one into believing that there are endless shortcuts to heaven, the desire par excellence? It may be impossible to fool God, but deceiving one's self is easy.

The ardent Christian will insist that faith conquers all and that Jesus was sent to earth to forgive the human frailties he took issue with. I am all for forgiveness, which Jesus instructed we practice, for its soothing quality has a healing effect, and it is a necessary ingredient in the resolution of any emotionally charged disagreement, but how often should one take advantage of Jesus's divine pardon? Should they expect it at the drop of a hat? Should it be expected at all? Does one arbitrarily determine each time the blessing occurs? Is it a cure-all for whatever ails them spiritually? If a pastor is consulted, is their official okay supposed to ease the anxiety and automatically clear the slate? Is it too commonly used as a crutch to explain away or cover up that which necessitated it in the first place? Those who use this "Christ card" with regularity have a tendency to view themselves through rose-colored glasses. The ego is strong in them, perhaps too strong to gain them celestial privileges.

Believing in God's forgiveness provides the solace to help penitent Christians work through some of their trials, but when it is framed within absolute terms, an undue burden is put on one's moral flaws, shadowing a person in the obligatory fear. Jesus voiced numerous strong demands, some of which a momentary confession or fleeting act of penance cannot hope to rectify. According to scripture, he said that failure to conform to them would put one's eternal salvation in serious jeopardy. When considering those that are vague in nature and virtually impossible to sustain, the inability to find a resolution must be unnerving, leading one to live in doubt or ignore the problem. For instance, how is the threshold for the forgiveness of one's materialism and quest for wealth determined? If Jesus were with us today, he would assuredly rail against our excesses and lament that the Holy Ghost finds a sacrilegious bedfellow in modern capitalism. How much like a child should one be to guarantee them safe entrance to heaven? If one is married and occasionally fantasizes about various members of the opposite sex, is it a matter of time before they feel the heat? If you ask me, there are too many uncertainties producing huge gray areas. How does one know if the Lord has looked upon their progress with favor?

Please take note of this inconsistency: Employment of the divine pardon neutralizes the efficacy of the immortal threat. On the one hand, Jesus talks about a hellish punishment as the consequence of sin; on the other, all is forgiven. Could it be that those threats were just so much hot air? Were they his?

Reading Jesus's words can leave me feeling punch-drunk. His radical wisdom is captivating in its raw beauty, but then he spoils it with that infernal "or else." At times, the Prince of Peace sounds hostile. It is understandable that he was angry about the hypocrisy enveloping the existing power structure. Making references to everlasting pain is another thing. Threatening the populations of whole cities with Judgment Day reprisals because of their reluctance to repent and pay homage to his mighty works is representative of an affronted ego, using fear to leverage his divine purpose. Fear is the tool of the tyrant and autocrat. Jesus was not about power and all about personal fulfillment. Why would he provide it with such a fertile breeding ground from which to ply its deviltry? Once again, I sense the presence of other hands in this.

Fear does have value as a motivator. It can encourage one to follow orders and provoke people into toeing the line. It foments insecurity, making it more likely that a person will seek the aid of outside consolation, especially for spiritual comfort.

While fear can initiate a turn for the better, if one is serious about continuing in a positive direction, it is best that it be left behind. The answers essential for growth are explored most effectively when the mind is composed and clear of worry and pressure. Their candor can be compromised if one detects the slightest evidence of penalty that might be incurred for personal revelations being unearthed. Initially, newfound disclosures are often unsettling. They need time

Lawrence K. Zeisler

to be apprehended and ripen into wisdom with the comfort it evokes. Fear does not respect comfort or patience.

Speaking of the "or else" factor, Jesus's descriptive account of the end times reinforces the dread coexisting with his message of love and understanding, only adding to the confusion. I suppose a true believer would be able to explain away its value as a divine scheme culminating in Christ's glorious return. Others surely interpret it as a grotesque nightmare scenario, fatalistically surrendering the earth and many of its human inhabitants to the whims of a fanciful future. The words of Jesus describe the event:

> "For nation shall rise against nation, and kingdom against kingdom; and there shall be famines, and pestilences, and earthquakes, in divers places. All these are the beginnings of sorrows."[2]

He adds:

> "Now the brother shall betray the brother to death, and the father the son; and children shall rise up against their parents, and shall cause them to be put to death."[3]

Regardless of how you paint it, Jesus's radiant future earth-bound reign is predicated upon copious quantities of temporal suffering. This opens a whole new can of questions. The punitive element is conspicuous throughout the narrative, relegating any who dare oppose his deity banishment to a crumbling planet. Apparently, good and moral people guilty of nothing more than the sin of nonbelief are included. Some religious believe that those who never had exposure to the Christian gospel will be punished because of the original sin of Adam and Eve! I reckon that even a loving god has only so much tolerance. It appears that Jesus harbors a good degree of the Old Testament fire and brimstone after all. Apparently, it's him or else. I refuse to repent if it means doing so puts my salvation ahead of the earth and the unconverted innocents upon it.

Where does that leave the faithful or elect? Why, in heavenly bliss. No matter that many of them, in pursuit of their final reward, shirked responsibility for the worldly woes that signaled the hastening of their savior's grand prediction. The term *elect* connotes superiority, in turn laying the groundwork for feelings of exceptionalism. I thought Jesus stressed equality, not differences. Perhaps this type of thinking drives the righteous zeal of those trying to foist their will upon social issues. Perhaps it's becoming clear that the same force (ego) that feeds one's selfishness and fear is at the center of the consensus interpretation of the Christian faith.

Was Jesus's need to fulfill Old Testament doomsday prophesies so important that he made a burnt offering of the Creation? Why the need for the future grand reentrance? It sounds like one gigantic ego massage. Didn't he foresee that his planetary neglect would jeopardize its health and aggravate the suffering of the multitudes in distant times to come? Of course not, because he was only a man. Perhaps *men* is a correct term as it relates here—men ignorant of the impact their words would have on the future. Woe be it if Jesus is something much more.

Talk about metaphysical anxiety. Was life so mundane and intimidating that the only hope for true joy rested upon its annihilation? How can any Christian call their

Lawrence K. Zeisler

religion "earth sensitive" with this incorporated in its ideology?

Does the story of Jesus's resurrection lose its luster if it's viewed as that exalted state one can ascend to after breaking free of the ego's clutches? What if a mortal Jesus experienced a love so genuine that he felt no division between himself and God, a kinship he knew we all had the potential to feel here and now without the need of a ministerial intermediary, one that could be realized only while immersed in the present without desire for gain or fear of loss? Apparently, he felt that divesting oneself of worldly attachments encouraged the prospect. Witness the words he spoke:

> Think not that I am come to send peace on earth: I came not to send peace, but a sword. For I am come to set a man at variance against his father, and the daughter against her mother, and the daughter in law against her mother in law. And a man's foes shall be they of his own household. He that loveth father or mother more than me is not worthy of me: and he that loveth son or daughter more than me is not worthy of me. And he that taketh not his cross, and followeth after me, is not worthy of me. He that findeth his life shall lose it: and he that loseth his life for my sake shall find it.[4]

In response to a question by his disciple, Peter, he said this:

> And Jesus said unto them, Verily I say unto you, That ye which have followed me, in the regeneration when the Son of man shall sit in the throne of his glory, ye also shall sit upon twelve thrones, judging

the twelve tribes of Israel. And every one that hath
forsaken houses, or brethren, or sisters, or father, or
mother, or wife, or children, or lands, for my name's
sake, shall receive an hundredfold, and shall inherit
everlasting life.[5]

If the above verses are applied to an eternal life after death, their implication is that one must forsake all one holds dear before the desired end can be achieved—a heartless command and near impossibility especially in twenty-first-century America. It is a burden that a loving Jesus would not saddle one with. If their meaning plays out in the mortal sphere, the message is much less unnerving, suggesting that harmony in this life can best be gained by freeing oneself of things that divert one's attention from pondering the divine while engaged in undistracted self-contemplation. It can also be read as a summons to banish personal bias, which clouds objectivity and impairs a clear and equable assessment of a given matter. When one is asked to pick and choose between a family member or someone outside while weighing the merits of a controversy, all things being equal (or unequal, for that matter), the blood relation will almost always get the benefit of the doubt at the other's expense.

Released of the uncompromising quality imposed by the promise of an immortal aftermath, the readers can approach Jesus's demands in a more sensible manner and work on bettering themselves in a setting still surrounded by loved ones without fear of penalty. This is another example of how the immortal threat imposes an undue strain upon the free will. The want for immortality strikes at the core of some of the central issues of Jesus's teachings.

Continuing down the heretical road, the contention here

is that Jesus's final sacrifice required greater courage if he died a mortal, and though his message would continue to resound with unswerving love, its impact would be lost on many.

There is no greater sacrifice than to die for a noble cause, but are a few hours of suffering such a terrible price to pay knowing an eternity of bliss is soon to follow? The whole "plotting" aspect seems disingenuous, giving Jesus's earthly machinations a staged quality, the outcome of which was preordained. To an immortal Jesus, the pain endured on the cross would be little more than an inconvenient, albeit painful, hiccup in a wonderful, grand picture. The knowledge of the reward corrupted the purity of the sacrifice.

The crucifixion and resurrection complement one another. When near the end of his evangelizing, with danger imminent, if Jesus had fled his accusers and died a natural death, even something as awe-inspiring as rising from the dead would not have withstood the rigors of the ages. The sacrifice had to be made. It was in the plan. Even the devil did his part, darkening the heart of Judas Iscariot before implementing the great betrayal. Apparently, the poor man's suicide was written into the script as well.

Was sacrifice even involved? It might be asked if the immortal Jesus felt pain. Some of the miracles were otherworldly. It is possible that one who cured the suffering of others was exempt from it. Did he automatically shut down his miraculous nature (the manifestation of his godly power) during and before the crucifixion?

A mortal Jesus would have had to rely on faith, not concrete knowledge, to lessen the pain of his final sacrifice. Even the strongest faith carries with it some semblance of uncertainty. It is uncertainty that gives added meaning to Jesus's sacrifice and illustrates its true beauty while amplifying the strength of his convictions. Jesus the man gives nobility to sacrifice, while his immortal counterpart falls woefully short.

Jesus's actions speak volumes: the life of sacrifice and distaste of hypocrisy, his unparalleled honesty, and his unerring faith in God's love are emblematic of one who "walked the walk." Without the benefit or crutch of immortality, that walk required much more grit and determination.

Heaven and hell color Jesus's message with an authoritarian ring and give him a hard edge that detracts from his humanity. They hang over the worshipper like a pall and produce an undercurrent of fear and guilt. The obsession with his immortality engenders desire, which places him at a distance, but without pressure to tend to the immortal soul, one is free to probe its depths in a much calmer setting, enabling a better comprehension of what they and Jesus are all about.

History betrays the violence and culture altering perpetrated in Jesus's name. When he said to spread his gospel, did he mean at any cost? Those in positions of power who exploited Church doctrine to further their ambitions could thank the resurrection for making their task easier. It would have been difficult for a fair share of Christ's "soldiers" to rationalize their rapacious practices, especially where women and children were concerned, if not sheltered by the belief in eternal life for those people struggling against their righteous might. There is irony in a logic that justified the sacrifice of countless heathen souls so that the survivors had a chance to save their own.

The words "blessed are the meek for they shall inherit the earth" and "truly, I say to you, as you did it to one of the least of these my brethren, you did it to me" are prime examples of Christ's love. Notice the change in meaning if the phrases concluded with "but only if they believe in eternal life beside the Father and me."

If Jesus is the true son of God, as Christians believe, by virtue of his omniscience, would he not have been able to foresee the bloodshed and carnage? If he is not omniscient, would not the all-knowing Father have been aware of the future misuse of his religion and taken pains for Jesus to specify in no uncertain terms never to wreak havoc in his name? It's clear that admonitions by Jesus such as "turn the other cheek" and "love your enemies" did not leave a firm enough imprint, especially when those involved were standing in the way of conquest. The philosophy driving America's territorial expansion was expressed in the term "manifest destiny," which advocated that the emerging nation was destined by Divine Providence to extend its dominion over the continent.

We must ask ourselves if we are talking about the more affable God of New Testament times, of whom Christ is a reflection, or the God of the Old Testament, who gave license to kill in his name.

> But in the cities of these peoples that the Lord your God gives you for an inheritance, you shall save alive nothing that breathes, but you shall utterly destroy them, the Hittites and the Amorites, the Canaanites and the Perizzites, the Hivites and the Jebusites, as the Lord your God has commanded; that they may not teach you to do according to all their abominable practices which they have done in the service of their gods, and so to sin against the Lord your God.[6]

It is obvious that one could kill under chosen circumstances. This contradiction between the violent side of God and his sixth commandment to Moses is perplexing. Apparently the faithful are not similarly vexed. Such unquestioning acceptance most likely accounts for the militant nature of otherwise peaceful members of the Christian flock.

The Old Testament God was demanding and extremely concerned about the tendency of his subjects to stray from the chosen path. The Bible is teeming with stories about them abandoning their belief, succumbing to sinful and dissolute habits, God's meting out punishment, his eventual forgiveness, and reestablishment of the law. Though he could be patient, forgiving, and compassionate, his arrogance, pride, jealousy, and thirst for vengeance often prevailed. Dare I say he was egotistic? The above factors prompted Mark Twain to state that God reminded him of a man.

Let's assume, for the sake of discussion, that God "saw the light" and softened his "eye for an eye" outlook enough to honor us with Christ's presence. Why would a loving God bless only one enclave of the world and ignore the rest of humankind? Imagine how much less blood would have been spilled if all God's children had known Jesus personally. More is the pity that their first exposure often came as Christian teaching was being rammed down their throats.

There are reminders of the Old Testament God sprinkled throughout the New Testament, some of which have been mentioned. Consider the fate of poor Ananias in the book of Acts who secretly maintained a portion of the profits from his sale of land while the rest of the faithful were selling their holdings and turning the revenue over to the apostles for the common good. For this, he was accused of lying to God. With no chance to repent, the penalty for his dishonesty was death. The same fate befell his wife who knew of the scheme. As is written in the Bible, the lesson spread dread among any who heard of the event.

It would be a blatant oversimplification to presume that Christianity alone fostered the forays responsible for civilization's heavy-handed spread. The lust for new lands and their resources, intense competition among rival powers, and curiosity played parts in promoting the centuries-long clamor heard round the world. Hostility and conflict appear to be inescapable. It could well be argued that Jesus represents the best attempt to bleed the poison from the system—more reason why it's strange he would make the cornerstone of his teaching something that provided the psyche with such a golden opportunity to sow the infection. The resurrection has possible abuse written all over it. The idea of an eternal resting place, free of pain and want, is a wonderful vision. Any well-intentioned souls who honestly wanted to give the earth's peoples a chance to share in the final reward notwithstanding, the vision got eaten alive, equipping man with an excuse to conquer and pacify in the name of love.

Granted, the violence has greatly diminished. Western man has largely lost the taste for military conquest and glory. Treat the imperialistic aspect of this narrative as a lesson in history, but the fact the events occurred in the past does not dismiss the fact that they happened. The primary arguments that have been discussed are topical.

Any motive tarnishes love's purity. The resurrection (with its correlatives, heaven and hell) has proven to be too big to handle. In spite of the fact that it's seen as a source of comfort and a strong incentive to practice virtue, it has saddled adherents with a burden that produces guilt, self-righteousness, intolerance, and fear. How sad that its factual necessity preempts its symbolic value. Too bad it met head-on with the ego and lost.

Upon analysis, it appears that the physical resurrection is a concept rather than reality, an instrument employed by those who sought to control the course of events. Its authors had honorable intentions, two of which were more than likely a desire to bring order and consolation to those adhering to its dictates. No one can ever hope to decipher the full extent of their motives; in the end, all inquiry is reduced to inference, but one has their intuition, historical perspective, and learned understanding of human nature. They tell me that taking the resurrection literally exposes numerous inconsistencies and contradictions that mortally wound its credibility and do Jesus a disservice. Then again, perhaps a wonderful promise with horrific undertones makes strange sense for a faith that combines the principles of love, humility, and forgiveness with limitless power, domination, and implied and spoken threats.

When human thoughts are dignified with a divine stamp, their status is elevated, saddling them with an intolerable burden of proof. When revelations are believed to emanate from a perfect or all-knowing source, there is no margin of error. The Church would insist the Bible meets this mark. Others disagree.

We all share equally in the earth, regardless of personal belief or financial status. It is the connective tissue that binds us. Jesus's greatest failure was to overlook that fact. Our only hope lies in its resurrection; not his, at least as written.

Lawrence K. Zeisler

Chapter 10

"Logic and sermons never convince, The damp of the night drives deeper into my soul."

—Walt Whitman

M any would argue that the Judeo-Christian God helped bring order from chaos, which more than compensates for any unfortunate side effects. Perhaps, but as with medicine, side effects hamper a treatment's effectiveness.

The civilizing of humankind has a long record of achievement. It accomplished the goal of buffering us from nature's beguilements. Hence, the freedom is there to worship her beauty, wonder, and generosity, even gaze in awe at her savagery with a compassionate eye and without fear of reverting to hedonistic practices like the people during biblical times. Her absence from the divine equation has proved disastrous and helped spawn a capitalist economy whose ego-based desire for material gain exploited her riches at will. Not until her pain became our pain did we take notice.

The ego is at the root of the problem, and its reach is long and its grip strong. What can be done about it?

The following discussion will be predicated on a noncombative approach to reining it in. The key is not to attack the ego with the intention of purging it, for that would invite the conflict it thrives on. The trick is to observe it and watch how it works. This means looking without approval or disapproval, any notion of right and wrong. Observe it quietly, passively, with no goal or objective, no obligation to improve. Only an accepting mind can remain tranquil enough to indulge in this observation. Acceptance is so critical that an official definition is provided: "Acceptance is an unabashed affirmation of whatever one is thinking or feeling at present, uninfluenced by an inner voice dictating that she or he is or should be thinking, feeling, or experiencing something else."

Acceptance does not mean acquiescence or justification. It does mean that before one can assume full responsibility for their feelings and thoughts, they must be able to watch them uninhibited by self-criticism. Uninhibited, as it applies here, is synonymous with openness and humility. Do you recall that a truly humble nature seeks nothing for its own, for seeking involves motive? That to want anything corrupts the innocence and honesty that are key components of self-understanding? One should have no expectations.

Even the attempt to imitate Christ, which is good in that it signifies one is seeking improvement, will thwart this exercise. Sounds strange, doesn't it? Jesus, whose gospel exuded humility, asked to be removed from the picture. It doesn't seem strange when it's understood that judgment opposes the personality by calling it into question. One is not to judge themselves against another standard. They are to calmly witness their thoughts and actions and the motives behind both. In essence, watch your motives with no particular reason or motive in mind.

If using Christ as a standard, when confronted with personal bias or vice, there is always the chance of succumbing to the temptation to sabotage one's attention and disrupt the flow of events with a preemptive bid for perfection. In other words, to seek a result, however noble it may be, implies that one wants a resolution or end. When conformity to that end takes precedence, the time and interest required for self-understanding are jeopardized.

Don't take this as a repudiation of Jesus; his love and compassion are inspirational. It would behoove everyone to read the Gospels with conviction and digest the aspects of their contents dealing with ethical behavior. Using those ethical standards as a guideline can point one in the proper direction and help promote a recognition of the goodness within, but if the guidelines remain the object of attention, the urge to copy them produces the strong probability that one will fail to adequately acknowledge their actual, current condition.

It's naive to assume one can grasp an ideal, much less maintain it. An ideal, defined here as an image of perfection to be sought, is not present reality. It may be what one hopes or thinks reality should be, but *should* is not *is*. The aware person sooner or later faces the fact that they can aspire after but never become someone else. Anyone who yearns to be like Jesus, or anyone else for that matter, places the source of contentment outside themselves and always a thought away.

If the memory of someone stirs a sense of envy, it would be best to look at the unsettling feeling without condoning or condemning it. If it is condoned, one will submit to it and thereby sustain the envy. On the other hand, if one elects to try to override or subdue the envy by concentrating on and seeking to emulate the idea of a better state of mind, it is possible that the disturbance that caused the memory will subside temporarily, but where does it go? It goes straight back to the unconscious, where it can begin working its subtle influence again. Although comparing oneself to an ideal may cause a particular object of envy to recede from conscious view, one's envious feelings for that object still thrive within, ready to impose their rule upon the mind at any time. This stopgap method of dealing with the problem of vice fuels the hypocrisy of the self-righteous. It is a Band-Aid at best, for it does not deeply explore the vice itself.

The acceptance approach promoted here would not automatically silence one's envy for good. Self-observation must be ongoing and ready to respond to the personality's fickle nature. One should never become complacent about or satisfied with their progress. The ego can convince you that this or that vice has been thoroughly dealt with and overcome when in truth you only think so. Every day I face recurring ideas I felt confident I had cleansed myself of.

By putting the focus on oneself and nowhere else, a personal intimacy will evolve, but from where does the information innate to the intimacy come? Like a ladle scooping soup from a large pot, it's drawn from the deep well of the unconscious, gradually revealing more of its secrets and giving the ego less places to hide, effectively reducing the rate and range of its influence.

Only a humble nature can repel the ego. A humble mind is a quiet mind, one cleared of any purpose or motive, desire or prejudice. It is an open mind attuned to present reality and possessed of an innocence that never presumes (the ego presumes) to have all the answers. It, like the truth, is not contentious, and like love, is steady, balanced, and unmoved by those forces that would cause it disturbance. Wanting a change (looking elsewhere) causes disturbance by denying one's present state; Truth and love exist nowhere but the present.

Lawrence K. Zeisler

Meister Eckhart substantiates this when he puts disinterest as the optimum condition for receiving God:

> *Perfectly disinterested, a man has no regard for anything, no inclination to be above this or below that, no desire to be over or under; he remains what he is, neither loving nor hating, and desiring neither likeness to this or unlikeness to that. He desires only to be one and the same; for to want to be this or that is to want something; and the disinterested person wants nothing.*[1]

When one is in sync with life's flow and not expecting resolution or personal gain, the pressure to find answers is removed. Living in the present, free of time's constraint, one can give their undivided attention. With no reason to be morally correct, they can engage themselves with total honesty, for the subconscious fear of failing to live up to expectations is a cause of self-deceit and discontentment. The more one acquires self-familiarity, the less they will rely upon the opinions and ideas that formerly provided guidance while trying to adapt the mind to fit within their predetermined and rigid parameters. Only then can one quietly observe life with interest and curiosity and become familiar with whatever they are thinking and feeling, be it good or bad, without question (distraction), and without the need to form a biased, hasty conclusion.

Jesus was on the mark when he preached the virtues of humility and self-denial. When he said we should become like children, he meant, among other things, that we should lower the barrier to God's love, which the "well of goodness" and the truth it contains comprises. Hoping to eventually achieve Christ-like attributes by means of virtuous conduct in this life clouds the realization of the inalienable Truth, as does the belief in physical union with God after death. Both approaches are inherently selfish and require that the desired states will occur in due time. Children aren't stifled by expectations or thoughts of time.

The object is not to dispute desire's place in the cosmos or to question its contribution to personal improvement and appreciation of life, but because of its reliance on time, it is an unsettled state. Love, on the other hand, is a constant and always with us (timeless), emerging only when the mind is free of motive, want, and other diversions. It can be characterized as unqualified ingenuousness and should be distinguished from "being in love," though its presence does make loving life and others effortless. This innocence is the well from which all loving acts spring. Our hectic, time-drenched lifestyle complicates matters and interferes with the state most conducive to love.

By no means does said innocence make one unaware of the nature of things. Don't confuse it with childlike naivety. Its open, uncluttered vision is possessed of a clarity that comprehends their nature all the better—a clarity manifested with greater regularity among those persons with diminished egos, a condition arrived at after an exhaustive revelatory soul search disclosing the multifaceted aspects of the personality.

Please recall the opening quote of Chapter 5 from the Talmud: "If you add to the truth you subtract from it." The ego's protective shield is a vast construct that attempts to do just that. It is a resistance to what one is, a mind-altering phenomenon that diverts us from realizing the most sensible and uncomplicated natural state possible. The truth is that there

Lawrence K. Zeisler

is nothing more conducive to health and happiness than the feeling of harmony and mental equilibrium that love provides. God is described as the reality underlying existence. He is truth at its most profound. Love is assuredly truth.

Love and inner truth are so entwined that making distinctions is difficult. Perhaps there are none. Tampering with the inner core's composition is like, to coin a friend's pet phrase, "gilding the lily." Suffice it to say that both compose clear awareness.

The truth-love core honors the distinctiveness of each individual but views everything in the field of vision in relationship, not as a group of disassociated objects. Its awareness extends to the global level, recognizing the lands, seas, and air as the glue cementing the earth; the waves lapping the shoreline connect and don't divide liquid and solid.

The capacity to abandon oneself to the moment, unfettered by opinions and established principles, is the basis of freedom and self-reliance. Tapping into one's natural center is the source of strength, allowing one to assume full responsibility for their actions with dignity and calm. When this center, not the ego, is linked to the truth outside (the environment), the reactions to life are constructive. We are the masters of our own fate. The Greeks were on the money when they coined the phrase "know thyself."

To know oneself puts one in contact with who they honestly are, free of the desire to be someone or something other, a realization achieved only on the heels of a methodical breakdown of the ego with its array of distortions and doubts that prevent one from experiencing love's reassuring qualities. Love's innate peace is the font of contentment and self-confidence, being the substrate from which all creative action and feelings of self-worth emanate. It is not concerned about personal achievement, though it sets the groundwork for administering productive, beneficent acts. Every one of us is blessed with this quality. All of one's worldly accomplishments will only be temporary fixes reflecting an unfulfilled, insatiable need when responding to egocentric urges.

J. Krishnamurti has this to say about personal responsibility:

As human beings, you and I, what can we do, not only to change the world but ourselves—-what can we do? Will somebody tell us? People have told us; the priests who are supposed to understand these things better than laymen like us, they have told us and that hasn't led us very far. We have the most sophisticated human beings; even they have not led us very far. We cannot depend on anybody, there is no guide, there is no teacher, there is no authority, there is only oneself and one's relationship with another and the world, there is nothing else. When one realizes that, faces that, either it brings great despair from which comes cynicism, bitterness and all the rest of it, or in facing it, one realizes that one is totally responsible for oneself and for the world, nobody else; when one faces that, all self-pity goes. Most of us thrive on self-pity, blaming others, and this occupation doesn't bring clarity.[2]

If self-observation is adhered to, you will become proficient at noticing how the ego works on the feelings. If you are insulted, you might see how by taking the offense personally, the ego impulsively jumps to its own defense and goads you to make a rash response. You will most

Lawrence K. Zeisler

likely become aware that some anger is only natural, but it fades when it is understood that hasty reactions are almost always counterproductive unless you must act in your physical defense. If you must raise your voice, a point can usually be made effectively without screaming and hurling expletives … usually.

It is not being suggested that ego-inspired anger is any less real than anger untarnished by its presence. I am saying that the less the anger is affected by the ego, the less damaging the consequences will be. Feelings are immediate, ever-changing responses to life and pose no threat to an intellect that understands their ways. The ego, on the other hand, sees that motion as a peril to the pride and prejudices it zealously clings to, and it will try to secure its hold. A feeling has nothing to hide, but a mind concerned with the need to influence one does, so it projects the blame. So long as a feeling is held hostage by a prejudiced thought, it will not only be magnified but most likely play over and over like a broken record.

The mature mind is cooperative, not controlling. It recognizes the value of emotional freedom. By observing and accepting feelings as they are, it gains familiarity with and an understanding of them. Growth involves pain. How much excess discomfort do we cause by engaging in constant warfare with ourselves?

Existence is an endless chain of interactions with people, things, oneself, and the subsequent reactions. If one wants to establish any semblance of order in life, they must continually scrutinize those reactions. For instance, I have little patience when working on mechanical projects; even minor ones such as changing a car's oil or replacing a washer on a leaking faucet can be bothersome. Sometimes a frustrating reaction prevents the completion of a task, but where does the frustration come from? Part of it stems from submission to the fixed concept that I'm not suited to that kind of work. Clearly some things are more appealing and come easier to us than others. More patience is devoted to natural inclinations.

Patience is essential to the proper completion of a project. Could it be that I wouldn't detest mechanical ones so much if I didn't consent to the mental images that make them seem so arduous and unexciting? What motivates the image or idea? Is the project really beyond my capabilities, or would I rather believe I don't have the time or have better things to do? Is it the chore per se or the thought of inconvenience that is behind the mental block and impatience?

It is rewarding to master something that had been perceived as distasteful or too difficult to attempt. Accomplishments build confidence and are indicators of our potential and measures of personal growth. Every little bit helps. It's surprising what one can achieve by quieting distracting thoughts that can cast doubt.

Many insist that the ego pushes us to improve by driving our competitive instinct. They argue it is the force behind the urge to beat the other guy and that without the desire to win, the chance for advancement is inhibited. I recall a situation where I felt threatened by a coworker. One day I girded myself and vowed to outperform him. I did perform at a higher level that day, and for that I thank my hurt pride, but if I had been more mature, there would have been no need to label him "the enemy" and prove myself. True creativity and a sound work ethic issue from deeper within and provide their own inspiration. Proceeding from a positive standpoint mitigates anxiety

Lawrence K. Zeisler

and resentment and provides an added benefit: it enables one to learn from a competitor and use that knowledge to expand their own skill base.

Peace exists in the present or, stated differently, in the eternal Now. The moments I enjoyed my children most were those when I gave them my undivided attention. I recall times when my play surrendered some of its delight because by 6:20 p.m., I was thinking about the 6:30 news. How readily we fail to let go to the moment.

Peace is a personal matter, but many of us lay our psyche in the laps of therapists and take their hands while studying matters uniquely individual. Granted, external help, be it friends or professionals, is necessary; no one is an island, but others can only assist one so far through the maze of urges and needs that must ultimately be encountered alone. One shouldn't be so prideful as to shut out advice, but on the other hand, overdependence upon others can weaken one's resolve. Commitment to self-understanding requires heart and courage, traits that outside motivation may be able to inspire but can never produce. The sooner one taps into their source of inner strength, the sooner they will be able to take control of their development—free of charge.

I recall a scene from an episode in the television series *M*A*S*H*. The protagonist, Hawkeye, consulted the army camp psychiatrist, Sydney, because of some unsettling dreams he was experiencing. The dreams were subconscious expressions of the pain and fear amassed over the numerous operations he had performed on soldiers. Their intensity had him worrying about his sanity. Knowing Hawkeye for the compassionate man he was, Sydney declared, "You're probably the sanest man in this camp." He knew it was only natural for a caring individual to feel thus. After a quality-filled interchange, Hawkeye regained his composure. Another's counsel can be priceless, especially if it is empathetic.

Some people have deep-rooted conditions like anxiety, depression, and obsession that can't be rectified during a brief oral exchange. Cognitive behavioral therapy is a relatively short-term, focused psychotherapy that centers on how one is thinking, behaving, and interacting today rather than in early childhood. It provides the patient with important self-help skills that are reinforced during homework assignments. The goal is to assist in breaking out of the negative thought patterns that compromise well-being so as to increase one's effectiveness in dealing with real-life issues, better enabling them to face reality with an improved outlook. Every effort is made to set the patient on their own two feet so that they can become their own therapist. CAT scans have revealed that the brains of cognitive therapy patients experienced physical changes not unlike those of patients who take drugs but without the side effects and dependency.

With self-knowledge comes tolerance; having been there already, one can see where others are coming from. We all laugh, cry, desire, envy, love, hate, dream, feel hurt, and seek recognition. The tendency to take things personally—the root of so much conflict—will subside proportionate to the extent one identifies with others, and tolerance will increasingly win out over anger.

I once worked with a young man who tested my patience almost daily. He was more skilled in some areas of the masonry trade and not shy about letting me know it. In order to gain his respect, my associates advised me to straighten him out with a stiff uppercut, and believe me, I was tempted. I could see he had a severe problem with self-esteem, one that he massaged by making himself the picture of perfection. His comments were more a result of this need than of outright animosity toward me. I believe most of us possess the trait to some extent; his was just an extreme case.

A distinction between self-importance and self-confidence is called for. The genuinely self-confident person doesn't have to broadcast their attributes, for their actions speak for them. They exude an undisturbed calm, a quiet humility, unlike the self-important person whose pride and vanity cry out for attention. The need for attention signifies a lack in one's character, and lack of contentment is endemic to vices. Upon realizing this, one can better accept dishonorable actions directed at them. When it is perceived that dishonesty, hostility, and undue criticism issue from an unhappy and unsettled source, empathy tempers the reflexive call for retribution.

The question is not whether we should experience negative feelings; their visitations are inevitable. What we do with them upon arrival is important. Their severity will be linked directly to the ego's degree of control. The control will be relinquished sooner if the matter is observed with a calm, uncritical, intent eye. If self-observation is continued with total dedication, when that emotion visits again, it will come in the front door, be greeted and recognized, and escorted to the back door where it will exit, leaving nary a trace.

Nature, like feelings, reveals her true face under relaxed and friendly conditions and when approached with an open mind. It's amazing how much one misses when distracted. We plow through life immersed in our pursuits and, in so doing, fail to stop and smell the flowers.

Accepting nature's intractable ways assists in accepting the emotions, for it makes you aware that change is a universal constant. Accepting both enhances the comfort level. It is reassuring to know what it means to be human and to realize the fruitlessness of expecting consistent virtue and pleasure with the attendant pressure and frustration. Maintain the faith in your inner goodness, a goodness reflecting a Truth responsible for life's beauty and harshness. Any action made in response to that exploration proceeds from firm footing.

It has been intimated that Christianity is inclined toward a spiritual split personality. The confusion is exhibited in what can be termed the soft and hard sides of Judeo-Christian thought. On the one hand, it is affirmed that God is the universal reality saturating life with his love. On the other, he is conceived as a ruling monarch standing above and scrutinizing all he surveys. When the mind seeks to manipulate the feelings and exploit nature, it is showing greater regard for the hard side, and its efforts denote division. When it moves in harmony with the entire complex, the soft side prevails, and its insights register communion.

Before one can love with all their heart or unconditionally, the mind must be free of ego. Walt Whitman's celebrated poem "Song of Myself" is a testimonial to a loving soul. His was not the stilted and selfish love of an ego for itself, as the title might imply, but the free and expansive love of a mind united with all life.

Some folks unfamiliar with Whitman might ask, "Why did he boast about himself so? Where was his humility? Did he have no shame?" My reply would be, "What shame is there in lauding the Divine?" Whitman caught a glimpse of it and felt its presence infusing all things.

Clear and sweet is my soul, and clear and sweet is all

Lawrence K. Zeisler

that is not my soul.[3]

I hear and behold God in every object, yet under-
stand God not in the least,
Nor do I understand who there can be more won-
derful than myself.[4]

Whitman did not think of himself as separate or superior. His ego temporarily vanished, exposing the "well of good-ness" and the truth therein. There is no shame in self-adulation when the mind is mirroring one's inner goodness, that part of oneself that is undivided like a child. In praising himself, he was praising everything. Could Whitman have found the kingdom of heaven?

Unlike the saints while undergoing their trials, Whitman immersed himself in life. Like the saints, he bathed in divine love—different roads, same destination. There is no one set way to enlightenment or, as the religious would say, God. Like Jesus, he did not find death problematic.

(No array of terms can say how much I am at peace
about God and about death.)[5]

And as to you Death, and you bitter hug of mortality,
it is idle to try to alarm me.[6]

While so inspired, Whitman was beyond good and evil, beyond morality. It's regrettable some link right and wrong with absolute good and evil, for that involves fear, and fear is the ego's handmaiden. Craving a future life with Christ involves desire, creating tension between what you are and what you want to be. Trying to cleave to the virtues while engaged in a fateful struggle for the immortal soul weakens the chance of realizing the ever-present truth and love that form our core, not beyond our grasp. Combined with the mentality of extravagance promoted by society, these factors put demands on the faithful that contribute to a disquieted nature. They hinder self-observation by making it difficult to accept oneself whatever their condition.

To allay the insecurity, Christians seek God and pray for his company. They feel penitent acts and self-restraint will draw God to act in their behalf. Contributing money to charity, they strive for divine approval. Denying themselves pleasures, they wonder if God has noticed. If these acts, well-intentioned and kind as they might be, are designed to bring God to them, they will amount to little more than ego massages. While God is perceived to be "other," any sense of satisfaction gained will be short-lived, and the isolation associated with his distance will repave the way to self-doubt. This isolation from ourselves, felt by Christian and atheist alike, is responsible for the cancerous insecurity that leads us to rash personal, political, and technological decisions.

When one expresses true self-denial, they ask for nothing in return from God. Wanting something, even goodness, betrays motive, which spoils love's purity. One cannot force or coax love; it can't be attained through conscious effort. It always seems to appear when you least expect it, springing unsought from within.

Our inner unity is revealed only after a total surrender of self (ego). Only then is the mind hushed (free of motive) enough to entertain the truth. Once free of the ego's divisive nature, one's isolation dissolves, and their goodness bursts forth, not because they want it to but because they have

Lawrence K. Zeisler

no choice. In this state, one may feel the divine touching all life, making it easier to accept in its totality. Even time's frigid grip relaxes and with it the fear associated with our physical demise. Feeling thus, why would one want to harm or violate anyone or anything in a world they feel an intrinsic part of? Why would they yearn for material things that interfere with the simple beauty innate to this union? Surely morality, with its strenuous concepts of right and wrong, would be irrelevant.

The answer to the problem of death lies in attaining a deep personal familiarity with life. Life can be properly observed only when one is fully engaged in it, not preoccupied with attention-diverting distractions. The mind should be free of judgment, because if not, it will find disfavor with those qualities it associates with unpleasantness and pain. One must be able to accept the value of all life. If there is any question whatsoever, trust in its sacredness will be tainted by doubt, which it only takes a shred of to give disillusion a foothold.

I know this all sounds wonderful, but is it realistic? After all, society is constantly redirecting our attention. We are relentlessly bombarded with media coverage of tragedies that presses us to question the fairness of things. It is doubly difficult maintaining composure while trying to make sense of a planet out of kilter, one where invasive species and warming temperatures disrupt the natural order, imperiling its proper functioning and degrading its splendor. The ego's prejudices, desires, and fears are always at the ready, waiting to usurp the calm. One can easily lose grasp of the sacred while entangled in the commotion. It is for these very reasons why it was felt necessary to provide this material.

Exalted individuals have achieved states similar to that being described, proof that it is not beyond the scope of reason. These ideas are an attempt to share with you the human spirit's inherent elegance, a gentle yet firm countervailing force against the din. We all possess the spirit; even if you or I just catch glimpses of its potential they will prove meaningful.

That which created the known is responsible for the unknown. There is a method to the eternal rhythm of life and death. Their mutualism is undeniable. Trust in the known half of the equation, and the other half falls in place.

Go outside, and take the time to observe and feel. Stick your nose in the wind and inhale. Absorb the interplay of forces—the peace, the conflict—with an open mind, bearing in mind that it has worked since time immemorial. In short, embrace the essence of reality. You may begin to feel a part of it and sense a growing confidence in its benevolence.

I'm looking for an expression. Ah, I found it: peace of mind. A mind at peace is displaying real faith in the purpose of all natural things, not faith with a purpose in mind.

In Summation

THE RATIONAL MIND IS PERFORMING THE TASK OF EXTRI-
cating us from what it recognizes to be an inadequate world
with results running the gamut from marvelous to madness.
Science and technology have proved double-edged swords
whose supernormal feats provide undreamt miracles while
leading us to the brink of annihilation.

Darwin's term "survival of the fittest" could be superim-
posed on the present capitalistic system. Nowhere else are
the winners and losers better defined and the failures forced
to endure the agonizing sting of lost esteem. Some face their
declines, grow stronger, and retrench. Others, not so capable,
become lost in the gaping abyss, exiled amid the surrounding
prosperity. In such a setting of highs and lows, mental illness
proliferates, respecting neither success nor failure.

Two of our most cherished freedoms are the inalienable
rights to produce and to spend as we please, but when the
ego determines the standards-it, not the dollar, is the root
of all "evil"- greed, pride, and selfishness overcome us to the
point that we lose touch with ourselves and undervalue the
earth's priceless, life-supporting qualities. We are creating
an "improved" world whose god is the profit motive with
all the pleasures it affords.

Worshipping the profit motive—many upstanding business folks don't bow at its altar—makes for dollars but not
always sense. It has produced a system that works, but at
what cost? When unchecked, it prefers to obey its own set

of dictates whose parameters often stray beyond reasonable restraints. It hardens the wills of its uncompromising adherents, generates excessive waste, and can take the eye off vital matters. Competition is healthy, but competition run amok is not. Corporate capitalists, in particular, have been known to blur the line between unscrupulous practices and product development while looking to inflate their portfolios at any cost; often at the expense of both consumers and employees. How much more could be accomplished if the head yielded ground to the heart, if the monetary reward could more effectively coexist with the virtuous one? What's that expression, "virtue is its own reward"? Those upholding this axion work to serve people, not just the bottom line.

Wouldn't it be something if more than a small minority of the wealthiest offered to share more of the burden? Did I just spout that Pollyannaish statement? Perhaps reliance on the government to forcibly direct their moral compass is more realistic. This may prove difficult, considering their stranglehold on politics. Unfortunately, the recently passed GOP tax bill designed to benefit the privileged while throwing crumbs at the rest exacerbates the dilemma by magnifying the ever-widening gap between the haves and have nots. Wall Street's gains come at the expense of Main Street. And the wealthy owe the environment a favor, especially the "carbon barons" in their midst. It's estimated that those breathing the rarefied air enjoyed by the richest 1 percent of the world's citizenry, on average, use 175 times more carbon than the disadvantaged souls scraping by in the bottom 10 percent of the property barrel.

The system buckles under its weight, fueling an upward spiral where the cost of living skyrockets, companies find it more profitable to produce goods on the other side of the globe, liberal political correctness advances a culture of unending grievance in which plaintiffs jockey for advantage by issuing claims of insult and discrimination, breadwinners are forced to work longer hours and borrow more, consumers often pay substantially more for brand-name prescription drugs sold here than in foreign countries, people slide deeper into credit card and college debt, growing numbers of citizens are declaring bankruptcy, stress levels rise, drug intake proliferates, suicide is increasing, and families succumb to dysfunction. In the "land of the free," the shackles are being set ever tighter. Even reality has been hobbled, forced to compete with an array of nonsensical imitations looking to hoodwink any receptive ear.

Despite the pressing need for common sense and common ground, the two major political parties continue to battle like pubescent youngsters vying for a maiden's attention. A key victim of the internecine bickering is our beleaguered healthcare system, which has fallen prey to the debate over what composes fair and affordable coverage. In a recent report surveying healthcare in eleven high-income countries, the United States was the only one without universal coverage, and it was found to have the highest costs and lowest overall performance of the group. For example, knee replacements cost $28,000 on average in our country while they run about $18,000 in the United Kingdom. Instead of fine-tuning the Affordable Care Act, which displayed positive gains in coverage and access to care, Republican members of Congress sought to gut it and institute a replacement that would only intensify the current dilemma. Thankfully, their efforts were ill-fated. Most other developed countries fare better on a range of quality of life indicators including working conditions, longevity, mothers' well-being, school performance, crime, and violent death rates. In general, the state provides care and support to those who need extra assistance. They appear to display a greater sense of decency toward their fellow countrymen than we.

Society is run by a faceless assemblage of special interests, lobbyists, and industry groups, not unlike a vast machine over which we have little voice. Add to that mix the ultra-wealthy individuals who use their riches to shape the political agenda in a manner conducive to their own interests. The laws are growing in complexity; keeping abreast of every legal nuance that might be of consequence is like trying to negotiate an ever-thickening minefield.

Only time will tell if we can break out of this perplexing cluster of interrelations. The way isn't through ever-increasing entanglements unless, at their zenith, we raise a collective voice in one deafening primal scream and shatter the spell.

The global economy is forcing us to take a hard look at ourselves. While it is true that goods produced cheaper overseas have had an adverse effect on some American jobs, and certain countries bend the rules to their advantage, it is erroneous to believe that renegotiating strict trade deals full of threats will necessarily solve the problem. The world is increasingly interconnected, and we share space with competing economic powerhouses such as the EU and China. Canada and Mexico are two of our largest trading partners. Sensible regulatory safeguards protecting the public and environment—cultivated under the Obama administration and eviscerated by Trump's, employed by the EU, United Kingdom, and others on the world stage—may compel the United States to conform or suffer losses in trade. That may prove difficult in a country where corporate lobbyists spend millions shaping congressional legislation. Too often monetary incentives encourage those seeking reelection to put self-interest before the common good. It is imperative that we treat others with respect when maneuvering for advantage in this crowded setting, keeping in mind that automation, nanotechnology, 3-D printing, and productivity gains on our soil contribute to job loss.

If one "does their own thing" within the realm of the law, it's deemed acceptable, but when does freedom become abused? At what point does the pursuit of pleasure and material wealth overstep its bounds? If the earth, its vanishing creatures, and the starving multitudes across the planet could give voice, their answers would differ radically from most of ours. Although the last few decades have witnessed significant progress in the alleviation of world poverty, far too many people still struggle under it's pitiless yoke.

There are folks who assume that the earth is here for us to do with as we please. Some right-wing Christians are included among the group. Even the most misguided must have a visceral sense that an indifferent shepherd can't responsibly tend to Creation—as if that matters to them. They stubbornly follow commands designed for an ancient, victimized people looking to gain a foothold in a sparsely populated world and literally interpret scriptures that aid them in facilitating their own self-serving interests (sometimes taking liberties with the contents if they are vague about a matter of passion as is the case with abortion). This is not meant to imply that all their views are outdated or erroneous or that their actions are necessarily without honorable intent. Like any religion, many of the elements included in their faith are timeless. Wisdom can be found throughout the Old and New Testaments.

These members of the flock are extremists, the closest

thing we have to Islamic fundamentalists. If their power was not so great and voices far less strident, their machinations would be little more than petty irritations. However, they are conspiring to unravel the separation between church and state and assiduously campaigning for conservative judges who, if appointed to the Supreme Court and the thirteen United States courts of appeals, could shape the law for decades.

Fear stains the Christians' reverence. It has proven a failed incentive to divine comfort. Using the threat of godly reprisals (especially hell) as a means to prevent wrongdoing is an affront to God's dignity, giving him a tyrannical look that hampers the human spirit's growth by filling it with unnecessary dread and self-doubt.

Existing alongside the fear is a perception of privilege. By honing the conviction that it knows precisely what the unknown wants of us, Christianity gives God an exclusive, some might say sanctimonious, air. This helps to explain why members of the religion have had an historical tendency to gaze with condescension upon those faiths and traditions acknowledging an eternal presence but unable to call upon an all-powerful god to justify their world-altering ambitions.

The fact that growing numbers of Christians are lightening their versions of hell, coupled with an endorsement of other belief systems, are signs their faith is maturing. It is sinking in that we and the earth are in this together, but will it ever be understood that we come from a source that humans alone can marvel at and seek familiarity with but have no more an awareness of its and our why and wherefore than the humble church mouse scurrying among the pews? Isn't it time to lay to rest the longing for sacred rec-

Lawrence K. Zeisler

ognition that clogs the vessels linking the heart with this most fundamental Truth?

The Native American spirits dwelled in an awe-inspiring world. Those who worshipped those spirits blended science with religion and found balance. Our scientific and religious institutions are just beginning to show signs of conciliation. If the relation blossoms, which will have meant that cool, equable heads have prevailed, perhaps one day we will bless the ground on which we walk.

It would be advantageous to heed the wisdom of the Iroquois and institute the farsighted principles of the concept of the "seventh generation." It expressed that before vital decisions could be made, their proposed impact upon the next seven generations of people had to be weighed. The belief was predicated upon a basic understanding of and respect for nature. Our understanding of her is considerable, though there is still much to learn. Nonetheless, understanding without comparable respect rings hollow.

I am compelled to state my case as bluntly as possible, because desperate times make for desperate measures. The window of opportunity is closing fast on the environment. The countless symbiotic relationships of which it is composed are steadily unraveling. Failure to act now on issues such as global warming, deforestation, ocean contamination, and land degradation will exponentially amplify the rate of the devastation. It doesn't help that data compiled by researchers at the Global Carbon Project projects that the world is on pace to discharge a record 37.1 gigatons of planet-warming CO_2 emissions in 2018, with likely continued growth in 2019. Of the major economies, only the EU's output has remained relatively flat.

The earth and its creatures do not have our power of reason, but they are the embodiment of that whose genius far exceeds our own. We think of miracles as extraordinary events surpassing all known natural powers as if present conditions border on the mundane. I find this disconcerting, a glaring symptom of how far we've strayed from a reverent state. Given the chance to ponder in solitude for a thousand years, the most erudite mind would be hard pressed to conceive a miracle as exalted as rain or breathing or pain or pleasure or joy or sadness or a flower or a butterfly.

The natural world is sacrificial to the core. The story of Jesus revolves around his supreme sacrifice. Hence, sacrifice is incorporated in both faith and reality. The ego renounces sacrifice, preferring to pursue its own selfish ends instead. An island unto itself, it fears any selfless action that endangers it, and all *sincere* sacrifice is selfless. It would have its life enhanced at any cost and disregards the state of those natural conditions that make life possible for all.

The ego doesn't want to lose all that it has accumulated mentally and materially, and the thought of deprivation fills it with dread. It takes pride in the prejudices that give it its identity and the wealth and material that make it noticed. All this "clutter" diverts one from the universal harmony that illuminated souls of all cultures have felt. This truth is expressed most eloquently through Jesus. His faith was so refined and his inner unity so pronounced that he knew that death itself could not sever his deep affiliation with that which binds all things.

The marvelous human brain provides the wherewithal to devise solutions to the heavy-handed impact its actions have imposed on the planet. Moreover, it affords us the opportunity to modify the divine engineering to improve

Lawrence K. Zeisler

the quality of life. Biotechnology's potential has barely been scratched; major developments in medicine, food production, and environmental improvement are imminent. If guided by the admiration and deference due the processes like diversity, decomposition, and natural balance that have been so fundamental to life's long march through time, there is little reason why its endeavors can't seamlessly blend with Mother Nature.

We cannot return to the time when the waters ran pristine, but we can work on their purification. The degree to which this is accomplished will depend in large part on our energy choices and smart improvements in the production process. There will be hard choices. In the short term, outdated jobs will be lost and some companies strained, but others will take their place. To this end, providing educational benefits geared toward technical training designed to meet cutting-edge job opportunities is of the essence. It is noted that vehicle prices will temporarily increase during the initial days of the overdue switchover to primarily electric and possibly hydrogen-fueled vehicles; government-sponsored incentives would help defray costs. Inconvenience is to be expected during a time of transition—a foreign concept to minds made languid with expectations of entitlement.

Hydrogen is particularly appealing as a source of energy. When combined with oxygen in a fuel cell, electricity is produced that can run one or more electric motors propelling a zero-emission vehicle. Water vapor is the only by-product. However, because there is so little free hydrogen gas in the atmosphere, it must be separated from source materials and purified. That production induces differing degrees of environmental impacts, making it currently impractical on a large-scale. One method, electrolysis, splits water molecules into gaseous forms of oxygen and hydrogen and produces no global warming emissions. If the source of the electricity needed to generate the process is based on fossil fuel, the total emissions will be considerable but not if the power is raised from renewable sources. The most common method of hydrogen gas collection comes from natural gas and causes methane to react with steam with its attendant release of CO_2 and negative atmospheric impact. The water produced as a by-product of the fuel cell process will have to be effectively dealt with. Future advances in hydrogen production technology will most likely address these hurdles.

Biodiesel, a fuel derived from recycled vegetable oils, restaurant greases, and animal fats, is a clean-burning and biodegradable alternative to the petroleum-based fuels now powering most diesel engines that has proved successful. The industry supports nearly forty-eight thousand jobs in areas including agriculture, manufacturing, transportation and service, and it enjoys continued growth. A University of Missouri study has calculated that if a metropolitan region produced one hundred million gallons of biodiesel annually, it would provide around six thousand new jobs. Energy-efficient environmental practices will improve our competitiveness in the global economy. The international market is awaiting the benefits of environmentally sound technologies.

A more sensible world won't be without its fair share of work. Implementation of a government plan to revitalize our deteriorating national infrastructure is essential, one organized around reducing carbon pollution while making us more resilient to the everyday stresses created by the changing climate. Someone must develop, produce, and repair the machinery businesses are installing to aid the environment. The US recycling industry employs more than one million people. Think of the possibilities: widespread

Lawrence K. Zeisler

desalinating plants, gigantic solar arrays stationed in the deserts providing energy for colder, less sunlit regions, windmills converting wind into power, negative emissions technologies sucking greenhouse gases from the air, factories churning out state-of-the-art, environment-compatible building materials and energy systems geared toward new construction as well as retrofitting highly efficient heating and cooling equipment in older buildings, electrified mass-transit systems, home weatherization, cleanup of the oceans and land, use of organic farming methods on a commercial basis, and development and extensive deployment of battery-powered cars, buses, trains, and planes.

Viewed overall, the natural world has effectively withstood the test of time. To not revere it courts disaster as is evidenced by the planet's presently imperiled state. Restoring the earth is the proper path of progress.

I'll leave you with this quote from Commander Frank Borman, crew member of the Apollo 8 mission. Recounting his view of our planet from lunar orbit, he stated that "It was the most beautiful, heart-catching sight of my life, one that sent a torrent of nostalgia, of sheer homesickness, surging through me. It was the only thing in space that had any color to it. Everything else was either black or white, but not the Earth."

There is no place like home. Nowhere.

Notes

Introduction
1. "Stewards of the Earth." *E Magazine* 13, no. 6 (2002), 36.
2. Aldo Leopold, *A Sand County Almanac* (Oxford: Oxford University Press, YEAR), 209–10.
3. Thomas À Kempis, *The Imitation of Christ* (Penguin Books, 1952), 46–47.

Chapter 1
1. *National Geographic* 195, no. 2 (1999).
2. *National Geographic* January (1983), 24.
3. Lindsay Brownell, "Sticky When Wet: Strong Adhesive for Wound Healing," The Wyss Institute, July 27, 2017.

Chapter 2
1. Damian Carrington, "Pesticides Damage Survival of Bee Colonies, Landmark Study Shows," *The Guardian* June 29, 2017.
2. William Neuman and Andrew Pollack, "Farmers Cope with Roundup-Resistant Weeds," *The New York Times* May 3, 2010
3. Allison Wilson, "New Research Links Neonicotinoid Pesticides to Monarch Butterfly Declines," October 21, 2015.

Chapter 3
1. Richard Erdos and John (Fire) Lame Deer. *Lame Deer, Seeker of Visions* (Simon and Schuster), 1972), 112.

Chapter 4

1. J. Krishnamurti, *Talks and Dialogues* (Avon Books, 1970), 83.

Chapter 5

1. Thomas Merton, *New Seeds of Contemplation* (New Directions, 1961), 38.

Chapter 6

1. Keith Hansen, "Breastfeeding: A Smart Investment in People and in Economics" *The Lancet*, 2016.
2. "Our Smartphone Addiction Is Costing the Earth," David Nield, *TechRadar* August 4, 2015, URL.

Chapter 7

1. Merton, *New Seeds of Contemplation*, 25.

Chapter 8

1. Raymond Blakney, *Meister Eckhart* (New York: Harper & Row, 1941), 33.
2. Alan Watts, *The Supreme Identity* (Vintage Books, 1972), 184.
3. Walt Whitman, *Leaves of Grass* (New York and Scarborough, Ontario: New American Library, 1980), 72–73.
4. Mark 10:25 (Revised Standard Version) (Cleveland and New York: World Publishing Company, 1962).
5. Matt. 7:21–23 (RSV) (Cleveland and New York: World Publishing Company, 1962).
6. Matt. 7:1–3 (RSV) (Cleveland and New York: World Publishing Company, 1962).
7. À Kempis, *The Imitation of Christ,* 73.
8. Blakney, *Meister Eckhart*, 47.

9. À Kempis, *The Imitation of Christ*, 40.
10. Ibid, 42.
11. His Holiness the Dalai Lama, *Ethics for the New Millennium* (New York: Riverhead Books, 1999), 139–40.
12. "Yes! A Journal of Positive Futures," *Positive Futures Network* Fall 2001, 1.
13. Merton, *New Seeds of Contemplation*, 24.

Chapter 9
1. Matt. 18:3–4 (RSV) (Cleveland and New York: World Publishing Company, 1962).
2. Matt 24:7-8 (Authorized King James Version) (London and New York: Collins' Clear-Type Press, 1957).
3. Mark 13:12 (Authorized King James Version) (London and New York: Collins' Clear-Type Press, 1957).
4. Matt. 10: 34–39 (AKJV) (London and New York: Collins' Clear-Type Press, 1957).
5. Matt. 19: 28–29 (AKJV) (London and New York: Collins' Clear-Type Press, 1957).
6. Deut. 20:16–18 (RSV) (Cleveland and New York: World Publishing Company, 1962).

Chapter 10
1. Blakney, *Meister Eckhart*, 83.
2. Krishnamurti, *Talks and Dialogues*, 117.
3. Whitman, *Leaves of Grass*, 51.
4. Ibid, 94.
5. Ibid, 94.
6. Ibid, 94.